THE BOOK ®

Gearbox overhaul manual

Maintenance • Dismantling • Overhaul • Reassembly

Ian Barnes

(3473-192)

ABCDE
FGHIJ
KLMNO
PQRST

© Haynes Publishing 1998

A book in the **Haynes Service and Repair Manual Series**

ISBN 1 85960 473 0

British Library Cataloguing in Publication Data
A catalogue record for this book is available from the British Library.

Printed by **J H Haynes & Co Ltd, Sparkford, Nr Yeovil, Somerset BA22 7JJ, England**

Haynes Publishing
Sparkford, Nr Yeovil, Somerset BA22 7JJ, England

Haynes North America, Inc
861 Lawrence Drive, Newbury Park, California 91320, USA

Editions Haynes S.A.
Tour Aurore - La Défense 2, 18 Place des Reflets,
92975 PARIS LA DEFENSE Cedex, France

Haynes Publishing Nordiska AB
Box 1504, 751 45 UPPSALA, Sweden

Introduction

This gearbox overhaul manual is aimed at the more experienced mechanic who has some experience of transmission dismantling and reassembly, and already has most of the specialised tools needed for such work. The gearboxes covered are those fitted to the most popular cars (see *Applications*), and is written with the assumption that the gearbox is already removed from the car.

Before a decision is taken to overhaul a gearbox, the cost of replacement parts should be investigated. A reconditioned gearbox may be no more expensive than the cost of parts needed for overhaul, and a reputable reconditioner will provide a guarantee. Buying a good second-hand gearbox from a car breaker is another possibility which may be worth considering. This is not intended to deter the reader from proceeding with an overhaul, but rather to point out the need to consider the economics of the situation.

This manual has drawings and descriptions to show the function of the various components so that their layout can be understood. Tasks are described and photographed in a clear step-by-step sequence. The illustrations are numbered by the Section number and paragraph number to which they relate - if there is more than one illustration per paragraph, the sequence is denoted alphabetically.

Acknowledgements

Thanks are due to Duckhams Oils, who provided lubrication data. Certain illustrations are the copyright of Citroën Cars Ltd, Ford Motor Company, Peugeot Talbot Motor Company Limited and Vauxhall Motors Limited, and are used with their permission. Thanks are also due to Sykes-Pickavant Limited, who provided some of the workshop tools, and to all those people at Sparkford who helped in the production of this manual, especially Andy Legg and Matthew Minter.

This manual is not a direct reproduction of the vehicle manufacturers' data, and its publication should not be taken as implying any technical approval by the vehicle manufacturers or importers.

We take great pride in the accuracy of information given in this manual, but vehicle manufacturers make alterations and design changes during the production run of a particular vehicle of which they do not inform us. No liability can be accepted by the authors or publishers for loss, damage or injury caused by errors in, or omissions from, the information given.

Contents 0•3

0•4 Contents

REPAIRS

This list is not exhaustive; it indicates the mainstream models to which particular gearboxes were fitted. Precise details of applications were not available for some of the older models.

Model	Years	Gearbox chapter
Austin Maestro 1.3 & 1.6 litre	All	VW 084 & 020 gearboxes
Austin Montego 1.3 & 1.6 litre	All	VW 084 & 020 gearboxes
Austin/Rover Metro	1980 to 1991	Austin/Rover Metro gearbox
Austin/Rover Mini	From 1969	Austin/Rover Mini gearbox
Citroën AX	All	Citroën/Peugeot MA gearbox
Citroën BX 1.6 1.7, & 1.9 litre	All	Citroën/Peugeot BE gearbox
Citroën C15 Van	All	Citroën/Peugeot BE gearbox
Citroën Visa GTI & diesel	All	Citroën/Peugeot BE gearbox
Citroën Xantia	All	Citroën/Peugeot BE gearbox
Citroën XM non-turbo	All	Citroën/Peugeot BE gearbox
Citroën ZX 1.1 & 1.3 litre	All	Citroën/Peugeot MA gearbox
Citroën ZX 1.6, 1.8, 1.9 & 2.0 litre & diesel	All	Citroën/Peugeot BE gearbox
Ford Capri 2.8 litre	From 1982	Ford B & N gearboxes
Ford Cortina 1.6 & 2.0 litre ohc	1970 to 1976	Ford B & N gearboxes
Ford Cortina 2.0 litre	1976 to 1983	Ford B & N gearboxes
Ford Escort	1980 to 1990	Ford J & K gearboxes
Ford Escort Mexico & RS	1975 to 1980	Ford B & N gearboxes
Ford Fiesta	1983 to 1995	Ford J & K gearboxes
Ford Fiesta Classic	1995 to 1996	Ford J & K gearboxes
Ford Granada & Scorpio	1977 to 1988	Ford B & N gearboxes
Ford Orion	1983 to 1990	Ford J & K gearboxes
Ford Sierra & Sapphire 1.6, 1.8, 2.0, 2.3, 2.8 & 2.9 litre	All	Ford B & N gearboxes
Ford Sierra 4x4	All	Ford B & N gearboxes
Ford Transit 2.0 & 2.5 litre	1986 to 1988	Ford B & N gearboxes
Opel Ascona 1.3 litre	1981 to 1988	Vauxhall F10 gearbox
Opel Ascona 1.6, 1.8 & 2.0 litre	1981 to 1988	Vauxhall F16 gearbox
Opel Astra 1.4 litre	1991 to 1994	Vauxhall F10 gearbox
Opel Astra 1.8 & 2.0 litre sohc	All	Vauxhall F16 gearbox
Opel Corsa	1983 to 1993	Vauxhall F10 gearbox
Opel Corsa 1.2 & 1.4* litre	1993 to 1998	Vauxhall F10 gearbox
Opel Kadett 1.2 & 1.3 litre	1979 to 1990	Vauxhall F10 gearbox
Opel Kadett 1.6 & 1.8 litre	1979 to 1990	Vauxhall F16 gearbox
Opel Vectra 1.4 litre	1988 to 1995	Vauxhall F10 gearbox
Opel Vectra 1.8 & 2.0 litre sohc	1988 to 1995	Vauxhall F16 gearbox
Peugeot 106	All	Citroën/Peugeot MA gearbox
Peugeot 205 1.0, 1.1 & 1.4 litre TU engines	All	Citroën/Peugeot MA gearbox
Peugeot 205 1.6 & 1.9 litre	All	Citroën/Peugeot BE gearbox
Peugeot 305 1.6 & 1.9 litre	All	Citroën/Peugeot BE gearbox
Peugeot 306 1.1, 1.4 & 1.6 litre	All	Citroën/Peugeot MA gearbox
Peugeot 309	All	Citroën/Peugeot BE gearbox
Peugeot 405	All	Citroën/Peugeot BE gearbox
Peugeot 406 1.6, 1.8, 1.9 & 2.0 litre	All	Citroën/Peugeot BE gearbox
Talbot Alpine, Solara, Minx & Rapier	1982 to 1986	Citroën/Peugeot BE gearbox
Talbot Horizon	1984 to 1986	Citroën/Peugeot BE gearbox
Vauxhall Astra 1.2 & 1.3 litre	1980 to 1990	Vauxhall F10 gearbox
Vauxhall Astra 1.6 & 1.8 litre	1980 to 1990	Vauxhall F16 gearbox
Vauxhall Astra 1.4 litre	1991 to 1994	Vauxhall F10 gearbox
Vauxhall Astra 1.8 litre	1991 to 1998	Vauxhall F16 gearbox
Vauxhall Astra 2.0 litre sohc	1991 to 1998	Vauxhall F16 gearbox
Vauxhall Belmont 1.2 & 1.3 litre	All	Vauxhall F10 gearbox
Vauxhall Belmont 1.6 & 1.8 litre	All	Vauxhall F16 gearbox
Vauxhall Cavalier 1.3 litre	1981 to 1988	Vauxhall F10 gearbox
Vauxhall Cavalier 1.4 litre	1988 to 1995	Vauxhall F10 gearbox
Vauxhall Cavalier 1.6, 1.8 & 2.0 litre	1981 to 1988	Vauxhall F16 gearbox
Vauxhall Cavalier 1.8 & 2.0 litre sohc	1988 to 1995	Vauxhall F16 gearbox
Vauxhall Corsa 1.2 & 1.4* litre	All	Vauxhall F10 gearbox
Vauxhall Nova**	All	Vauxhall F10 gearbox
VW Golf	All	VW 084 & 020 gearboxes
VW Jetta	All	VW 084 & 020 gearboxes
VW Polo	1982 to 1994	VW 084 & 020 gearboxes
VW Scirocco	All	VW 084 & 020 gearboxes
VW Vento	All	VW 084 & 020 gearboxes

*not 1.4 hatchback with MPi (C14SE engine)   **not 1.4 SR or 1.6 GTE/GSi

Working on your car can be dangerous. This page shows just some of the potential risks and hazards, with the aim of creating a safety-conscious attitude.

General hazards

Scalding

• Don't remove the radiator or expansion tank cap while the engine is hot.
• Engine oil, automatic transmission fluid or power steering fluid may also be dangerously hot if the engine has recently been running.

Burning

• Beware of burns from the exhaust system and from any part of the engine. Brake discs and drums can also be extremely hot immediately after use.

Crushing

• When working under or near a raised vehicle, always supplement the jack with axle stands, or use drive-on ramps. *Never venture under a car which is only supported by a jack.*
• Take care if loosening or tightening high-torque nuts when the vehicle is on stands. Initial loosening and final tightening should be done with the wheels on the ground.

Fire

• Fuel is highly flammable; fuel vapour is explosive.
• Don't let fuel spill onto a hot engine.
• Do not smoke or allow naked lights (including pilot lights) anywhere near a vehicle being worked on. Also beware of creating sparks (electrically or by use of tools).
• Fuel vapour is heavier than air, so don't work on the fuel system with the vehicle over an inspection pit.
• Another cause of fire is an electrical overload or short-circuit. Take care when repairing or modifying the vehicle wiring.
• Keep a fire extinguisher handy, of a type suitable for use on fuel and electrical fires.

Electric shock

• Ignition HT voltage can be dangerous, especially to people with heart problems or a pacemaker. Don't work on or near the ignition system with the engine running or the ignition switched on.

• Mains voltage is also dangerous. Make sure that any mains-operated equipment is correctly earthed. Mains power points should be protected by a residual current device (RCD) circuit breaker.

Fume or gas intoxication

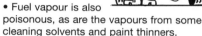

• Exhaust fumes are poisonous; they often contain carbon monoxide, which is rapidly fatal if inhaled. Never run the engine in a confined space such as a garage with the doors shut.
• Fuel vapour is also poisonous, as are the vapours from some cleaning solvents and paint thinners.

Poisonous or irritant substances

• Avoid skin contact with battery acid and with any fuel, fluid or lubricant, especially antifreeze, brake hydraulic fluid and Diesel fuel. Don't syphon them by mouth. If such a substance is swallowed or gets into the eyes, seek medical advice.
• Prolonged contact with used engine oil can cause skin cancer. Wear gloves or use a barrier cream if necessary. Change out of oil-soaked clothes and do not keep oily rags in your pocket.
• Air conditioning refrigerant forms a poisonous gas if exposed to a naked flame (including a cigarette). It can also cause skin burns on contact.

Asbestos

• Asbestos dust can cause cancer if inhaled or swallowed. Asbestos may be found in gaskets and in brake and clutch linings. When dealing with such components it is safest to assume that they contain asbestos.

Special hazards

Hydrofluoric acid

• This extremely corrosive acid is formed when certain types of synthetic rubber, found in some O-rings, oil seals, fuel hoses etc, are exposed to temperatures above 400°C. The rubber changes into a charred or sticky substance containing the acid. *Once formed, the acid remains dangerous for years. If it gets onto the skin, it may be necessary to amputate the limb concerned.*
• When dealing with a vehicle which has suffered a fire, or with components salvaged from such a vehicle, wear protective gloves and discard them after use.

The battery

• Batteries contain sulphuric acid, which attacks clothing, eyes and skin. Take care when topping-up or carrying the battery.
• The hydrogen gas given off by the battery is highly explosive. Never cause a spark or allow a naked light nearby. Be careful when connecting and disconnecting battery chargers or jump leads.

Air bags

• Air bags can cause injury if they go off accidentally. Take care when removing the steering wheel and/or facia. Special storage instructions may apply.

Diesel injection equipment

• Diesel injection pumps supply fuel at very high pressure. Take care when working on the fuel injectors and fuel pipes.

⚠ *Warning: Never expose the hands, face or any other part of the body to injector spray; the fuel can penetrate the skin with potentially fatal results.*

Remember...

DO

• Do use eye protection when using power tools, and when working under the vehicle.

• Do wear gloves or use barrier cream to protect your hands when necessary.

• Do get someone to check periodically that all is well when working alone on the vehicle.

• Do keep loose clothing and long hair well out of the way of moving mechanical parts.

• Do remove rings, wristwatch etc, before working on the vehicle – especially the electrical system.

• Do ensure that any lifting or jacking equipment has a safe working load rating adequate for the job.

DON'T

• Don't attempt to lift a heavy component which may be beyond your capability – get assistance.

• Don't rush to finish a job, or take unverified short cuts.

• Don't use ill-fitting tools which may slip and cause injury.

• Don't leave tools or parts lying around where someone can trip over them. Mop up oil and fuel spills at once.

• Don't allow children or pets to play in or near a vehicle being worked on.

Length (distance)

Inches (in)	x 25.4	= Millimetres (mm)	x 0.0394	=	Inches (in)
Feet (ft)	x 0.305	= Metres (m)	x 3.281	=	Feet (ft)
Miles	x 1.609	= Kilometres (km)	x 0.621	=	Miles

Volume (capacity)

Cubic inches (cu in; in³)	x 16.387	= Cubic centimetres (cc; cm³)	x 0.061	=	Cubic inches (cu in; in³)
Imperial pints (Imp pt)	x 0.568	= Litres (l)	x 1.76	=	Imperial pints (Imp pt)
Imperial quarts (Imp qt)	x 1.137	= Litres (l)	x 0.88	=	Imperial quarts (Imp qt)
Imperial quarts (Imp qt)	x 1.201	= US quarts (US qt)	x 0.833	=	Imperial quarts (Imp qt)
US quarts (US qt)	x 0.946	= Litres (l)	x 1.057	=	US quarts (US qt)
Imperial gallons (Imp gal)	x 4.546	= Litres (l)	x 0.22	=	Imperial gallons (Imp gal)
Imperial gallons (Imp gal)	x 1.201	= US gallons (US gal)	x 0.833	=	Imperial gallons (Imp gal)
US gallons (US gal)	x 3.785	= Litres (l)	x 0.264	=	US gallons (US gal)

Mass (weight)

Ounces (oz)	x 28.35	= Grams (g)	x 0.035	=	Ounces (oz)
Pounds (lb)	x 0.454	= Kilograms (kg)	x 2.205	=	Pounds (lb)

Force

Ounces-force (ozf; oz)	x 0.278	= Newtons (N)	x 3.6	=	Ounces-force (ozf; oz)
Pounds-force (lbf; lb)	x 4.448	= Newtons (N)	x 0.225	=	Pounds-force (lbf; lb)
Newtons (N)	x 0.1	= Kilograms-force (kgf; kg)	x 9.81	=	Newtons (N)

Pressure

Pounds-force per square inch (psi; lbf/in²; lb/in²)	x 0.070	= Kilograms-force per square centimetre (kgf/cm²; kg/cm²)	x 14.223	=	Pounds-force per square inch (psi; lbf/in²; lb/in²)
Pounds-force per square inch (psi; lbf/in²; lb/in²)	x 0.068	= Atmospheres (atm)	x 14.696	=	Pounds-force per square inch (psi; lbf/in²; lb/in²)
Pounds-force per square inch (psi; lbf/in²; lb/in²)	x 0.069	= Bars	x 14.5	=	Pounds-force per square inch (psi; lbf/in²; lb/in²)
Pounds-force per square inch (psi; lbf/in²; lb/in²)	x 6.895	= Kilopascals (kPa)	x 0.145	=	Pounds-force per square inch (psi; lbf/in²; lb/in²)
Kilopascals (kPa)	x 0.01	= Kilograms-force per square centimetre (kgf/cm²; kg/cm²)	x 98.1	=	Kilopascals (kPa)
Millibar (mbar)	x 100	= Pascals (Pa)	x 0.01	=	Millibar (mbar)
Millibar (mbar)	x 0.0145	= Pounds-force per square inch (psi; lbf/in²; lb/in²)	x 68.947	=	Millibar (mbar)
Millibar (mbar)	x 0.75	= Millimetres of mercury (mmHg)	x 1.333	=	Millibar (mbar)
Millibar (mbar)	x 0.401	= Inches of water (inH₂O)	x 2.491	=	Millibar (mbar)
Millimetres of mercury (mmHg)	x 0.535	= Inches of water (inH₂O)	x 1.868	=	Millimetres of mercury (mmHg)
Inches of water (inH₂O)	x 0.036	= Pounds-force per square inch (psi; lbf/in²; lb/in²)	x 27.68	=	Inches of water (inH₂O)

Torque (moment of force)

Pounds-force inches (lbf in; lb in)	x 1.152	= Kilograms-force centimetre (kgf cm; kg cm)	x 0.868	=	Pounds-force inches (lbf in; lb in)
Pounds-force inches (lbf in; lb in)	x 0.113	= Newton metres (Nm)	x 8.85	=	Pounds-force inches (lbf in; lb in)
Pounds-force inches (lbf in; lb in)	x 0.083	= Pounds-force feet (lbf ft; lb ft)	x 12	=	Pounds-force inches (lbf in; lb in)
Pounds-force feet (lbf ft; lb ft)	x 0.138	= Kilograms-force metres (kgf m; kg m)	x 7.233	=	Pounds-force feet (lbf ft; lb ft)
Pounds-force feet (lbf ft; lb ft)	x 1.356	= Newton metres (Nm)	x 0.738	=	Pounds-force feet (lbf ft; lb ft)
Newton metres (Nm)	x 0.102	= Kilograms-force metres (kgf m; kg m)	x 9.804	=	Newton metres (Nm)

Power

Horsepower (hp)	x 745.7	= Watts (W)	x 0.0013	=	Horsepower (hp)

Velocity (speed)

Miles per hour (miles/hr; mph)	x 1.609	= Kilometres per hour (km/hr; kph)	x 0.621	=	Miles per hour (miles/hr; mph)

Fuel consumption*

Miles per gallon (mpg)	x 0.354	= Kilometres per litre (km/l)	x 2.825	=	Miles per gallon (mpg)

Temperature

Degrees Fahrenheit = (°C x 1.8) + 32

Degrees Celsius (Degrees Centigrade; °C) = (°F - 32) x 0.56

It is common practice to convert from miles per gallon (mpg) to litres/100 kilometres (l/100km), where mpg x l/100 km = 282

Whenever servicing, repair or overhaul work is carried out on the car or its components, observe the following procedures and instructions. This will assist in carrying out the operation efficiently and to a professional standard of workmanship.

Joint mating faces and gaskets

When separating components at their mating faces, never insert screwdrivers or similar implements into the joint between the faces in order to prise them apart. This can cause severe damage which results in oil leaks, coolant leaks, etc upon reassembly. Separation is usually achieved by tapping along the joint with a soft-faced hammer in order to break the seal. However, note that this method may not be suitable where dowels are used for component location.

Where a gasket is used between the mating faces of two components, a new one must be fitted on reassembly; fit it dry unless otherwise stated in the repair procedure. Make sure that the mating faces are clean and dry, with all traces of old gasket removed. When cleaning a joint face, use a tool which is unlikely to score or damage the face, and remove any burrs or nicks with an oilstone or fine file.

Make sure that tapped holes are cleaned with a pipe cleaner, and keep them free of jointing compound, if this is being used, unless specifically instructed otherwise.

Ensure that all orifices, channels or pipes are clear, and blow through them, preferably using compressed air.

Oil seals

Oil seals can be removed by levering them out with a wide flat-bladed screwdriver or similar implement. Alternatively, a number of self-tapping screws may be screwed into the seal, and these used as a purchase for pliers or some similar device in order to pull the seal free.

Whenever an oil seal is removed from its working location, either individually or as part of an assembly, it should be renewed.

The very fine sealing lip of the seal is easily damaged, and will not seal if the surface it contacts is not completely clean and free from scratches, nicks or grooves. If the original sealing surface of the component cannot be restored, and the manufacturer has not made provision for slight relocation of the seal relative to the sealing surface, the component should be renewed.

Protect the lips of the seal from any surface which may damage them in the course of fitting. Use tape or a conical sleeve where possible. Lubricate the seal lips with oil before fitting and, on dual-lipped seals, fill the space between the lips with grease.

Unless otherwise stated, oil seals must be fitted with their sealing lips toward the lubricant to be sealed.

Use a tubular drift or block of wood of the appropriate size to install the seal and, if the seal housing is shouldered, drive the seal down to the shoulder. If the seal housing is unshouldered, the seal should be fitted with its face flush with the housing top face (unless otherwise instructed).

Screw threads and fastenings

Seized nuts, bolts and screws are quite a common occurrence where corrosion has set in, and the use of penetrating oil or releasing fluid will often overcome this problem if the offending item is soaked for a while before attempting to release it. The use of an impact driver may also provide a means of releasing such stubborn fastening devices, when used in conjunction with the appropriate screwdriver bit or socket. If none of these methods works, it may be necessary to resort to the careful application of heat, or the use of a hacksaw or nut splitter device.

Studs are usually removed by locking two nuts together on the threaded part, and then using a spanner on the lower nut to unscrew the stud. Studs or bolts which have broken off below the surface of the component in which they are mounted can sometimes be removed using a stud extractor. Always ensure that a blind tapped hole is completely free from oil, grease, water or other fluid before installing the bolt or stud. Failure to do this could cause the housing to crack due to the hydraulic action of the bolt or stud as it is screwed in.

When tightening a castellated nut to accept a split pin, tighten the nut to the specified torque, where applicable, and then tighten further to the next split pin hole. Never slacken the nut to align the split pin hole, unless stated in the repair procedure.

When checking or retightening a nut or bolt to a specified torque setting, slacken the nut or bolt by a quarter of a turn, and then retighten to the specified setting. However, this should not be attempted where angular tightening has been used.

For some screw fastenings, notably cylinder head bolts or nuts, torque wrench settings are no longer specified for the latter stages of tightening, "angle-tightening" being called up instead. Typically, a fairly low torque wrench setting will be applied to the bolts/nuts in the correct sequence, followed by one or more stages of tightening through specified angles.

Locknuts, locktabs and washers

Any fastening which will rotate against a component or housing during tightening should always have a washer between it and the relevant component or housing.

Spring or split washers should always be renewed when they are used to lock a critical component such as a big-end bearing retaining bolt or nut. Locktabs which are folded over to retain a nut or bolt should always be renewed.

Self-locking nuts can be re-used in non-critical areas, providing resistance can be felt when the locking portion passes over the bolt or stud thread. However, it should be noted that self-locking stiffnuts tend to lose their effectiveness after long periods of use, and should then be renewed as a matter of course.

Split pins must always be replaced with new ones of the correct size for the hole.

When thread-locking compound is found on the threads of a fastener which is to be re-used, it should be cleaned off with a wire brush and solvent, and fresh compound applied on reassembly.

Special tools

Some repair procedures in this manual entail the use of special tools such as a press, two or three-legged pullers, spring compressors, etc. Wherever possible, suitable readily-available alternatives to the manufacturer's special tools are described, and are shown in use. In some instances, where no alternative is possible, it has been necessary to resort to the use of a manufacturer's tool, and this has been done for reasons of safety as well as the efficient completion of the repair operation. Unless you are highly-skilled and have a thorough understanding of the procedures described, never attempt to bypass the use of any special tool when the procedure described specifies its use. Not only is there a very great risk of personal injury, but expensive damage could be caused to the components involved.

Environmental considerations

When disposing of used engine oil, brake fluid, antifreeze, etc, give due consideration to any detrimental environmental effects. Do not, for instance, pour any of the above liquids down drains into the general sewage system, or onto the ground to soak away. Many local council refuse tips provide a facility for waste oil disposal, as do some garages. If none of these facilities are available, consult your local Environmental Health Department, or the National Rivers Authority, for further advice.

With the universal tightening-up of legislation regarding the emission of environmentally-harmful substances from motor vehicles, most vehicles have tamperproof devices fitted to the main adjustment points of the fuel system. These devices are primarily designed to prevent unqualified persons from adjusting the fuel/air mixture, with the chance of a consequent increase in toxic emissions. If such devices are found during servicing or overhaul, they should, wherever possible, be renewed or refitted in accordance with the manufacturer's requirements or current legislation.

OIL CARE
FOLLOW THE CODE

OIL BANK LINE
0800 66 33 66

Note: It is antisocial and illegal to dump oil down the drain. To find the location of your local oil recycling bank, call this number free.

With any fault-finding, the first step is to decide where to begin investigations. Sometimes this is obvious, but on other occasions, a little detective work will be necessary. The person who makes half a dozen haphazard adjustments or replacements may be successful in curing a fault (or its symptoms), but will be none the wiser if the fault recurs, and ultimately may have spent more time and money than was necessary. A calm and logical approach will be found to be more satisfactory in the long run. Always take into account any warning signs or abnormalities that may have been noticed in the period preceding the fault.

Bear in mind that faults which may at first sight be due to the gearbox can in fact have some other cause. In particular, clutch maladjustment or malfunction can make engagement of gears difficult, while propeller shaft or driveshaft joint wear can give rise to vibration apparently coming from the gearbox.

Gearboxes which whine or rumble, or on which the synchromesh can easily be 'beaten', may carry on for a long time in such a state. As a rule of thumb, noises which start suddenly and rapidly get worse are more of a cause for concern than those which develop slowly. The use of proprietary oil additives, whilst frowned on by vehicle manufacturers and oil companies alike, can sometimes have a palliative effect.

Always check the oil level and verify that the correct grade of oil is in use before proceeding to any other fault diagnosis.

Transmission noisy in neutral
- [ ] Input shaft bearings worn (noise apparent with clutch pedal released, but not when depressed)
- [ ] Clutch release bearing worn (noise apparent with clutch pedal depressed, probably less when released)
- [ ] Oil type incorrect or level too low
- [ ] Excessive shaft endplay

Transmission noisy only when moving (in all gears)
- [ ] Mainshaft bearings worn
- [ ] Differential bearings worn
- [ ] Wear of differential crownwheel and mainshaft pinion teeth
- [ ] Oil type incorrect or level too low
- [ ] Excessive shaft endplay

Transmission noisy in only one gear
- [ ] Worn, damaged or chipped gear teeth

Transmission noisy when cornering
- [ ] Driveshaft or wheel bearing worn
- [ ] Differential bearing worn

Transmission jumps out of gear
- [ ] Worn synchroniser units
- [ ] Worn selector shaft detent plungers or springs
- [ ] Worn selector forks
- [ ] Selector linkage damaged or adjustment incorrect

Ineffective synchromesh
- [ ] Worn synchroniser units or baulk rings
- [ ] Selector linkage out of adjustment

Difficulty in engaging gears*
- [ ] Selector linkage damaged or adjustment incorrect
- [ ] Worn selector forks or selector mechanism
- [ ] Clutch fault
- [ ] Seized input shaft pilot bearing in flywheel (Ford type B or N only)

Vibration
- [ ] Lack of oil
- [ ] Worn bearings
- [ ] Driveshaft or propeller shaft joints worn
- [ ] Propeller shaft flange bolts loose (when applicable)
- [ ] Engine or gearbox mountings worn or loose

Lubricant leaks
- [ ] Ineffective oil seals
- [ ] Gearbox housing joint leaking

Before being able to engage reverse gear, it is normal to have to wait a couple of seconds with the clutch pedal fully depressed, the engine idling and the vehicle stationary. This is not a fault.

The maintenance intervals in this manual are based on those provided by the vehicle manufacturers for vehicles driven daily. If you wish to keep your gearbox in peak condition at all times, you may wish to check the oil level, or renew the oil, more frequently than specified. A good practice, where possible, would be to renew the oil regularly instead of just checking the level.

If frequent topping-up of the gearbox oil is required, this can only be due to a leak which should be found and rectified before it becomes serious. (This does not necessarily apply to the Mini or Metro, where the gearbox and engine share the same oil.)

Besides attention to lubrication, check the security and condition of the gearbox mountings and attachments from time to time. On gearboxes with external linkages, also check the security and condition of articulating joints, rubber bushes and the like.

Austin/Rover Metro gearbox*

All models	Renew every 6000 miles or 6 months, whichever comes first

Austin/Rover Mini gearbox*

All models	Renew every 6000 miles or 6 months, whichever comes first

Citroën/Peugeot BE gearbox

Without filler/level plug	Renew every 2 years**
With filler/level plug	Check level every 36 000 miles

Citroën/Peugeot MA gearbox

All models	Check level every 36 000 miles

Ford B & N gearboxes

All models	Check level every 12 000 miles or 12 months, whichever comes first

Ford J & K gearboxes

All models	Check level every 12 000 miles or 12 months, whichever comes first

Vauxhall F10 gearbox

Models up to 1984	Check level every 6000 miles or 6 months, whichever comes first
Models from 1984	Check level every 18 000 miles or 24 months, whichever comes first

Vauxhall F16 gearbox

Models up to 1984	Check level every 6000 miles or 6 months, whichever comes first
Models from 1984	Check level every 18 000 miles or 24 months, whichever comes first

VW 084/020 gearbox

Models up to 1992	Check level every 10 000 miles or 12 months, whichever comes first
Models from 1992	Check level every 20 000 miles or 24 months, whichever comes first

*Lubricant shared with engine
**The mileage interval varies according to model

Refer to the approrpriate Chapter for oil capacity and location of drain and filler/level plugs.

Austin/Rover Metro gearbox

Models up to July 1983 — Multigrade engine oil, viscosity SAE 15W/50
(Duckhams Hypergrade Petrol Engine Oil)

Models from August 1983 — Multigrade engine oil, viscosity SAE 10W/40
(Duckhams Hypergrade Petrol Engine Oil or Duckhams QXR Premium Petrol
Engine Oil)

Austin/Rover Mini gearbox

Models up to July 1983 — Multigrade engine oil, viscosity SAE 10W/30, 10W/40 or 20W/50
(Duckhams Hypergrade Petrol Engine Oil or Duckhams QXR Premium Petrol
Engine Oil)

Models from August 1983 — Multigrade engine oil, viscosity SAE 10W/40
(Duckhams QXR Premium Petrol Engine Oil)

Citroën/Peugeot BE gearbox

Without filler/level plug — Multigrade engine oil, viscosity SAE 10W/40 or 15W/40
(Duckhams Hypergrade Petrol Engine Oil)

With filler/level plug — Gear oil, viscosity SAE 75W/80
(Duckhams Hypoid PT 75w/80w)

Citroën/Peugeot MA gearbox

All models — Gear oil, viscosity SAE 75W/80
(Duckhams Hypoid PT 75w/80w)

Ford B & N gearboxes

B gearbox: — Gear oil, viscosity SAE 80EP, to Ford spec SQM 2C 9008-A
(Duckhams Hypoid 80w/90)

N gearbox:
4-speed & 4x4 — Gear oil, viscosity SAE 80EP, to Ford spec SQM 2C 9008-A
(Duckhams Hypoid 80w/90)

5-speed non-4x4 — Semi-synthetic gear oil to Ford spec ESD-M2C-175-A
(Duckhams Hypoid 75w/90S)

Transfer box (4x4) — Automatic transmission fluid to Ford spec SQM-2C 9010-A
(Duckhams Unimatic)

Ford J & K gearboxes

All models — Gear oil, viscosity SAE 80EP, to Ford spec SQM 2C 9008-A
(Duckhams Hypoid 80w/90)

Vauxhall F10 gearbox

Corsa 1993 to 1997 — GM 90 001 777 gear oil
(Duckhams Hypoid 80w/90)

All other models — Gear oil, viscosity SAE 80 or GM 90 188 629 gear oil
(Duckhams Hypoid 80w/90)

Vauxhall F16 gearbox

Astra/Kadett GTE — GM 90 188 629 gear oil

All other models — Gear oil, viscosity SAE 80 or GM 90 188 629 gear oil
(Duckhams Hypoid 80w/90)

VW 084 & 020 gearboxes

Models up to 1992 — Gear oil, viscosity SAE 80
(Duckhams Hypoid 75w/90S)

Models from 1992 — Gear oil, viscosity SAE 80 or 75W/90 (VW G50 gear oil)
(Duckhams Hypoid 75w/90S)

Chapter 1
Austin/Rover Metro gearbox

Contents

Specifications

General

Type	Four forward speeds and reverse; synchromesh on all forward speeds

Gear ratios (typical)

	1.0 HLE	All other models
1st	4.00 : 1	3.65 : 1
2nd	2.31 : 1	2.19 : 1
3rd	1.44 : 1	1.43 : 1
Top	1.00 : 1	1.00 : 1
Reverse	4.03 : 1	3.67 : 1
Final drive	3.11 : 1	3.65 : 1

Primary gear

Endfloat	0.089 to 0.165 mm (0.0035 to 0.0065 in)
Thrust washers available	2.84 to 2.89 mm (0.112 to 0.114 in)
	2.89 to 2.94 mm (0.114 to 0.116 in)
	2.94 to 2.99 mm (0.116 to 0.118 in)
	2.99 to 3.04 mm (0.118 to 0.120 in)

Idler gear

Endfloat	0.102 to 0.178 mm (0.004 to 0.007 in)
Thrust washers available	3.35 to 3.37 mm (0.132 to 0.133 in)
	3.40 to 3.42 mm (0.134 to 0.135 in)
	3.45 to 3.47 mm (0.136 to 0.137 in)
	3.50 to 3.53 mm (0.138 to 0.139 in)

Laygear

Endfloat	0.05 to 0.15 mm (0.002 to 0.006 in)
Thrustwashers available	3.12 to 3.14 mm (0.123 to 0.124 in)
	3.17 to 3.20 mm (0.125 to 0.126 in)
	3.22 to 3.25 mm (0.127 to 0.128 in)
	3.30 to 3.32 mm (0.130 to 0.131 in)

Third motion shaft

Endfloat	0 ± 0.025 mm (0 ± 0.001 in)

Lubrication

Oil capacity (with engine)	4.8 litres (8.5 pints)
Lubricant type/specification	See *Recommended lubricants and fluids*

1

Torque wrench settings

	Nm	lbf ft
Bellcrank lever pivot pin nut	29	21
Drain plug	41	30
Final drive pinion nut	207	153
First motion shaft nut	207	153
Flywheel housing nuts and bolts	25	18
Gearbox case studs:		
3/8 in diameter	11	8
5/16 in diameter	8	6
Gearbox case stud nuts:		
3/8 in diameter	35	26
5/16 in diameter	25	18
Gearbox case to crankcase	8	6
Speedometer gear housing bolts	8	6
Speedometer gear housing nuts	25	18
Third motion shaft bearing retaining bolts	18	13

1 General description

The manual gearbox incorporates four forward speeds and one reverse speed, with synchromesh engagement on all forward gears.

Gearshift is by means of a floor-mounted lever, connected by a remote control housing and extension rod to a selector shaft located in the bottom of the gearbox casing. The selector shaft incorporates an interlock spool, and a stub on the end of the shaft is in contact with a bellcrank lever assembly, which in turn moves the selector forks and the reverse idler gear to select the required gear (see illustration).

The final drive (differential) unit is attached to the rear of the gearbox casing, and the final drive gear is in mesh with a splined pinion on the end of the third motion shaft.

A drain plug incorporating a magnetic swarf collector is screwed into the right-hand side of the gearbox casing.

1.1 Exploded and phantom views of the gearbox

1 Laygear thrustwashers
2 Needle roller bearing(s) (1 or 2 off large)
3 Laygear
4 Layshaft
5 Reverse idler gear shaft
6 Bush
7 Reverse idler gear
8 Bracket
9 Oil pick-up pipe
10 Final drive pinion nut
11 Lockwasher
12 Final drive pinion
13 Bearing retainer
14 Shaft locking plate
15 Shim
16 Circlip
17 Bearing
18 1st speed gear
19 Needle roller bearing
20 Journal
21 Baulk ring
22 Synchro unit spring
23 1st/2nd synchro hub
24 1st/2nd synchro sleeve and reverse gear
25 Baulk ring
26 Thrust washer
27 2nd speed gear
28 Split needle roller bearing
29 Third motion shaft
30 Locking plungers
31 Locking plunger and spring
32 Synchro unit spring
33 Nut
34 Spigot bearing
35 Circlip

36 Main bearing cap oil seal
37 Gearbox casing
38 O-ring
39 Oil strainer
40 O-ring
41 Dowel
42 Gasket
43 3rd speed gear
44 Split needle roller bearing
45 Thrust washer
46 Baulk ring
47 3rd/top synchro hub
48 3rd/top synchro sleeve
49 Needle roller bearing
50 Baulk ring
51 First motion shaft
52 Bearing
53 Circlip
54 First motion shaft gear
55 Lockwasher
56 Endplate
57 Gasket
58 Speedometer drivegear
59 Speedometer drive housing
60 Speedometer drive pinion
61 Bush
62 Seal
63 Clamp and bearing
64 Blanking plate
65 Thrust washer
66 Differential pinion
67 Selector shaft
68 1st/2nd speed selector fork
69 Roll pin

70 3rd/top speed selector fork
71 Gasket
72 Differential housing
73 Bush
74 Spring ring
75 Differential gear
76 Thrust washer
77 Thrust block
78 Differential gear
79 Differential pinion
80 Thrust washer
81 Roll pin
82 Differential cage
83 Bush
84 Bearing
85 Pinion pin
86 Gasket
87 Side cover
88 Bush
89 Oil seal
90 Inner CV joint
91 Oil seal
92 Bush
93 Side cover
94 Gasket
95 Shim
96 Bearing
97 Final drive gear
98 Selector shaft
99 Drain plug
100 Bellcrank lever assembly
101 Interlock spool
102 Oil seal
103 Detent ball, spring, sleeve and O-ring

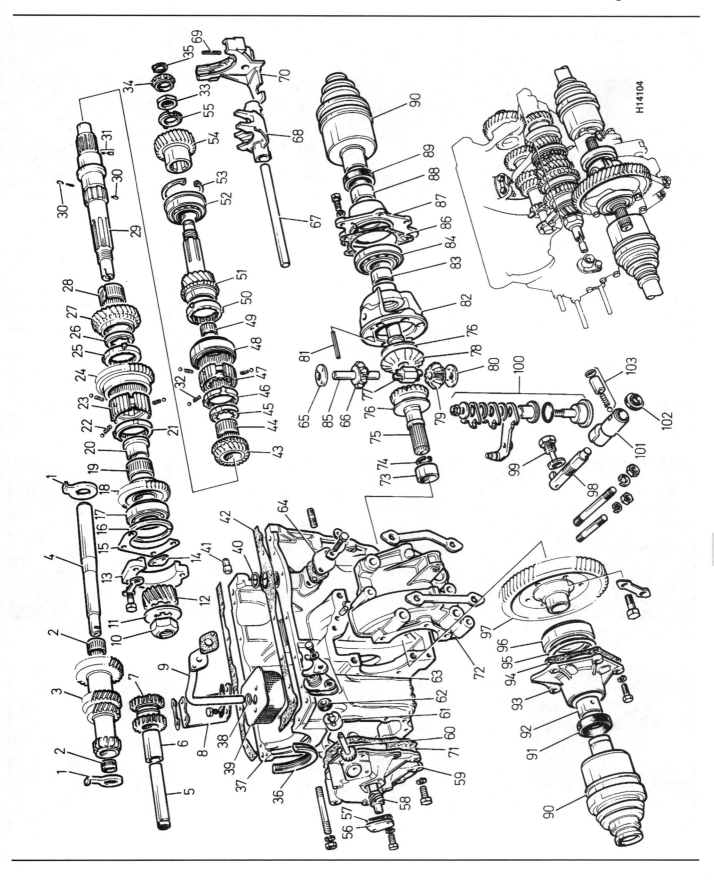

H14104

1

2.3 Extracting the spigot-bearing circlip

2.5a Removing the nut . . .

2.5b . . . and first motion shaft gear

2 Dismantling into assemblies

1 Remove the final drive (differential) unit.
2 Remove the final drive pinion.
3 Extract the circlip from the end of the first motion shaft (see illustration).
4 Flatten the locktab then, with first and top gear selected, loosen the first motion shaft nut and unscrew it to the end of the thread to push off the spigot bearing. Screw in the nut and use a spanner to tap the bearing off the shaft.
5 Unscrew and remove the nut and lockwasher, then slide the gear from the first motion shaft (see illustrations).
6 Move the selector forks to select neutral.
7 Flatten the locktabs then unbolt the third motion shaft bearing retainer.
8 Remove the reverse shaft/layshaft locking plate and the bearing adjustment shims (see illustrations).
9 Flatten the locktabs and unscrew the oil pick-up pipe retaining bolts. Remove the blanking plate and gaskets and withdraw the oil pick-up pipe (see illustrations).
10 Push the layshaft out and withdraw it from the transfer gear end of the gearbox (see illustration).
11 Flatten the locktabs and unscrew the oil strainer bracket retaining bolts (see illustration).
12 Remove the small thrustwasher, then withdraw the laygear and large thrustwasher from the gearbox (see illustration).
13 Extract the large circlip from the first motion shaft bearing groove (see illustration).
14 Refit the first motion shaft nut and use a puller or slide hammer to remove the first motion shaft, complete with bearing.
15 Using a soft metal drift, drive the third motion shaft towards the clutch end of the gearbox, but do not disengage the 3rd/4th synchro sleeve from its hub, otherwise the synchro balls and springs will be ejected.
16 Insert open-ended spanners over the third motion shaft between the 1st speed gear and

2.8a Location of the reverse shaft/layshaft locking plate

2.8b Third motion shaft bearing retainer shim

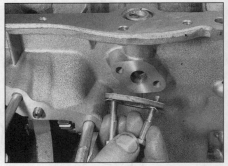

2.9a Removing the blanking plate . . .

2.9b . . . and oil pick-up pipe

2.10 Removing the layshaft

2.11 Removing the oil strainer bracket bolts

2.12 Removing the laygear

2.13 Extracting the first motion shaft bearing circlip

2.16a Using a spanner . . .

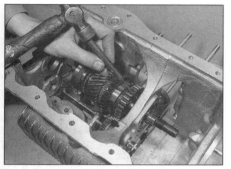

2.16b . . . and drift to remove the third motion shaft bearing

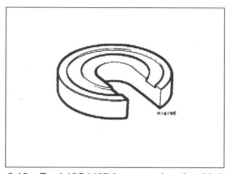

2.16c Tool 18G1127 for removing the third motion shaft bearing

2.17a Removing the third motion shaft . . .

the bearing, then tap the end of the third motion shaft to partially remove the bearing. Fully remove the bearing with a suitable drift, or alternatively obtain tool 18G1127 **(see illustrations)**.

17 Withdraw the third motion shaft from the gearbox, and also remove the oil strainer **(see illustrations)**.

18 Remove the reverse idler shaft and gear **(see illustration)**.

19 Drive the roll pin from the 3rd/4th selector fork and selector shaft **(see illustration)**.

20 Remove the selector shaft and withdraw the selector forks **(see illustration)**.

21 Unscrew the selector bellcrank lever pivot post nut, and withdraw the washer, bellcrank

2.17b . . . and oil strainer

2.18 Removing the reverse idler shaft and gear

2.19 Removing the 3rd/4th selector fork roll pin

2.20 Removing the selector shaft and forks

2.21a Removing the selector bellcrank lever pivot post nut

1

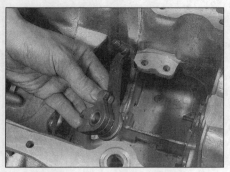

2.21b Removing the bellcrank levers

2.22 Removing the interlock spool and selector shaft

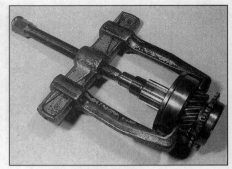

3.3 Removing the first motion shaft bearing

levers, intermediate washers, and pivot sleeve. Note the lever positions on the sleeve **(see illustrations)**.
22 Remove the interlock spool and selector shaft from inside the gearbox casing **(see illustration)**.

3 First motion shaft - dismantling and reassembly

1 Examine the gear teeth for wear and chipping and the dog teeth for wear. Check the gear and shaft splines for wear by refitting the gear and attempting to move the gear within the splines.

2 Check the spigot needle roller bearing for wear; also check the bearing surfaces of the first and third motion shafts.
3 Spin the ball-bearing by hand and check it for roughness. To remove the bearing, position the outer race over an open vice and drive the first motion shaft out of the inner race. Alternatively use a suitable puller **(see illustration)**.
4 Renew the components as necessary. Fit the new ball-bearing by resting the coned end of the shaft on a block of wood, and, using a suitable length of tube against the inner race, drive it fully onto the shaft. Make sure that the bearing flanged end is towards the splined end of the shaft.

4 Laygear, reverse idler gear, and shafts - dismantling and reassembly

1 Examine the gear teeth for wear and chipping, particularly the spur teeth. Remove the needle roller bearings from the laygear and check them for wear. Check the bearing surfaces of the laygear, reverse idler gear, and the corresponding shafts for wear and pitting **(see illustration)**.
2 Renew the laygear thrustwashers if the laygear endfloat is greater than the maximum given in the Specifications.
3 Renew the laygear and reverse idler gear components as necessary.

5 Third motion shaft - dismantling and reassembly

1 Remove the top baulk ring from the end of the shaft, and press off the 3rd/top synchro unit. Remove the third baulk ring **(see illustrations)**.
2 Depress the locking plunger with a screwdriver, then turn the thrustwasher until its splines are aligned with those on the shaft. Remove the thrustwasher, plunger, and spring **(see illustrations)**.

4.1 Laygear, shaft and bearings

5.1a Removing the top baulk ring . . .

5.1b . . . 3rd/top synchro unit

5.1c . . . and 3rd baulk ring

5.2a Depress the locking plunger . . .

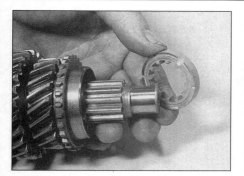

5.2b ... remove the thrustwasher ...

5.2c ... plunger and spring from the third motion shaft

5.3a Removing the 3rd gear...

3 Remove the 3rd gear and split needle roller bearing **(see illustrations)**.

4 Remove the 1st gear from the speedometer drive end of the shaft, followed by the needle roller bearing and bush **(see illustrations)**.

5 Remove the 1st baulk ring and press off the 1st/2nd synchro unit. Remove the 2nd baulk ring **(see illustrations)**.

6 Turn the 2nd gear to align the holes, then depress the two locking plungers and turn the thrustwasher until its splines are aligned with those on the shaft **(see illustrations)**.

7 Remove the thrustwasher and 2nd gear together, then remove the plungers and

5.3b ... and split needle roller bearing

5.4a Removing the 1st gear ...

5.4b ... needle roller bearing ...

5.4c ... and bush

5.5a Removing 1st baulk ring ...

5.5b ... 1st/2nd synchro unit. ..

5.5c ... and 2nd baulk ring

5.6a Align the holes in the 2nd gear...

1

5.6b . . . and depress the locking plungers

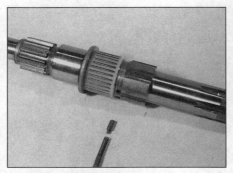

5.7a Removing the plungers and spring . . .

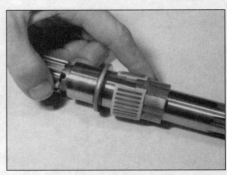

5.7b . . . and split needle roller bearing

spring followed by the split needle roller bearing **(see illustrations)**.

8 Mark the hub and sleeve of each synchro unit in relation to each other. Identify each baulk ring for position to ensure correct reassembly.

9 To dismantle the synchro units, wrap them each in cloth and push the hubs from the sleeves. Keep the balls and springs separate with each synchro unit **(see illustration)**.

10 Examine all the gear teeth for wear and chipping. Check the bearing surfaces on all components for excessive wear or pitting. Check the needle roller bearings for wear and damage to the cages. Check the splines on the third motion shaft, synchro-hubs and final

drive pinion for wear by refitting the components and attempting to move them within the splines. Check the thrustwashers, plungers and springs for wear and damage.

11 Check the synchro unit hub and sleeve splines for wear. Check the synchro unit springs and balls for wear. Fit each baulk ring on its respective gear cone, and check that it locks onto the taper before contacting the edge of the gear. If not, the complete synchro unit and baulk rings should be renewed.

12 Renew all components as necessary. During reassembly lubricate all bearing surfaces liberally with gear oil.

13 First assemble the synchro units, preferably using tool 18G572, although a jubilee clip may

be used instead. Locate the springs and balls in the hub and hold them depressed using the tool or clip **(see illustrations)**.

14 With the sleeve on a flat surface, insert the hub into the splines with the previous marks and the cut-outs aligned. Using a block of wood, give the hub a sharp tap to force it into the sleeve, together with the balls.

15 Repeat the procedure on the remaining synchro unit.

16 Grip the third motion shaft vertically in a soft-jawed vice with the speedometer drive end uppermost **(see illustration)**.

17 Locate the split needle roller bearing onto the shaft, and insert the spring and two plungers **(see illustration)**.

5.9 Synchro unit ball and spring

5.13a Assemble the synchro unit . . .

5.13b . . . and use a jubilee clip to depress the balls

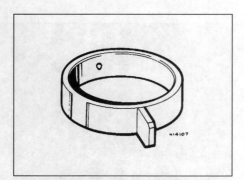

5.13c Tool 18G572 for installing synchro unit balls and springs

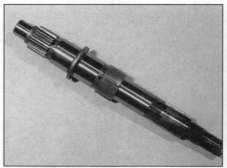

5.16 The dismantled third motion shaft

5.17 Split needle roller bearing and spring and plungers assembled to the third motion shaft

5.18 Fitting the 2nd gear

5.19 Installing the 2nd gear thrustwasher

5.26 Fitting the 3rd gear thrustwasher

18 Depress the plungers and fit the 2nd gear with the cone facing upwards **(see illustration)**. The plungers will be released after the gear has passed over them, but they cannot escape as the gear cone prevents this.
19 Locate the thrustwasher, machined grooves first, on the splines, then depress both plungers and push the thrustwasher over them **(see illustration)**. Turn the thrustwasher the width of one spline so that the plungers are released and the washer locked.
20 Fit the baulk ring to the 2nd gear. Press the complete 1st/2nd synchro unit onto the shaft splines, reverse gear teeth end first, at the same time engaging the 2nd baulk ring with the hub.

21 Locate the 1st baulk ring in the synchro hub cut-outs.
22 Locate the 1st gear bush on the shaft, flanged end first, followed by the needle roller bearing and 1st gear, raised cone end first.
23 Hold the gears in position, then invert the assembly in the vice.
24 Locate the 3rd gear needle roller bearing on the shaft, followed by the 3rd gear, gear end first.
25 Insert the spring and plunger into the hole in the shaft. Locate the thrustwasher, machined grooves first, on the splines.
26 Depress the plunger and push the thrustwasher over it **(see illustration)**. Turn the thrustwasher the width of one spline so

that the plunger is released and the washer locked.
27 Locate the 3rd baulk ring to the 3rd gear. Press the complete 3rd/top synchro unit onto the shaft splines, at the same time engaging the 3rd baulk ring with the hub. The raised section of the synchro sleeve must be towards the gear.
28 Locate the top baulk ring in the synchro hub cut-outs.

6 Transfer gears - dismantling and reassembly

1 Remove the C-shaped thrustwasher from the end of the crankshaft, and withdraw the backing ring, primary gear, and the notched thrustwasher **(see illustrations)**.
2 Remove the idler gear and thrustwashers from the flywheel housing or gearbox casing; identify the thrustwashers side for side **(see illustration)**.
3 Examine the gear teeth for wear and chipping. Check the primary gear splines and inner bushes for wear; also check the idler gear thrustwashers.
4 Check the idler gear needle roller bearings in the flywheel housing and gearbox casing, and the bearing surfaces of the idler gear for

6.1a Removing the thrustwasher. . .

6.1b . . . backing ring . . .

6.1c . . . primary gear. . .

6.1d . . . and notched thrustwasher from the crankshaft

6.2 Removing the idler gear

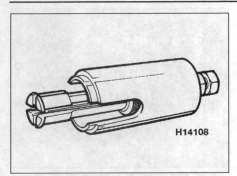

6.4 Tool 18G1288 for removing idler gear bearings

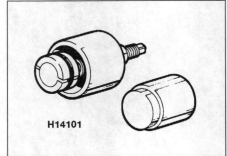

6.5 Tool 18G617C for removing first motion shaft spigot bearing outer race

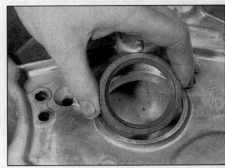

6.8 Installing the primary gear oil seal

wear. To remove the needle roller bearings, use tool 18G1288 or a similar puller **(see illustration)**.

5 Check the first motion shaft spigot bearing and race for damage. To remove the outer race from the flywheel housing, extract the circlip, and use tool 18G617C **(see illustration)**.

6 Drive the primary gear oil seal from the flywheel housing using a metal tube of suitable diameter.

7 Renew all components as necessary.

8 Using a block of wood, drive the new primary gear oil seal into the flywheel housing with the seal lip facing inwards **(see illustration)**.

9 Using a length of metal tube, drive the first motion shaft spigot bearing outer race

squarely into the flywheel housing. If available use tool 18G617C. Fit the retaining circlip in its groove **(see illustration)**.

10 Using a length of metal tube, drive the idler gear needle roller bearings squarely into the flywheel housing and gearbox casing until just recessed below the housing/casing surface. Use tool 18G1289 if available **(see illustration)**. The chamfered end of the bearings should be inserted first.

11 Locate the notched thrustwasher (chamfered side first) onto the end of the crankshaft, followed by the primary gear (gear end first), backing ring and C-shaped thrustwasher.

12 Using a feeler blade between the backing ring and gear, check that the primary gear endfloat is as given in the Specifications **(see**

illustration). If not, note the measured endfloat, then remove the notched thrustwasher and measure its thickness. An alternative thrustwasher must now be selected and fitted to correct the endfloat.

7 Selector components and gearbox housings - dismantling and reassembly

1 Examine the bellcrank lever components, the selector forks and the selector shaft for wear and damage, and renew them as necessary **(see illustrations)**.

2 If the bellcrank lever pivot post is worn, drive it out of the gearbox casing using a

6.9 First motion shaft spigot and idler gear bearings in the flywheel housing

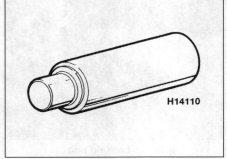

6.10 Tool 18B1289 for fitting idler gear bearings

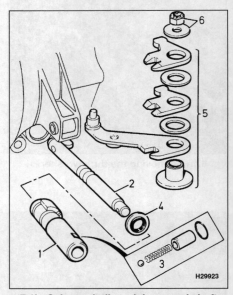

7.1b Selector bellcrank lever and shaft components

1 *Interlock spool*
2 *Selector shaft*
3 *Detent ball, spring, sleeve and O-ring*
4 *Oil seal*
5 *Bellcrank levers and pivot sleeve assembly*
6 *Pivot post nut and washer*

6.12 Checking the primary gear endfloat

7.1a Interlock spool and selector shaft

length of metal tubing, while supporting the casing with blocks of wood.

3 Renew and lubricate the O-ring seal, and drive the new pivot post into the gearbox casing.

4 Unbolt the endplate and gasket from the speedometer drive housing and withdraw the speedometer gear.

5 Wash the gearbox casing, flywheel housing and speedometer drive housing with paraffin and wipe dry with lint-free cloth. Thoroughly examine the housings for cracks and damage and renew them as necessary.

6 Check the speedometer drivegear for wear and chipping; also check the pinion. Renew them as necessary.

7 Fit the drivegear into the housing, and fit the endplate with a new gasket. Tighten the bolts.

8 Reassembly

Note: *Before reassembly, all components must be clean. During reassembly, all bearings and bearing surfaces should be lubricated with gear oil.*

1 Insert the selector shaft into the interlock spool, then locate them in the gearbox casing from inside with the stub facing away from the pivot post.

2 Fit the pivot sleeve, bellcrank levers, and intermediate washers onto the pivot post,

8.8 Fitting the third motion shaft bearing

8.10 Installing the first motion shaft

8.3 Inserting the selector shaft through the forks

then fit the washer and tighten the self-locking nut to the specified torque.

3 Locate the selector forks in the casing in their correct order, then insert the selector shaft through the casing and forks **(see illustration)**.

4 Align the hole in the selector shaft with the hole in the 3rd/4th selector fork. Drive in the roll pin with a punch until it is flush with the surface of the fork.

5 Engage the reverse idler gear groove with the reverse bellcrank lever, with the groove towards the transfer gear end of the gearbox. Insert the shaft through the casing and idler gear with the slotted end towards the speedometer drive end of the gearbox.

6 Position the oil strainer loosely in the casing **(see illustration)**.

7 Install the third motion shaft assembly into

8.9 Installing the needle roller bearing in the first motion shaft

8.11a Checking the first motion shaft bearing circlip groove width

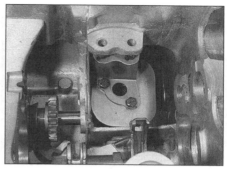

8.6 Oil strainer location

the gearbox, at the same time engaging the two selector forks with their corresponding synchro units.

8 Locate the ball-bearing over the third motion shaft with the circlip towards the speedometer drive end of the gearbox **(see illustration)**. Hold a block of wood against the inner end of the third motion shaft, then drive the bearing into the centre web of the casing using a length of tubing on the bearing outer track.

9 Locate the needle roller bearing into the end of the first motion shaft **(see illustration)**.

10 Using a length of tubing on the ball-bearing outer track, drive the first motion shaft and bearing into the casing, making sure that it engages the third motion shaft spigot **(see illustration)**.

11 Using feeler blades or tool 18G569, determine the width of the first motion shaft bearing circlip groove **(see illustrations)**. If it is between 2.44 and 2.49 mm (0.096 and 0.098 in) the circlip part number 2A3710 should be used; if it is between 2.49 and 2.54 mm (0.098 and 0.100 in) circlip part number 2A3711 should be used. If the original bearing is being re-used, the original circlip can be fitted.

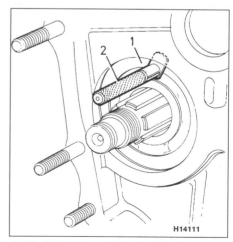

8.11b Using tool 18G569 to determine the thickness of the first motion shaft bearing circlip

1 Bearing   2 Tool

8.13 Laygear needle roller bearing

8.14a A laygear thrustwasher (arrowed)

8.14b Checking the laygear endfloat

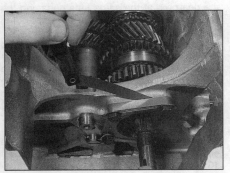

8.16 Checking for third motion shaft bearing endfloat

8.23 Tightening the first motion shaft nut

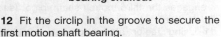

8.24 Fitting the first motion shaft spigot bearing

12 Fit the circlip in the groove to secure the first motion shaft bearing.

13 Insert the needle roller bearings into the laygear **(see illustration)**.

14 Using grease, stick the laygear thrustwashers in position on the casing and lower the laygear between them. Insert the layshaft from the transfer gear end of the gearbox. Check that the endfloat is as given in the Specifications **(see illustrations)**.

15 Turn the ends of the layshaft and reverse idler shaft until the slots are parallel to and facing each other, then insert the locking plate.

16 Install the third motion shaft bearing retainer without any shims, and tighten the bolts evenly and firmly. Using feeler blades, determine the gap (if any) between the retainer and the casing **(see illustration)**. Deduct the specified bearing endfloat from the result to give the thickness of shims to fit.

17 Remove the retainer, then fit the selected shims beneath the reverse shaft layshaft locking plate to give the specified third motion shaft bearing endfloat.

18 Refit the retainer and tighten the bolts evenly and in diagonal sequence to the specified torque.

19 Engage 1st and top gear to lock the gears.

20 Fit the final drive pinion.

21 Check the third motion shaft endfloat and, if as specified, bend the locktabs onto one flat of each bolt to lock them.

22 Fit the speedometer drive housing.

23 Slide the first motion shaft gear (flanged end first) onto the first motion shaft splines. Fit the lockwasher and nut, and tighten the nut to the specified torque **(see illustration)**. Bend the locktab to lock the nut.

24 Drive the spigot bearing, flange end first, onto the end of the first motion shaft and fit the circlip into the groove **(see illustration)**.

25 Move the selector forks to select neutral, then rotate the selector shaft and spool

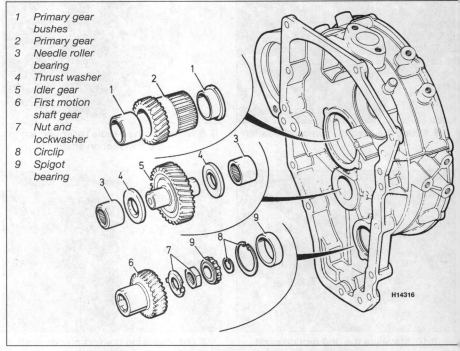

1 Primary gear bushes
2 Primary gear
3 Needle roller bearing
4 Thrust washer
5 Idler gear
6 First motion shaft gear
7 Nut and lockwasher
8 Circlip
9 Spigot bearing

8.31 Exploded view of the transfer gears and flywheel housing

clockwise into engagement with the bellcrank levers.

26 Insert the oil pick-up pipe into the strainer.
27 Locate new gaskets either side of the casing with the blanking plate on the outside. Fit the lockwasher and bolts, and tighten the bolts. Bend the locktabs to lock the bolts.
28 Fit the oil strainer bracket bolts and lockwasher, and tighten them. Bend the locktabs to lock the bolts.
29 Fit the final drive (differential) unit.
30 Lubricate the gears and bearings liberally with gear oil.

Refitting

31 If either the idler gear, idler gear thrustwashers, flywheel housing, or gearbox casing have been renewed, one of the two methods given below must be followed in order to determine the idler gear thrustwasher thickness **(see illustration)**. With either procedure, a selection of thrustwashers and an extra flywheel housing gasket should be obtained before starting work.

Gearbox separated from engine

32 Fit the idler gear to the gearbox casing needle roller bearing, together with a medium-size thrustwasher **(see illustration)**. Locate a small size thrustwasher on the outside of the idler gear.
33 Fit the flywheel housing with a new gasket to the gearbox casing, and tighten the nuts and bolts to the specified torque **(see illustration)**.
34 Using a feeler blade behind the flywheel housing, check the idler gear endfloat with the feeler blade between the inner thrustwasher and idler gear **(see illustration)**. If the endfloat is not as specified, select a different outer thrustwasher of a thickness which will correct the endfloat.
35 Remove the flywheel housing and discard the gasket. Fit the correct outer thrustwasher, then fit the gearbox using the remaining new gasket.

8.32 Removing the idler gear

Gearbox attached to engine

36 Fit the idler gear to the gearbox casing needle roller bearing together with a medium size thrustwasher.
37 Fit a thin washer followed by a wax washer and a further thin washer from tool 18G1089 to the flywheel side of the idler gear **(see illustration)**.
38 Fit the flywheel housing with a new gasket and tighten the nuts and bolts to the specified torque.

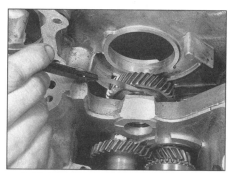

8.34 Checking the idler gear endfloat (gearbox separated from engine)

8.33 Fitting the flywheel housing gasket

39 Unscrew the nuts and bolts and remove the flywheel housing and gasket.
40 Remove the thin washers and wax washer, and measure their thickness carefully with a micrometer. Subtract the specified endfloat, and fit a thrustwasher of the resulting thickness to the flywheel side of the idler gear.
41 Discard the gasket just used, then fit the flywheel housing with the remaining new gasket.

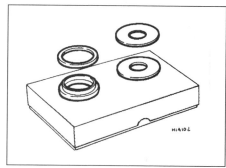

8.37 Tool 18G1089 for calculating idler gear thrustwasher thickness

1

Notes

Chapter 2
Austin/Rover Mini gearbox

Contents

Specifications

General

Type .... Four forward and one reverse gear, synchromesh action on all forward gears

Gear ratios (typical)

Up to 1985:	850 & 998	1098	1275
1st	3.52 : 1	3.52 : 1	3.33 : 1
2nd	2.22 : 1	2.22 : 1	2.09 : 1
3rd	1.43 : 1	1.43 : 1	1.35 : 1
Top	1.00 : 1	1.00 : 1	1.00 : 1
Reverse	3.54 : 1	3.54 : 1	3.34 : 1
Final drive	3.76 : 1	3.44 : 1	3.44 : 1

From 1985:	All models
1st	3.65 : 1
2nd	2.19 : 1
3rd	1.43 : 1
Top	1.00 : 1
Reverse	3.67 : 1
Final drive	3.11 : 1

Laygear

Endfloat .... 0.05 to 0.15 mm (0.002 to 0.006 in)

Primary gear

Endfloat .... 0.10 to 0.18 mm (0.004 to 0.007 in)

Idler gear

Endfloat .... 0.10 to 0.18 mm (0.004 to 0.007 in)

Lubrication

Oil capacity (with engine) .... 4.2 litres (7.5 pints)
Lubricant type/specification .... See *Recommended lubricants and fluids*

Torque wrench settings

	Nm	lbf ft
Engine to gearbox casing	8	6
First motion shaft nut	207	153
Flywheel housing nuts and bolts	25	18
Gearbox casing studs		
3/8 in UNC	11	8
3/8 in UNF	35	26
Gearbox casing studs		
5/16 in UNC	8	6
5/16 in UNF	25	18
Gearbox drain plug	35	26
Mainshaft (final drive pinion) nut	207	153
Mainshaft bearing retainer bolts	18	13
Speedometer drive housing nuts	25	18

2

1 General description

The manual gearbox fitted to all models covered by this manual comprises four forward and one reverse gear. All forward gears are engaged through baulk ring synchromesh units to obtain smooth silent gearchanges **(see illustrations)**. The gearbox is housed within an aluminium casing bolted to the lower face of the engine, and shares the engine lubricating oil. The differential assembly is contained within a separate housing bolted to the rear of the gearbox casing.

On early models, movement of the gear lever is transmitted to the selector forks by a

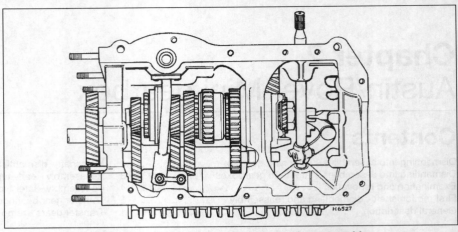

1.1a Internal view of the early type gearbox assembly

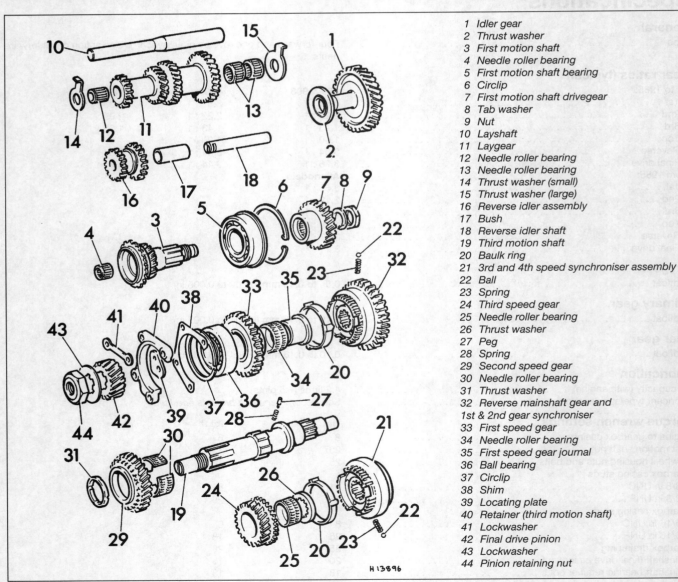

1	Idler gear
2	Thrust washer
3	First motion shaft
4	Needle roller bearing
5	First motion shaft bearing
6	Circlip
7	First motion shaft drivegear
8	Tab washer
9	Nut
10	Layshaft
11	Laygear
12	Needle roller bearing
13	Needle roller bearing
14	Thrust washer (small)
15	Thrust washer (large)
16	Reverse idler assembly
17	Bush
18	Reverse idler shaft
19	Third motion shaft
20	Baulk ring
21	3rd and 4th speed synchroniser assembly
22	Ball
23	Spring
24	Third speed gear
25	Needle roller bearing
26	Thrust washer
27	Peg
28	Spring
29	Second speed gear
30	Needle roller bearing
31	Thrust washer
32	Reverse mainshaft gear and 1st & 2nd gear synchroniser
33	First speed gear
34	Needle roller bearing
35	First speed gear journal
36	Ball bearing
37	Circlip
38	Shim
39	Locating plate
40	Retainer (third motion shaft)
41	Lockwasher
42	Final drive pinion
43	Lockwasher
44	Pinion retaining nut

1.1b Exploded view of the gear train and related components

selector lever, two relay shafts and a ball-and-socket joint. The gear lever is mounted either on the rear of the differential casing or externally in a remote control housing, which is bolted to the rear of the differential. In this case an additional shaft transmits movement of the gear lever to the relay shafts.

A revised gear selector mechanism with a simpler and more positive rod-change remote control linkage is incorporated in the later type

gearboxes (see illustration). Movement of the gear lever is transmitted to the selector forks by an external selector rod, a selector shaft, and a bellcrank lever assembly. The gear lever is mounted in a remote control housing attached to the vehicle floor via rubber mountings.

Drive is transmitted from the clutch to the gearbox by means of three transfer gears. On the end of the crankshaft is the primary gear.

When the clutch pedal is depressed the primary gear remains stationary while the crankshaft revolves inside it. On releasing the clutch pedal the drive is taken up and the primary gear revolves with the crankshaft at crankshaft speed.

Drive is taken from the primary gear, through an intermediate gear, to the first motion shaft drivegear, which is a splined fit on the nose of the first motion shaft.

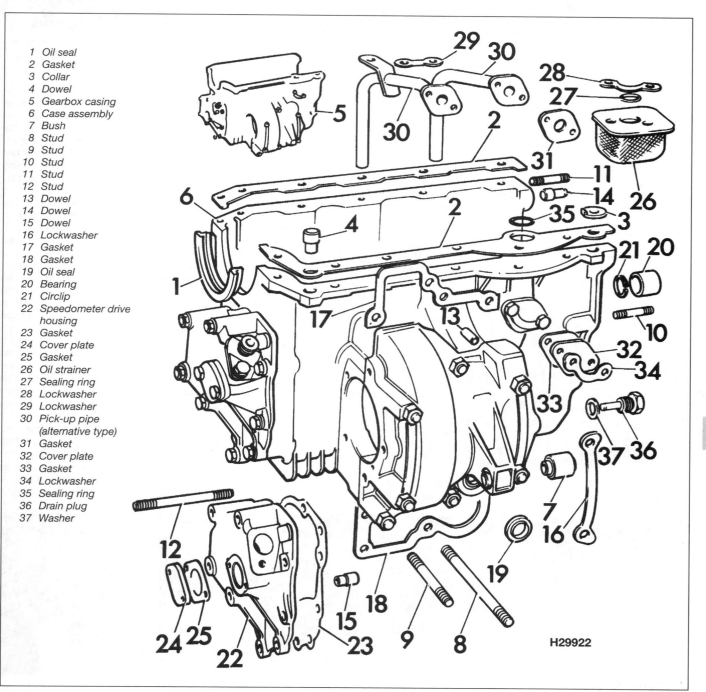

1 Oil seal
2 Gasket
3 Collar
4 Dowel
5 Gearbox casing
6 Case assembly
7 Bush
8 Stud
9 Stud
10 Stud
11 Stud
12 Stud
13 Dowel
14 Dowel
15 Dowel
16 Lockwasher
17 Gasket
18 Gasket
19 Oil seal
20 Bearing
21 Circlip
22 Speedometer drive housing
23 Gasket
24 Cover plate
25 Gasket
26 Oil strainer
27 Sealing ring
28 Lockwasher
29 Lockwasher
30 Pick-up pipe (alternative type)
31 Gasket
32 Cover plate
33 Gasket
34 Lockwasher
35 Sealing ring
36 Drain plug
37 Washer

H29922

1.3 Exploded view of the rod-change type gearbox casing

2.5 Removing the gearchange shaft and Woodruff key

2.8 Removing the interlocking change speed gate

2.10 Removing the oil strainer retaining bolts

2 Dismantling into assemblies - early type gearbox

Note: *Refer to Section 1 for differences between early and later type gearboxes.*

1 Position the gearbox on a strong bench so that it is at comfortable working height and easily accessible from both sides. Alternatively place the gearbox on a clean floor, preferably covered with paper.

2 Begin dismantling by removing the differential assembly.

3 Undo and remove the large hexagon-headed plug and washer from the front of the gearbox casing and then lift out the spring and reverse check plunger. **Note:** *On some models a reversing light switchis fitted in place of the hexagon plug.*

2.14a Unscrew the final drive pinion retaining nut. . .

4 Take off the idler gear from the side of the gearbox casing, together with its thrustwashers. Ensure that the thrustwashers are kept in their correct relative position either side of the gear.

5 Unscrew the clamp bolt and washer securing the selector lever to the gearchange shaft. Slide the gearchange shaft off the selector lever and withdraw it from the casing. Take care not to lose the Woodruff key from the shaft **(see illustration)**. Now lift out the selector lever and prise out the shaft oil seals if required.

6 Undo and remove the speedometer pinion housing cover retaining screw and lift off the cover and bush assembly. Now lift out the pinion.

7 Undo and remove the nuts and spring washers and lift off the engine mounting bracket and front cover.

8 Now lift out the interlocking change speed gate **(see illustration)**.

9 Knock back the locktabs and undo and remove the two bolts securing the oil suction pipe blanking plate to the rear of the casing. Lift off the blanking plate and gasket.

10 Knock back the locktabs and undo and remove the two bolts securing the oil strainer and suction pipe support bracket to the lug on the gearbox casing. Pull the suction pipe out of the oil strainer and remove it from the gearbox **(see illustration)**. The oil strainer cannot be removed at this stage.

11 From the flywheel housing side of the gearbox, extract the small circlip from the first motion shaft and then, using a puller or two screwdrivers, withdraw the small first motion shaft roller bearing from the end of the shaft.

12 Engage two gears simultaneously by moving two of the selector rods in or out. This will lock the mainshaft and prevent it from turning as the large retaining nuts are undone.

13 Tap back the lockwasher and undo and remove the first motion shaft retaining nut from the flywheel housing side of the gearbox. This nut will be very tight and it may be necessary to place the gearbox on the floor and have an assistant stand on the casing as the nut is undone. Now slide the first motion shaft gear off the shaft.

14 Tap back the lockwasher and, using a socket and extension bar inserted through the open end of the casing, undo and remove the final drive pinion retaining nut. This will also be tight and your assistant may be required again. With the nut removed, slide off the final drive pinion **(see illustrations)**.

15 Knock back the locktabs and undo and remove the bolts securing the mainshaft bearing retainer to the centre web of the gearbox casing. Lift off the bearing retainer and shim followed by the layshaft and reverse shaft locking plate **(see illustrations)**.

2.14b . . . and slide off the final drive pinion

2.15a Bend back the locktabs and remove the bearing retainer bolts . . .

2.15b . . . followed by the bearing retainer . . .

2.15c . . . shims and locking plate

2.18a Withdrawing the laygear . . .

2.18b . . . and thrustwashers

16 Measure the endfloat of the laygear using feeler gauges. If the endfloat is outside the limits specified then new thrustwashers must be fitted on reassembly.

17 Unlock the two previously locked mainshaft gears by moving the selector rods back to the neutral position.

18 Using a brass drift, tap the layshaft out of the gearbox casing towards the flywheel housing side, and lift off the laygear together with the two thrustwashers **(see illustrations)**.

19 Undo and remove the two plugs from the lower rear face of the gearbox and lift out the springs and interlocking plungers. Sludge in the bottom of the casing may prevent the

plungers from being removed but this will not affect the dismantling procedure. Take care that they are not lost or dislodged when cleaning the casing after dismantling.

20 Extract the large circlip from the flywheel housing side of the gearbox which retains the first motion shaft bearing in position. Now very carefully, using a brass drift, tap out the first motion shaft and bearing from the casing **(see illustrations)**.

21 Using a brass drift or soft-faced mallet, tap the mainshaft toward the flywheel housing side of the gearbox until a gap of about 25 mm (1 in) exists between the bearing and first gear. Now, using extreme care, tap the outer race of the bearing away from the

flywheel housing and out of the centre web of the casing. Tap each side of the bearing alternatively to prevent it from binding, and take care not to impose any load on the teeth of first gear. When the bearing is clear of the centre web slide it off the end of the mainshaft and withdraw it from the casing **(see illustration)**.

22 Now carefully lift the complete mainshaft assembly up and out of the gearbox **(see illustration)**.

23 Lift out the oil strainer assembly **(see illustration)**.

24 Tap out the reverse gear shaft **(see illustration)** and withdraw the gear and selector fork.

2.20a Extract the first motion shaft bearing circlip . . .

2.20b . . . and remove the shaft and bearing assembly

2.21 With extreme care, tap the mainshaft bearing out of the casing

2

2.22 Lifting out the mainshaft assembly. . .

2.23 . . . followed by the oil strainer

2.24 Removing the reverse gear shaft

2.25 Removing the selector fork locking screws

2.27 With the circlip removed, withdraw the reverse shift lever and pivot pin

25 Slacken the locknuts and then undo and remove the selector fork retaining locking screws (see illustration).
26 Slide the selector rods out of the forks and withdraw the rods and forks from the gearbox.
27 Remove the circlip from the reverse gear shift lever pivot pin and remove the lever (see illustration).

3 Dismantling into assemblies
- later type gearboxes

Note: *Refer to Section 1 for differences between early and later type gearboxes.*

1 Position the gearbox on a strong bench so that it is at comfortable working height and easily accessible from both sides. Alternatively, place the gearbox on a clean floor, preferably covered with paper.
2 Begin dismantling by removing the differential assembly.
3 Take off the idler gear from the side of the gearbox casing together with its thrustwashers. Ensure that the thrustwashers are kept in their correct relative positions on either side of the gear.
4 Undo and remove the speedometer pinion housing cover retaining screw and lift off the cover and bush assembly. Then lift out the pinion.
5 Undo and remove the nuts and spring washers and withdraw the engine mounting, adaptor, and front cover assembly.
6 Knock back the locktabs and undo and remove the two bolts securing the oil suction pipe blanking plate to the rear of the casing. Lift away the blanking plate and gasket.
7 Knock back the locktabs and undo and remove the two bolts securing the oil strainer

and suction pipe support bracket to the lug on the gearbox casing. Pull the suction pipe out of the oil strainer and remove it from the gearbox. The oil strainer cannot be removed at this stage.
8 From the flywheel housing side of the gearbox, extract the small circlip from the first motion shaft and then, using a puller or two screwdrivers, withdraw the small first motion shaft roller bearing from the end of the shaft.
9 Turn the selector shaft anti-clockwise until the operating stub and the interlock spool are disengaged from the bellcrank levers (see illustration).
10 Push the sliding collar of the third/fourth synchro-hub toward the flywheel housing end of the gearbox to engage fourth gear. Now push the sliding collar of the first second synchro-hub toward the gearbox centre web to engage first gear. This will lock the mainshaft and prevent it from turning as the large retaining nuts are undone.
11 Tap back the lockwasher and undo and remove the first motion shaft retaining nut from the flywheel housing side of the gearbox. This nut will be very tight and it may be necessary to place the gearbox on the floor and have an assistant stand on the casing as the nut is undone. When the nut is removed, slide the first motion shaft gear and lockwasher off the shaft.
12 Tap back the lockwasher and, using a socket and extension bar inserted through the open end of the casing, undo and remove the final drive pinion retaining nut. This nut will also be tight and your assistant may be required again. With the nut removed slide off the final drive pinion and lockwasher.
13 Return the first and fourth gears to the neutral position.
14 Knock back the locktabs and undo and remove the bolts securing the mainshaft bearing retainer to the centre web of the gearbox casing. Lift off the bearing retainer

and shim followed by the layshaft and reverse shaft locking plate.
15 Measure the endfloat of the laygear using feeler gauges. If the endfloat is outside the limits specified then new thrustwashers must be fitted on reassembly.
16 Using a brass drift, tap the layshaft out of the gearbox casing towards the flywheel housing side, and lift out the laygear together with the two thrustwashers.
17 Extract the large circlip from the flywheel housing side of the gearbox which retains the first motion shaft bearing in position. Now, very carefully using a brass drift, tap out the first motion shaft and bearing from the casing.
18 Using a brass drift or soft-faced mallet, tap the mainshaft toward the flywheel housing side of the gearbox until a gap of about 25 mm (1 in) exists between the bearing and first gear

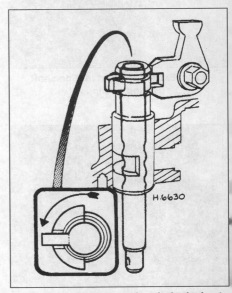

3.9 Selector shaft turned anti-clockwise to disengage bellcrank levers

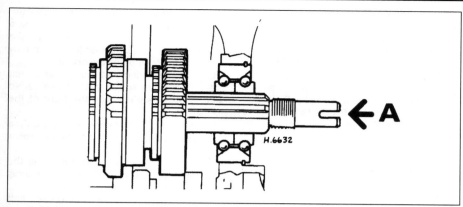

3.18 Removal of mainshaft from centre support bearing - A indicates direction of removal

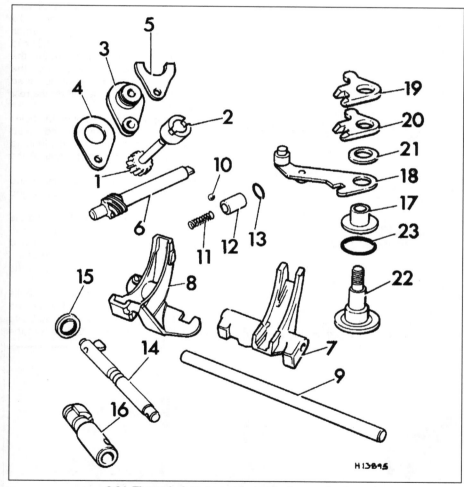

3 24 The rod-change gearbox selector mechanism

1 Speedometer pinion	9 Selector fork shaft	17 Bush
2 Bush	10 Detent ball	18 Reverse lever
3 Bush	11 Detent spring	19 Upper bell crank lever
4 Gasket	12 Detent sleeve	20 Centre bell crank lever
5 Retainer	13 O-ring	21 Spacer
6 Gear and spindle	14 Selector shaft	22 Pivot pin
7 1st and 2nd speed fork	15 Oil seal	23 O-ring
8 3rd and 4th speed fork	16 Interlock spool	

(see illustration). Take care that the sliding collar of the third/fourth synchro-hub does not become disengaged from the hub otherwise the detent balls and springs will be released.

19 Using extreme care tap the outer race of the bearing away from the flywheel housing end and out of the centre web of the casing. Tap each side of the bearing alternately to prevent it from binding, and take care not to impose any load on the teeth of first gear. As the bearing emerges it can be carefully levered the rest of the way out using a screwdriver inserted between the casing and the bearing circlip.

20 When the bearing is clear of the centre web, slide it off the end of the mainshaft and withdraw it from the casing.

21 Carefully lift the complete mainshaft assembly up and out of the gearbox.

22 Remove the oil strainer assembly.

23 Tap out the reverse gear shaft and withdraw the gear.

24 Using a small pin punch, drift out the rollpin securing the third/fourth selector fork to its shaft (see illustration).

25 Slide out the selector shaft and withdraw the two forks.

26 Undo and remove the bellcrank lever pivot post nut and washer.

27 Lift out the bellcrank levers, washers and pivot sleeve, noting the assembly sequence and the markings on the levers. Keep this assembly together to avoid confusion when refitting.

28 Withdraw the interlock spool and selector shaft from inside the gearbox casing.

29 If necessary, the bellcrank lever pivot post may be removed by drifting it downwards and out of the casing.

4 Examination and renovation

1 Thoroughly clean the interior and exterior of the gearbox casing. Check for any small parts that may have dropped into the gearbox during dismantling and recover them.

2 Examine the layshaft for signs of wear where the needle rollers bear. If a small ridge can be felt or if there is any deterioration of the surface hardening (see illustration),

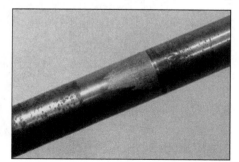

4.2a Deterioration of the layshaft surface hardening at the needle roller bearing journal . . .

2

4.2b ... will also cause wear on the bearings

renew the layshaft. Also inspect the needle roller bearings (see illustration). If the shaft is worn, the bearings will be worn and must be renewed. New thrustwashers should be fitted as a matter or course, referring to the charts in Sections 7 and 8 for the correct size.

3 Examine the laygear, reverse idler gear and the gears on the mainshaft for excessive wear and chipping of the teeth.

4 Inspect the synchronising rings on the mainshaft for wear, distortion or cracks. If difficulty was experienced when changing gear then the rings should be renewed. If the vehicle had a tendency to jump out of gear, then the complete synchro-hub of the relevant gear should be renewed.

5 Inspect the condition of the main ball-bearings, and also the small needle roller bearing and cage located on the front of the mainshaft. If there is any looseness between the inner and outer races, pitting of the balls or rollers, or roughness when the bearing is spun, then the bearing should be renewed. It is also advisable at this stage to check the condition of the idler gear bearings in the gearbox casing and flywheel housing. These bearings and the idler gear itself are notorious for wear and should be renewed if they show the slightest sign of such wear. Full information on these components will be found in Sections 9 and 10.

6 Examine the ends of the selector forks where they engage with the synchroniser-hubs. If possible compare the forks with new units to help determine the extent of the wear.

7 If it is necessary to renew the synchro-rings or the synchroniser-hubs or any of the mainshaft components, the mainshaft should now be dismantled as described in Section 6. If the first motion shaft or bearing require attention they should be dismantled as described in Section 5.

5 First motion shaft - dismantling and reassembly

1 To remove the bearing from the first motion shaft, slide the shaft between open vice jaws and support the outer race of the bearing on the top of the jaws.

2 Using a soft-faced mallet, drive the first motion shaft down and out of the bearing inner race. The strain placed on the bearing does not matter, as the bearing would not be removed unless it was being renewed. Alternatively, use a two-legged universal puller (see illustration).

3 To fit a new bearing, slide it onto the first motion shaft with the shoulder of the bearing towards the front of the shaft.

4 Now support the inner race of the bearing on protected vice jaws. and using a drift of suitable diameter inserted into the bearing hole at the rear of the gear, drive the shaft pulley into the bearing.

6 Mainshaft - dismantling and reassembly

1 Place the mainshaft on a clean uncluttered working surface and begin dismantling by sliding off the third/fourth synchro-hub and baulk rings from the front of the shaft.

2 Using a thin screwdriver or thin piece of

rod, press down the spring-loaded plunger and turn the splined thrustwasher so that a spline holds the plunger down and the thrustwasher is so positioned that it can now be slid off the front of the mainshaft.

3 Lift out the spring and plunger and then slide off the third speed gear and its caged needle roller bearing from the front of the mainshaft.

4 From the rear of the mainshaft withdraw the first speed gear and its caged needle roller bearing.

5 Using two screwdrivers carefully lever the first speed gear needle roller bearing journal rearwards and off the mainshaft.

6 Now slide off the first/second synchro-hub and the two baulk rings off the rear of the shaft.

7 The splined retaining thrustwasher securing the second speed gear in position is retained with two spring-loaded plungers. To compress the plunger, insert two small screwdrivers between the thrustwasher and the edge of the gear. Now rotate the thrustwasher so that the splines hold the plungers down and the thrustwasher is so positioned that it can now be slid off the rear of the mainshaft.

8 Insert two pieces of wire through the holes in the cone face of the second gear. Compress the two spring-loaded plungers and withdraw the gear from the rear of the mainshaft.

9 Finally lift out the spring and plunger and take off the second speed gear split caged needle roller bearing.

10 Should it be necessary to dismantle the synchro-hubs, place a rag around the hub to catch the balls and springs that will be ejected and then slide the inner hub out of the collar. Now recover the balls and springs from the rag.

11 To reassemble the hubs, hold the balls against spring pressure with your fingers, and with the help of an assistant slide the hub into the collar (see illustration). Ensure that the

5.2 Using a puller to remove the first motion shaft bearing

6.11 Synchro-hub balls and springs in position ready for assembly

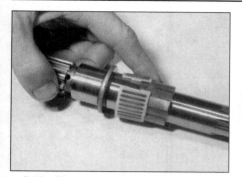

6.12a Place the two split halves of the
needle roller bearing in position . . .

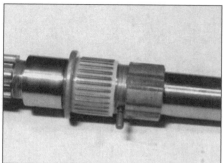

6.12b . . . and then insert the spring and
plungers

6.13 Depress the plungers and slide on
second gear

6.14 Fully compress the plungers with two thin pieces of rod and
slide on the thrustwasher

6.15 Rotate the thrustwasher to lock it in position

spaces in the collar align with the cut-outs in
the hub. Also ensure that the long boss on the
collar and hub are on the same side when
assembled.

12 Begin reassembly of the mainshaft by
placing the two split halves of the second
gear needle roller bearing in position, and then
insert the spring and plungers into the drilling
on the mainshaft **(see illustrations)**.

13 From the rear of the mainshaft, slide on
the second speed gear, flat face first, depress

the plungers and slide the gear over the
needle roller bearings **(see illustration)**.

14 Support the mainshaft in a vice with
suitable protected jaws and using two thin
pieces of rod inserted through the holes in the
cone of the gear, compress the two plungers
(see illustration).

15 Now slide the thrustwasher into position
and rotate it until the plungers can be heard to
click into position and lock the thrustwasher
(see illustration).

16 Place the baulk ring in position on the
second speed gear and then refit the
first/second synchro-hub with the long boss
towards the rear of the mainshaft **(see
illustrations)**.

17 Fit the first speed gear needle roller
bearing journal to the rear of the mainshaft
(see illustration) and tap it fully home using a
tube of suitable diameter.

18 Refit the first gear needle roller bearing,
the baulk ring and then first gear with the flat

2

6.16a Place the baulk ring in position. . .

6.16b . . . and refit the first/second
synchro-hub

6.17 Fit the first gear needle roller bearing
journal . . .

6.18a ... followed by the needle roller bearing

6.18b With the baulk ring in position, slide on first gear

6.19 At the other end of the mainshaft, assemble the third gear needle roller bearing

6.20a With the spring and plunger in place refit third gear ...

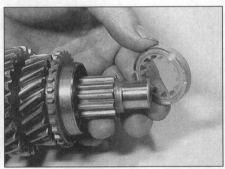

6.20b ... followed by the splined thrustwasher

6.21a Depress the plunger and push the thrustwasher fully home ...

6.21b ... then turn it until it locks into position

6.22a Finally refit the third gear baulk ring ...

6.22b ... the third/fourth synchro-hub ...

6.23 ... and the remaining baulk ring

side towards the rear of the mainshaft (see illustrations).

19 From the front end of the mainshaft, assemble the third gear needle roller bearing and then place the spring and plunger into the drilling in the shaft (see illustration).

20 Slide on the third speed gear, flat side first, followed by the splined thrustwasher (see illustrations). Ensure that the notch at the rear of the thrustwasher is adjacent to the plunger.

21 Depress the plunger and rotate the thrustwasher until the plunger can be heard to click into place, and then lock the thrustwasher (see illustrations).

22 Refit the baulk ring to the third speed gear (see illustration) and then slide on the third/fourth synchro-hub ensuring that the large boss on the hub faces the front of the mainshaft (see illustration).

23 Finally refit the remaining baulk ring to the front of the third/fourth synchro-hub (see illustration).

7 Reassembly -
early type gearbox

Note: *Before reassembly commences ensure that the gearbox casing is thoroughly clean, with all traces of old gaskets removed. Also ensure that all the components are clean and*

7.4 Reverse gear in position over the selector fork

7.5 Refitting the reverse gear shaft

dry and that a complete set of new gaskets is available.

1 Press the reverse lever operating pin into its bore in the bottom of the casing with the groove in the pin uppermost.

2 Press the reverse operating lever into place on the operating pin and fit operating lever retaining circlip.

3 Refit the reverse fork into the hole in the operating lever, ensuring that the offset in the fork is towards the rear of the gearbox casing.

4 Place the reverse gear into the gearbox casing with the machined groove of the gear engaged with the selector fork. **Note:** *The gear must be positioned with the groove towards the right-hand side of the casing* **(see illustration)**.

5 Lubricate the reverse gear shaft and pass it through the centre web of the casing, into reverse gear, and with the slotted end of the shaft facing upwards **(see illustration)**.

6 Fit the reverse gear detent spring into the drilling in the rear of the casing and then slide in the reverse detent plunger, flat side first **(see illustrations)**.

7 Slide the reverse selector rod through the centre web of the casing and into the reverse selector fork **(see illustration)**. Using a long

screwdriver, push the detent plunger in against spring pressure, while at the same time pushing the reverse selector rod through into the end of the casing.

8 Place the third and fourth gear selector fork in the casing and push the third and fourth gear selector rod in from the left of the casing so the rod enters the lower hole in the fork **(see illustration)**.

9 Place the first and second gear selector fork in the casing and push the first and second gear selector rod in from the left of the

casing so the rod enters the locating hole in the first and second gear selector fork, and also passes through the clearance hole in the third and fourth gear selector fork **(see illustration)**.

10 Line up the indentations in the rods with the holes in the forks and insert and tighten down the selector screws, lockwashers and locknuts. Make certain the locknuts are properly tightened down, and on no account omit the lockwashers. As the selectors lie in the bottom of the gearbox casing, if one

7.6a Place the reverse gear detent spring into the gearbox casing . . .

7.6b . . . followed by the detent plunger

2

7.7 Refitting the reverse selector rod into the fork

7.8 Refit the third/fourth selector fork and rod . . .

7.9 . . . followed by the first/second selector fork and rod

7.11a Fit a new oil seal to the oil strainer . . .

7.11b . . . and with the bracket attached, place the strainer in the gearbox casing

7.13 With the mainshaft in place, tap in the bearing

7.14a Position the small spigot bearing on the front of the mainshaft . . .

7.14b . . . and then insert the first motion shaft assembly . . .

works loose the whole gearbox must be stripped to tighten it.

11 Place the oil strainer sealing ring in the recess in the oil strainer (see illustration) and lightly grease the ring to help the oil pipe pass through easily when it is fitted later. Attach the oil strainer bracket to the oil strainer, fit the lockwasher and insert and tighten the two bolts securely. Turn up the tabs on the lockwasher. Place the strainer in position in the bottom of the casing (see illustration). Do not yet insert the bolts which hold the bracket to the lugs on the casing.

12 Refit the mainshaft assembly with the forked end of the shaft toward the left of the gearbox casing and with the synchroniser-hubs in place over the selector forks.

13 Ensure that the large circlip is in position in the retaining groove of the mainshaft bearing and refit the bearing, tapping it into the centre web of the casing with a tube of suitable diameter (see illustration).

14 Place the small caged needle roller bearing over the front of the mainshaft and then refit the first motion shaft and bearing assembly to the gearbox casing. Secure the

bearing in position with the large circlip (see illustrations).

15 Refit the first/second and third/fourth selector rod detent plungers to their drillings in the rear face of the gearbox casing. Refit the springs, plugs and sealing washers (see illustrations).

16 Place the standard size laygear thrustwasher into its location in the gearbox casing and retain it with a dab of grease on its rear face. Note: The large thrustwasher is of standard size and the smaller one selective.

17 Carefully lower the laygear into the gearbox

7.14c . . . and secure with the circlip

7.15a Insert the detent plungers and springs . . .

7.15b . . . and refit the plugs

7.17a Lower the laygear into the casing . . .

7.17b . . . and with the standard size thrustwasher fitted at the other end, measure the clearance

(see illustration), hold it against the thrustwasher and, using feeler gauges, measure the clearance at the other end (see illustration).

18 With the standard washer fitted and the gap between the end of the laygear and the casing measured, the selective washer can be decided upon. The washer required will have a thickness of the measured clearance minus the specified endfloat (see Specifications). The following table gives the available thrustwashers thicknesses.

Washer thickness
3.07 to 3.12 mm (0.121 to 0.123 in)
3.14 to 3.20 mm (0.124 to 0.126 in)
3.22 to 3.28 mm (0.127 to 0.129 in)
3.30 to 3.35 mm (0.130 to 0.132 in)

19 Now refit both thrustwashers to the gearbox casing and place the needle roller bearings in the laygear (see illustration). Lower the laygear into the gearbox, and by judicious manipulation insert the layshaft from the right-hand side of the casing and into the thrustwashers and laygear (see illustration). Note that when installed the slot in the layshaft must face downwards.

20 Now recheck the laygear endfloat which, if the correct thrustwashers have been selected, should be within the specified limits.

21 Refit the mainshaft bearing retainer to the centre web of the gear casing, but do not fit any shims at this stage. Lightly tighten the retaining bolts and then measure the clearance between the retainer and the gearbox casing centre web using feeler gauges (see illustration). Refer to the table below for the correct thickness of shims required.

Measured gap	Fit shims totalling
0.127 to 0.152 mm (0.005 to 0.006 in)	0.127 mm (0.005 in)
0.152 to 0.203 mm (0.006 to 0.008 in)	0.178 mm (0.007 in)
0.203 to 0.254 mm (0.008 to 0.010 in)	0.229 mm (0.009 in)
0.254 to 0.305 mm (0.010 to 0.012 in)	0.279 mm (0.011 in)
0.305 to 0.356 mm (0.012 to 0.014 in)	0.330 mm (0.013 in)
0.356 to 0.381 mm (0.014 to 0.015 in)	0.381 mm (0.015 in)

22 Now remove the retainer and place the shims in position, followed by the reverse gear shaft and layshaft locking plate. Ensure that the plate engages with the slots in the two shafts and then refit the bearing retainer, bolts

7.19a Now fit the appropriate thrustwashers to the face of the gearbox casing . . .

2

7.19b . . . and with the laygear held in position, insert the layshaft

7.21 Measuring the clearance between the mainshaft bearing retainer and casing

7.22a Fit the selected shims and the reverse/layshaft locking plate . . .

7.22b . . . followed by the bearing retainer

7.23a The final drive pinion . . .

7.23b . . . new lockwasher . . .

7.23c . . . and retaining nut can now be fitted

and locktabs. Tighten the bolts and bend over the locktabs **(see illustrations)**.

23 Fit the final drive pinion to the end of the mainshaft followed by a new lockwasher and the retaining nut **(see illustrations)**.

24 Engage two gears simultaneously by moving two of the selector rods in or out.

25 Tighten the final drive pinion retaining nut to the specified torque and then bend over the lockwasher **(see illustration)**.

26 Place the first motion shaft gear over the splines of the first motion shaft and then fit a new lockwasher and the retaining nut. Tighten the nut to the specified torque and then bend over the lockwasher **(see illustrations)**.

27 Return the selector rods to the neutral position.

28 Refit the small roller bearing to the end of the first motion shaft, tapping it on using a tube of suitable diameter. Ensure that the bearing is positioned with the flat face of the roller cage facing the gear. Secure the bearing with the circlip **(see illustration)**.

29 Lightly grease the end of the oil suction pipe and insert it into the hole in the centre of the oil strainer, taking care not to dislodge the rubber sealing ring.

30 The top flange on the bracket lies under the lug on the side of the gearbox casing. The oil pipe bracket lies on the top of the lug. Position the lockwasher and insert the two bolts through the two holes in the lug into the

7.25 After tightening the nut bend over the lockwasher

7.26a Next refit the first motion shaft gear . . .

7.26b . . . refit and tighten the retaining nut . . .

7.26c . . . and bend over the lockwasher

7.28 Secure the first motion shaft bearing in place with the circlip

7.30a Place a new gasket on the oil feed pipe flange . . .

7.30b . . . and refit the blanking plate from the other side

7.31a Fit a new gearchange shaft oil seal . . .

fixed nuts under the bracket flange. Place a new joint gasket between the pipe blanking plate and the flange on the outside of the casing, and a new gasket between the oil flange and the inside of the casing. Fit a new lockwasher and tighten up the two pairs of bolts. Turn up the tabs on both lockwashers **(see illustrations)**.

31 Refit the oil seal **(see illustration)** and partially insert the gearchange shaft into the gearbox casing. Refit the Woodruff key **(see illustration)** to the shaft, position the selector lever in the casing, and push the gearchange shaft through the hole in the lever so the Woodruff key mates with the slot in the selector lever. Push the shaft right into its housing in the gearbox case, and line up the cut out in the shaft with the hole for the clamp bolt in the lever. Insert and tighten the clamp bolt **(see illustration)** and turn up the tab on the lockwasher.

32 Refit the change speed gate **(see illustration)**, fit a new front cover gasket to the flange on the front of the casing; fit the front cover and insert and tighten up the bolts, nuts and springwashers as appropriate **(see illustrations)**.

33 Refit the reverse check plunger and the plunger spring in the hole in the casing; make sure the washer is under the head of the spring plug and tighten the plug securely **(see illustrations)**.

7.31b . . . slide the shaft into the casing and refit the Woodruff key

7.31c Engage the shaft with the selector lever and refit the clamp bolt

7.32a Refit the change speed gate . . .

7.32b . . . place a new gasket in position . . .

2

7.32c . . . and refit the front cover

7.33a Finally refit the reverse check plunger and spring . . .

7.33b . . . refit and tighten the spring plug

8.2 Refitting the interlock spool and selector shaft assembly

1 Selector shaft
2 Interlock spool
3 Pivot post washer and locknut
4 Bellcrank lever assembly

8.3a Rod-change type gear selector mechanism

34 Insert the speedometer spindle and gear through the front cover so the spindle engages the slot in the end of the mainshaft, fit the joint gasket and endplate and tighten down the two securing bolts and lockwashers.

35 Refit the speedometer pinion to the front cover and then fit the bush, gasket and pinion housing cover. Secure the cover with the bolt and washer.

36 The differential assembly can now be refitted to the gearbox casing. Before refitting the engine to the gearbox refer to Section 9 regarding removal and refitting of the transfer gears.

8 Reassembly - later type gearbox

Note: *Before reassembly commences, ensure that the gearbox is thoroughly clean with all trace of old gasket removed. Also ensure that all the components are clean and dry and that a complete set of new gaskets is available.*

1 Lightly lubricate a new O-ring oil seal and position it on the bellcrank lever pivot post. Drift the pivot post into the gearbox casing using a hammer and block of wood.

2 Refit the interlock spool to the selector shaft and insert this assembly into the gearbox casing. Position the operating stub of the selector shaft away from the bellcrank lever pivot post **(see illustration)**.

3 Insert the bellcrank lever assembly onto the pivot post, ensuring that the sleeve, levers and washers are in their correct order as noted during dismantling **(see illustrations)**. Push the assembly fully home and refit the pivot post washer and locknut. **Note:** *Do not rotate the interlock spool and selector shaft into engagement with the bellcrank levers until the mainshaft and first motion shaft nuts have been refitted and fully tightened.*

4 Place the third/fourth selector fork in the gearbox casing and engagement with

8.3b Refitting the bellcrank lever assembly onto the pivot post

the selector lever. Slide in the selector shaft until it just engages the fork **(see illustrations)**.

5 Place the first/second selector fork in position and then slide the selector shaft fully home. Align the holes in the third/fourth selector fork and the selector shaft and drift in

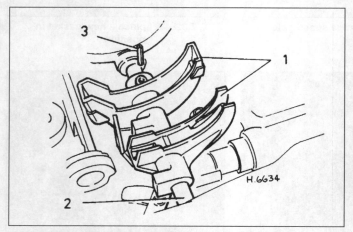

8.4a Rod-change type selector fork assembly

1 Selector forks   2 Selector shaft   3 Roll pin

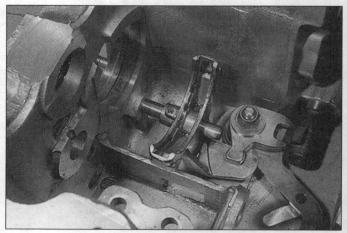

8.4b Position the third/fourth selector fork in the casing and insert the selector shaft

8.5a With the first/second selector fork in place push the selector shaft fully home . . .

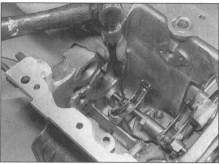

8.5b . . . align the holes and drift a new roll pin into the third/fourth fork

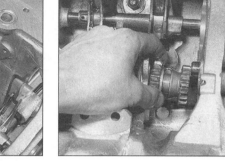

8.6 Lay the reverse idler in the casing and insert the reverse idler shaft

a new roll pin until it is flush with the fork boss **(see illustrations)**.

6 Lay the reverse idler gear in the casing, ensuring that the chamfer on the gear teeth faces the centre web of the gearbox casing, and that the gear is engaged with the pin on the reverse selector lever. Insert the reverse idler shaft through the gearbox centre web and into the gear. Rotate the shaft so that the slot faces upward **(see illustration)**.

7 Lubricate the oil strainer sealing ring to help the oil pipe pass through easily when it is fitted later. Place the strainer in position in the

bottom of the casing, but do not insert the bolts which hold the bracket to the lugs on casing at this stage **(see illustration)**.

8 Refit the mainshaft assembly with the forked end of the shaft toward the left of gearbox casing and with the synchroniser-hubs in place over the selector forks.

9 Ensure that the large circlip is in position in the retaining groove of the mainshaft bearing and refit the bearing, tapping it into the centre web of the casing with a tube of suitable diameter **(see illustration)**.

10 Insert the small caged first motion shaft

needle roller bearing into its location in the gear and then refit the first motion shaft and bearing assembly to the gearbox casing. Secure the bearing in position with the large circlip **(see illustrations)**.

11 Place the standard size laygear thrustwasher into its location in the gearbox casing and retain it with a dab of grease on its rear face **(see illustration)**. **Note:** *The large thrustwasher is of standard size and the smaller one selective.*

12 Carefully lower the laygear into the gearbox, hold it against the thrustwasher and,

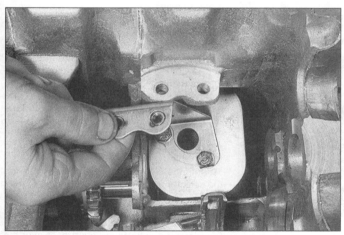

8.7 Positioning the oil strainer in the gearbox casing

8.9 With the mainshaft in place, refit the bearing

2

8.10a Insert the first motion shaft needle roller bearing into the recess in the gear . . .

8.10b . . . refit the first motion shaft assembly . . .

8.11 With the large thrust washer in position . . .

8.12 . . . lower the laygear into the gearbox and measure the clearance at the other end

8.14a Refit the needle roller bearings to the laygear . . .

8.14b . . . and with the thrustwasher and laygear in place, insert the layshaft

using feeler gauges, measure the clearance at the other end **(see illustration)**.

13 With the standard thrustwasher fitted and the gap between the end of the laygear and the casing measured, the selective washer can be decided upon. The washer required will have a thickness of the measured clearance minus the specified endfloat (see Specifications). The following table gives the available thrustwashers thicknesses.

Washer thickness
3.07 to 3.12 mm (0.121 to 0.123 in)
3.14 to 3.20 mm (0.124 to 0.126 in)
3.22 to 3.28 mm (0.127 to 0.129 in)
3.30 to 3.35 mm (0.130 to 0.132 in)

14 Now refit both thrustwashers to the gearbox casing and place the needle roller

bearings in the laygear **(see illustration)**. Lower the laygear into the gearbox, and by judicious manipulation insert the layshaft from the right-hand side of the casing and into the thrustwashers and laygear **(see illustration)**. When installed the slot on the end of the layshaft must face downward.

15 Recheck the laygear endfloat, which, if the correct thrustwashers have been selected, should be within the specified limits.

16 Refit the mainshaft bearing retainer to the centre web of the gearbox casing, but do not fit any shims at this stage. Lightly tighten the retaining bolts and then measure the clearance between the retainer and the gearbox casing centre web using feeler gauges **(see illustration)**. Refer to the

following table for the correct thickness of shims required.

Measured gap	Fit shims totalling
0.127 to 0.152 mm	0.127 mm
(0.005 to 0.006 in)	(0.005 in)
0.152 to 0.203 mm	0.178 mm
(0.006 to 0.008 in)	(0.007 in)
0.203 to 0.254 mm	0.229 mm
(0.008 to 0.010 in)	(0.009 in)
0.254 to 0.304 mm	0.279 mm
(0.010 to 0.012 in)	(0.011 in)
0.304 to 0.356 mm	0.330 mm
(0.012 to 0.014 in)	(0.013 in)
0.356 to 0.381 mm	0.381 mm
(0.014 to 0.015 in)	(0.015 in)

17 Having selected the required shims, remove the retainer and place the shims in position, followed by the reverse gear shaft and layshaft locking plate **(see illustration)**. Ensure that the locking plate engages with the slots in the two shafts and then refit the bearing retainer, bolts and shafts. Tighten the bolts and bend over the locktabs.

18 Fit the final drive pinion to the end of the mainshaft, followed by a new lockwasher and the retaining nut **(see illustrations)**.

19 Engage first and fourth gears, by moving the selector forks, to lock the mainshaft.

20 Tighten the final drive pinion nut to the specified torque and then bend over the lockwasher **(see illustration)**.

21 Place the first motion shaft gear over the splines of the first motion shaft, and then fit a

8.16 Measuring the clearance between the bearing retainer and the casing

8.17 Place the selected shims and the reverse/layshaft locking plate in position, then refit the bearing retainer

8.18a Refit the final drive pinion . . .

8.18b . . . a new lockwasher . . .

8.20 . . . and the retaining nut tightened to the specified torque

8.21a Slide the first motion shaft gear over the splines . . .

8.21b . . . refit the lockwasher and retaining nut . . .

8.21c . . . then tighten the nut to the specified torque

8.23a Drive the first motion shaft needle roller bearing onto the shaft . . .

8.23b . . . and secure with the circlip

new lockwasher and the retaining nut. Tighten the nut to the specified torque and then bend over the lockwasher (see illustrations).
22 Return the selector forks to the neutral position. Rotate the interlock spool and selector shaft into engagement with the bellcrank levers.
23 Refit the small roller bearing to the end of the first motion shaft, tapping it on using a tube of suitable diameter. Ensure that the

bearing is positioned with the flat face of the roller cage facing the gear. Secure the bearing with the circlip (see illustrations).
24 Insert the oil suction pipe into the hole in the centre of the oil strainer, taking care not to dislodge the rubber sealing ring.
25 The top flange on the oil strainer lies under the lug on the side of the gearbox casing. Position the lockwasher, and insert the two bolts through the two holes in the lug

into the fixed nuts under the bracket flange. Place a new joint gasket between the pipe blanking plate and the flange on the outside of the casing, and a new gasket between the oil pipe flange and the inside of the casing. Fit a new lockwasher and tighten up the two pairs of bolts. Turn up the tabs on both lockwashers (see illustrations).
26 Place a new gasket in position and refit the gearbox front cover, engine mounting and

8.25a Place a new gasket on the oil pick-up pipe . . .

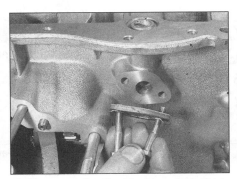

8.25b . . . and on the blanking plate, then refit the bolts and lockwasher to the blanking plate . . .

8.25c . . . and oil strainer, tightening both pairs of bolts fully

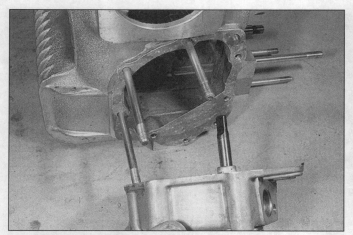

8.26 Refitting the gearbox front cover . . .

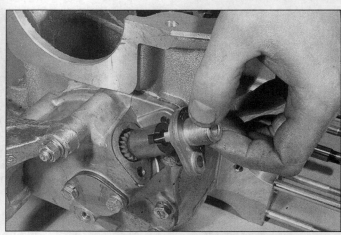

8.27 . . . and the speedometer pinion and housing assembly

adaptor **(see illustration)**. Refit and tighten the nuts, bolts and washers as appropriate.

27 Refit the speedometer pinion to the front cover and then fit the bush, gasket and pinion housing cover. Secure the cover with the bolt and washer **(see illustration)**.

28 The differential assembly can now be refitted to the gearbox casing. Before refitting the engine to the gearbox refer to Section 9 regarding removal and refitting of the transfer gears.

9 Transfer gears - removal and refitting

1 With the flywheel housing removed, the transfer gears are now exposed. The primary gear can be removed first by lifting off the U-shaped ring and retaining washer and sliding the gear off the end of the shaft. Now slide off the thrustwasher **(see illustration)**.

2 Lift the idler gear out of its needle roller bearing in the gearbox casing. Make sure that the thrustwashers (one on each side) are kept in their correct relative positions.

3 To remove the first motion shaft gear, first extract the circlip and withdraw the roller bearing, using a puller or two screwdrivers, from the first motion shaft. Now bend back the lockwasher and undo and remove the nut **(see illustration)**. To prevent the first motion shaft from turning as the nut is undone, put

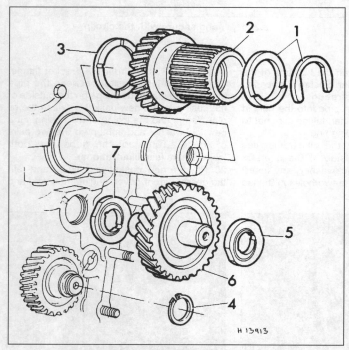

9.1 Transfer gear train

1	Retaining washer and U-ring	4	Circlip
2	Primary gear	5	Thrust washer
3	Thrust washer	6	Idler gear
		7	Thrust washer

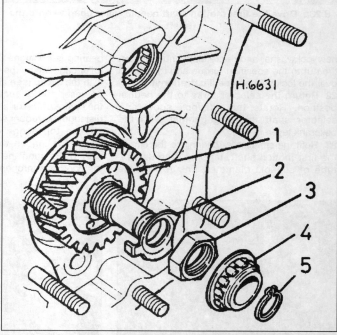

9.3 First motion shaft gear and bearing assembly

1	First motion shaft gear	4	Roller bearing
2	Lockwasher	5	Circlip
3	Retaining nut		

9.6 Using feeler gauges to measure the primary gear endfloat

9.8 Checking the endfloat of the idler gear

the gearbox in gear and then lock the drive flanges using blocks of wood between the flanges and gearbox casing. On later models tool 18G1088 may be needed.

4 Lift off the lockwasher and slide the gear off the first motion shaft.

5 Refitting the transfer gears is the reverse sequence to removal. However, the endfloat of the primary gear and idler gear must be checked, and if necessary adjusted, as described below before finally refitting the flywheel housing.

Primary gear

6 Refit the primary gear thrustwasher with its chamfered bore against the crankshaft flange. Slide on the gear and secure with the retaining washer and U-shaped ring. Using feeler gauges, measure the clearance between the end of the gear and the thrustwasher (see illustration). The correct endfloat is given in the Specifications. If the measured endfloat is outside the specified limits, selective thrustwashers are available from your dealer.

Idler gear

7 The endfloat of the idler gear can only be accurately measured with the engine removed from the gearbox. If a new idler gear, thrustwashers, gearbox casing or flywheel housing are being fitted then this must be done to allow the endfloat to be accurately measured. If, however, the original components are being refitted, it can be assumed that the endfloat will be as before and therefore satisfactory.

8 To check the endfloat, refit the flywheel housing after making sure the mating faces are clean and a new gasket is in position. Tighten the retaining nuts to the specified torque and then, using feeler gauges, measure the clearance between the thrustwasher and the side of the casing (see illustration). The endfloat should be as specified. Selective thrustwashers are available from your dealer to correct any deficiency. The flywheel housing can now be

removed, the engine positioned on the gearbox and the transfer gears and housing finally refitted.

10 Transfer gear bearings - removal and refitting

Note: *If the idler gear bearings in the flywheel housing or gearbox casing on the first motion shaft support bearing outer race require renewal, proceed as follows.*

1 Remove the flywheel and flywheel housing.
2 Heat the flywheel housing in boiling water. *On no account apply a direct flame to the housing.* If a receptacle large enough to hold the flywheel housing is not available, slowly pour boiling water over the area round the bearing.
3 Remove the retaining ring (where fitted) and carefully prise the bearing out of the casing, taking great care not to damage the bearing

housing. If possible use service tool 18G581.
4 When fitting a new bearing carefully drift it into position (having previously heated the housing as described above) until it is just clear of the retaining ring recess (where fitted). *On no account press the bearing right into the recess in the housing,* as this would mask the bearing oil supply hole which is at the rear of the recess.
5 To renew the idler gear needle roller bearing in the gearbox casing, separate the engine from the gearbox, remove the circlip and drift the bearing out of the casing. Alternatively, if service tool 18G581 is obtainable, the engine need not be separated from the gearbox (see illustration).
6 To refit the bearing, carefully drive it into position using a suitable drift and refit the circlips.
7 If the outer race of the first motion shaft roller bearing requires renewal, use the procedure described in paragraphs 2 and 3, or preferably obtain service tool 18G617A.

2

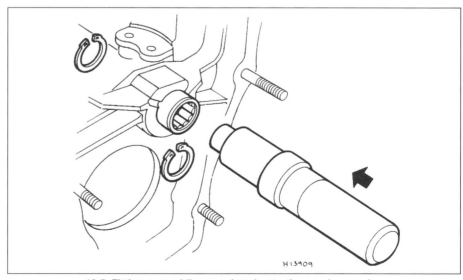

H13909

10.5 Fitting a new idler gear bearing to the gearbox casing

Notes

Chapter 3
Citroën/Peugeot BE gearbox

Contents

Specifications

General

Type	Four or five forward speeds, all synchromesh, one reverse gear
Designation	BE1/4 (four speed), BE1/5 (five speed) or BE3/5 (5-speed)

Gear ratios (typical)

Citroën Visa	Van	GTI	Diesel
1st	3.31 : 1	3.25 : 1	3.31 : 1
2nd	1.88 : 1	1.85 : 1	1.88 : 1
3rd	1.15 : 1	1.36 : 1	1.28 : 1
4th	0.80 : 1	1.07 : 1	0.97 : 1
5th	-	0.87 : 1	0.76 : 1
Reverse	3.33 : 1	3.33 : 1	3.33 : 1
Final drive	3.81 : 1	3.94 : 1	3.94 : 1

Citroën BX	BX 16	BX 17	BX 19
1st	3.31 : 1	3.31 : 1	3.31 : 1
2nd	1.88 : 1	1.88 : 1	1.88 : 1
3rd	1.28 : 1	1.28 : 1	1.36 : 1
4th	0.97 : 1	0.97 : 1	1.07 : 1
5th	0.76 : 1	0.76 : 1	0.87 : 1
Reverse	3.33 : 1	3.33 : 1	3.33 : 1
Final drive	4.19 : 1	4.19 : 1	3.69 : 1

Citroën Xantia	
1st	3.45 : 1
2nd	1.87 : 1
3rd	1.36 : 1
4th	1.07 : 1
5th	0.80 : 1
Reverse	3.33 : 1
Final drive	4.27 : 1

3

Citroën ZX	**Petrol**	**Diesel**
1st	3.42 : 1	3.46 : 1
2nd	1.81 : 1	1.85 : 1
3rd	1.28 : 1	1.28 : 1
4th	0.98 : 1	0.97 : 1
5th	0.77 : 1	0.76 : 1
Reverse	3.58 : 1	3.33 : 1
Final drive	4.29 : 1	3.94 : 1

Peugeot 205	**Standard**	**Close ratio**
1st	3.31 : 1	3.31 : 1
2nd	1.88 : 1	1.88 : 1
3rd	1.36 : 1	1.28 : 1
4th	1.07 : 1	0.97 : 1
5th	0.87 : 1	0.76 : 1
Reverse	3.33 : 1	4.06 : 1
Final drive	4.06 : 1	4.06 : 1

Peugeot 305	**Up to 12/86**	**From 1/87**
1st	3.31 : 1	3.25 : 1
2nd	1.88 : 1	1.85 : 1
3rd	1.36 : 1	1.36 : 1
4th	1.07 : 1	1.07 : 1
5th	0.87 : 1	0.87 : 1
Reverse	3.33 : 1	3.33 : 1
Final drive	4.19 : 1	4.19: 1

Peugeot 309	**BE1/4***	**BE1/5***	**GTI**
1st	3.31 : 1	3.31 : 1	2.92 : 1
2nd	1.88 : 1	1.88 : 1	1.85 : 1
3rd	1.15 : 1	1.28 : 1	1.36 : 1
4th	0.80 : 1	0.97 : 1	1.07 : 1
5th	-	0.76 : 1	0.87 : 1
Reverse	3.33 : 1	3.33 : 1	3.33 : 1
Final drive	4.43 : 1	3.81 : 1	3.67 : 1

Peugeot 405	**Except Mi 16**	**Mi 16**
1st	3.25 : 1	2.37 : 1
2nd	1.85 : 1	1.85 : 1
3rd	1.28 : 1	1.28 : 1
4th	0.97 : 1	0.96 : 1
5th	0.76 : 1	0.75 : 1
Reverse	2.58 : 1	2.58 : 1
Final drive	4.06 : 1	4.42 : 1

Talbot Alpine, Solara, Minx & Rapier	
1st	3.31 : 1
2nd	1.83 : 1
3rd	1.28 : 1
4th	0.97 : 1
5th	0.76 : 1
Reverse	3.33 : 1
Final drive	4.18 : 1

Talbot Horizon	
1st	3.31 : 1
2nd	1.88 : 1
3rd	1.28 : 1
4th	0.97 : 1
5th	0.76 : 1
Reverse	3.33 : 1
Final drive	3.81 : 1
From 1/87:	
1st	3.25 : 1
2nd	1.85 : 1

Lubrication

Approximate oil capacity (including final drive unit)	2.0 litres (3.52 pints)
Lubricant type/specification	See *Recommended lubricants and fluids*

Torque wrench settings

	Nm	lbf ft
Casing bolts	13	10
Crownwheel-to-cage bolts	65	48
Drain plug	30	22
Filler/level plug	20	15
Final drive casing:		
10 mm bolts	40	30
7 mm bolts	13	10
Final drive casing extension housing	15	11
Input shaft nut	55	41
Output shaft bearing retaining bolts	15	11
Output shaft nut	55	41
Rear cover bolts	13	10
Release bearing guide tube bolts	13	10
Reverse shaft locking plate bolt	15	11
Reverse shaft retaining bolt	20	15
Reversing lamp switch	25	18
Selector lever spring bracket	15	11
Speedometer drive locking bolt	13	10

3

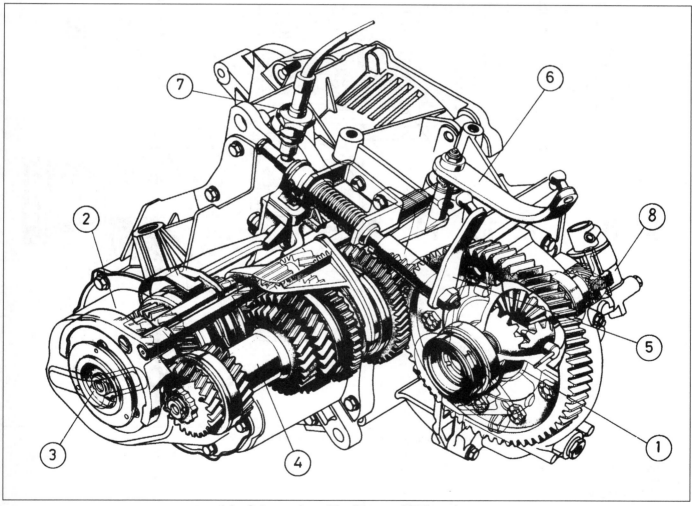

1.1a Cutaway view of the five-speed BE1 gearbox

1 *Final drive unit*
2 *5th gear housing*
3 *Input shaft*
4 *Output shaft*
5 *Engagement lever/shaft*
6 *Selector cover/shaft*
7 *Reverse release plunger*
8 *Speedometer drive housing*

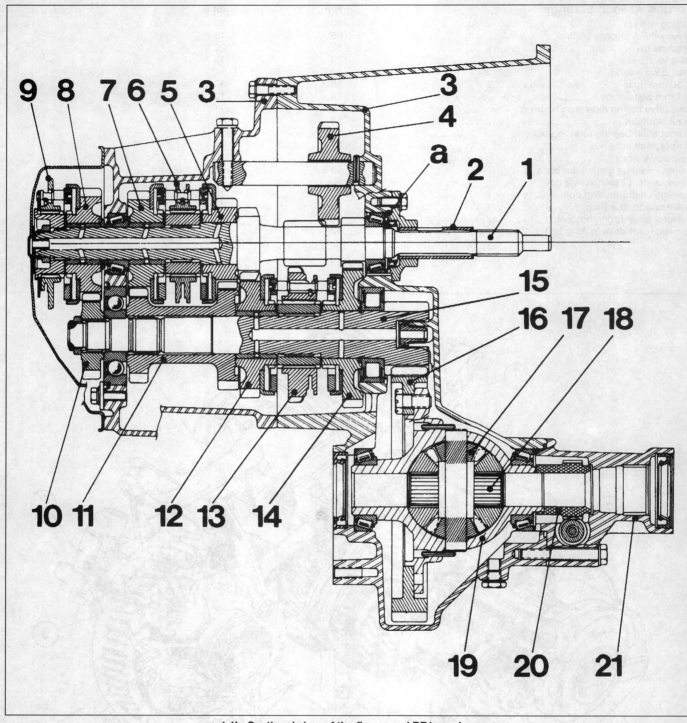

1.1b Sectional view of the five-speed BE1 gearbox

1   Input shaft
2   Release bearing guide tube
3   Casings
4   Reverse idler gear
5   3rd gear (driving)
6   3rd/4th synchro
7   4th gear (driving)
8   5th gear (driving)

9   5th synchro
10 5th gear (driven)
11 3rd/4th gears (driven)
12 2nd gear (driven)
13 1st/2nd synchro
14 1st gear (driven)
15 Output shaft
16 Crownwheel

17 Differential gear
18 Side gear
19 Differential carrier
20 Speedo driving gear
21 Extension housing
a   Selective shim - input shaft bearing
    preload

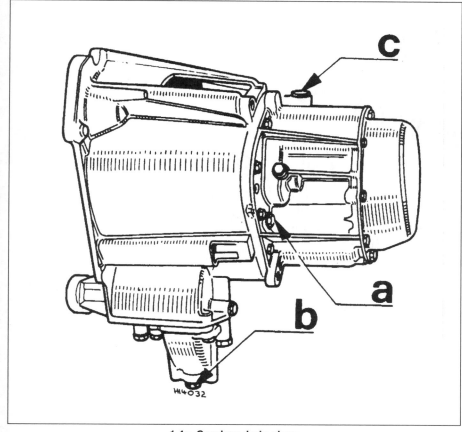

1.4a Gearbox drain plugs

A Gearbox drain plug (early models)
B Final drive drain plug

C Filler plug (early gearboxes, with two drain plugs)

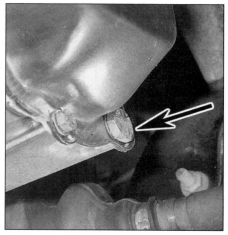

1.4b Gearbox filler/level plug on later gearboxes (arrowed)

1 General description

BE1 gearbox

This gearbox is a four- or five-speed, all synchromesh unit with integral final drive **(see illustrations)**. Drive is transmitted to the front wheels by the driveshafts, whose splined ends locate in either side of the final drive unit.

As is common practice with five-speed gearboxes, the fifth gear is housed in a bolt-on extension to the gearbox, the input shaft being extended through an intermediate plate to carry the 5th gear components.

Gear selection is by control rod and links from a floor-mounted gear lever. Inadvertent selection of reverse is prevented by a reverse release plunger, operated by cable from the gear lever.

On early gearboxes, two drain plugs are provided; one for the main gearbox, the other for the final drive differential. On later models, the gearbox drain plug has been deleted and the complete gearbox is drained through the final drive drain plug **(see illustrations)**.

Speedometer drive is taken from a pinion mounted on the right-hand side of the final drive unit.

BE3 gearbox

This is a development of the BE1 gearbox, and can be recognised by the revised gearchange pattern - reverse is positioned opposite 5th gear. Most overhaul procedures are the same, except many of the components are not interchangeable between the two gearboxes; major differences are indicated in the text.

2 Dismantling into assemblies

1 With the unit removed from the vehicle, clean and wipe dry all exterior surfaces.
2 Unbolt and remove the end cover.
3 Make alignment marks between the 5th gear synchro-hub and its sliding sleeve.

4 Engage 5th gear then drive out the spring pin securing 5th gear selector fork to the selector shaft.
5 Keeping 5th gear selected, engage one other gear to lock the shafts together.
6 Relieve the staking on the shaft nut collar, then unscrew and remove the input shaft nut.
7 Remove 5th gear synchro-hub, sleeve and selector fork from the input shaft. Be careful not to lose the detent ball from the fork.
8 Temporarily refit 5th gear sleeve and synchro-hub and engage 5th gear. Relieve the staking on the output shaft nut and remove the nut.
9 Remove 5th gear sleeve and hub.
10 Remove 5th gear and its bush, then lift off the spacer.
11 Unscrew and remove the output shaft rear bearing securing bolts and washers.
12 Prise out the output shaft bearing circlip. The circlip must be renewed so do not worry if it is damaged during removal.
13 Unbolt and remove the reverse selector shaft lockplate.
14 Remove the reverse idler shaft retaining bolt from the side of the gearbox casing.
15 Unbolt and remove the end casing bolts then separate the end casing from the main casing with gentle blows from a plastic mallet. Do not attempt to prise the casings apart with a lever. Note the position of the clutch cable bracket.
16 Engage reverse gear then remove the reverse idler gear and shaft by inserting a small screwdriver into the hole in the end of the shaft, disengaging the gear wheel as it is lifted out.
17 Turn 5th gear shaft clockwise and lift out the shaft.
18 Turn 1st/2nd-3rd/4th shaft clockwise using a screwdriver in the slot in the end of the shaft, and withdraw the shaft.
19 Turn 3rd/4th selector fork clockwise, and withdraw the fork.
20 Engage neutral.

3

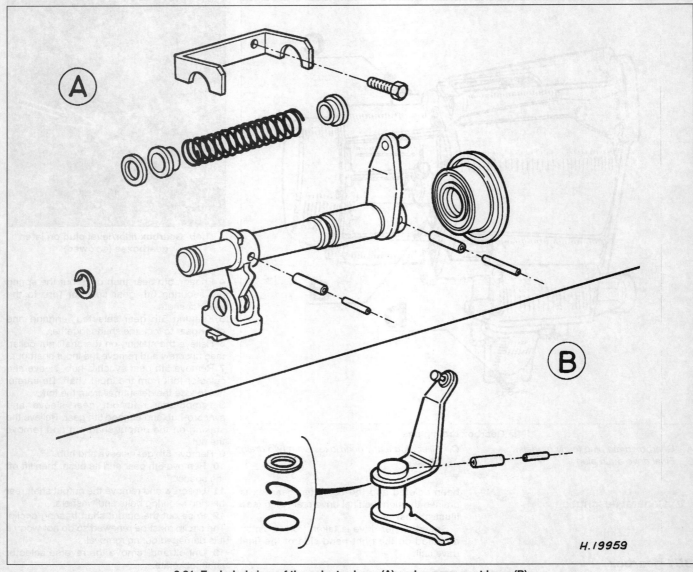

2.21 Exploded view of the selector lever (A) and engagement lever (B)

H.19959

2.32 Prising the input shaft oil seal from the clutch release bearing guide tube

21 Pull the selector lever fully out and downward, locking it against the casing **(see illustration)**.

22 Raise the interlock key then lift out both gear trains and 1st/2nd selector fork as a complete assembly.

23 Drift out the spring pin from the engagement lever.

24 Pull the lever from the engagement shaft and recover the spring, washer and seal.

25 Release the selector lever then push the engagement shaft inward to disengage its finger from the cut-out in the selector shaft, then remove the selector shaft and lever.

26 Recover the interlock key, selector finger, spacer, spring and washers.

27 Unbolt and remove the selector shaft spring bracket.

28 Undo the nut on the outside of the casing then remove the reverse selector lever and lift out the reverse release plunger and spring.

29 Remove the swarf collecting magnet from its slot in the casing.

30 Remove the reversing lamp switch.

31 Remove the clutch release arm and fork.

32 Remove the clutch release bearing guide tube and prise out the oil seal, being careful not to score the seal bore in the tube **(see illustration)**.

33 Extract the input shaft shim and bearing outer race.

34 If there have been signs of leakage from the selector shaft oil seal, prise out the seal from the casing.

35 If not already removed, unbolt and

withdraw the speedometer lockring and drive pinion **(see illustration)**.

36 Unbolt and remove the extension housing from the final drive.

37 Lift out the speedometer gear, recovering the O-ring seal and shim.

38 Unbolt and remove the final drive half-casing.

39 If the crownwheel bearings are to be re-used, mark the relationship of the bearing outer races and final drive housing.

40 Remove the engagement shaft and finger.

3 Examination and renovation

1 Clean all components and examine them thoroughly for wear and damage.

2 Circlips, roll pins, gaskets, oil seals and locking devices should all be renewed as a matter of course. Prise out the old oil seal from the clutch release bearing guide tube, but do not fit the new seal until reassembly. Renew the input and output shaft nuts.

3 If new input shaft or differential bearings are to be fitted, a selection of preload shims will be required. Read through the relevant procedures before starting work.

4 Input shaft - dismantling and reassembly

1 Remove the 3rd and 4th gear components from the input shaft by supporting the assembly under the 3rd gear and pressing or driving the shaft through. Protect the end of the shaft. Once the rear bearing is free, the other components can be removed from the shaft in order: 4th gear and its bush, 3rd/4th synchro sleeve and hub and 3rd gear **(see illustrations)**.

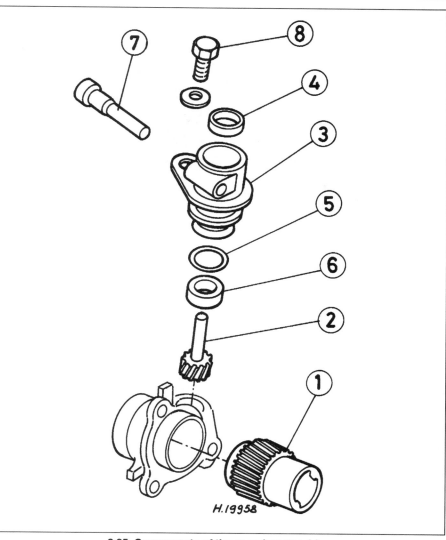

2.35 Components of the speedometer drive

1	Drive gear	4	Ring	7	Locking pin
2	Drive pinion	5	O-ring seal	8	Locking bolt
3	Housing	6	Ring		

4.1a Input shaft bearing . . .

4.1b . . . 4th gear. . .

4.1c . . . 4th gear bush . . .

3

4.1d . . . 3rd/4th synchro sleeve . . .

4.1e . . . synchro-hub . . .

4.1f . . . and 3rd gear

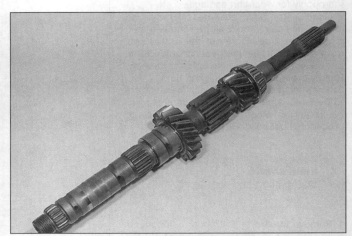

4.1g Input shaft with all components removed except the front bearing

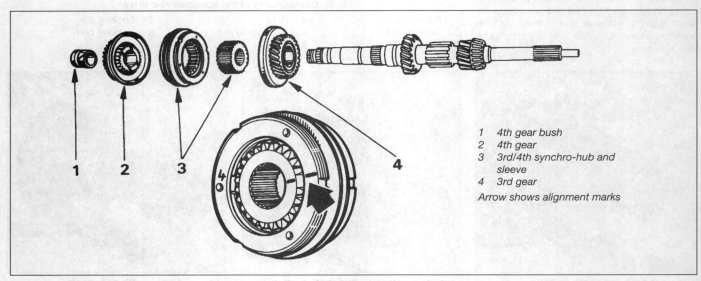

1 4th gear bush
2 4th gear
3 3rd/4th synchro-hub and sleeve
4 3rd gear
Arrow shows alignment marks

4.1h Exploded view of the input shaft

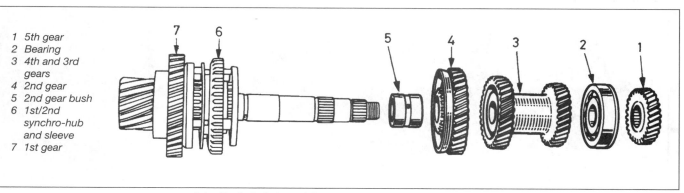

1 5th gear
2 Bearing
3 4th and 3rd gears
4 2nd gear
5 2nd gear bush
6 1st/2nd synchro-hub and sleeve
7 1st gear

5.1a Exploded view of the output shaft and components

2 Mark the synchro sleeve and hub relative to each other and to show which side faces 4th gear.

3 Remove the front bearing from the shaft, preferably with a press or a bearing puller. As a last resort it may be possible to support the bearing and drive the shaft through: be sure to protect the end of the shaft if this is done.

4 Once the input shaft bearings have been removed, they must be renewed. Press the rear bearing outer track from the end casing and press in the new track, making sure it enters squarely.

5 Before commencing reassembly, make sure that the input shaft is free from burrs and wear marks. Lubricate all parts as they are fitted.

6 Fit a new front bearing to the shaft, using a suitable tube to press or drive it home.

7 Fit 3rd gear, 3rd/4th synchro-hub and sleeve, 4th gear and its bush. Take care not to get 3rd and 4th gears mixed up, they are similar in appearance (4th gear has more teeth). If the original synchro components are being refitted, observe the mating marks made during dismantling.

8 Fit a new rear bearing to the shaft, again using a piece of tube.

9 The input shaft is now reassembled.

5 Output shaft - dismantling and reassembly

1 Remove 5th gear and the rear bearing from the output shaft (see illustrations). Use a puller or bearing extractor if they are a tight fit on the shaft.

2 Remove 3rd/4th gear assembly, 2nd gear and its bush (see illustrations).

3 Make alignment marks between the 1st/2nd synchro-hub and sleeve, then remove them from the shaft (see illustrations).

5.1b Output shaft rear bearing

5.2a 3rd/4th gear assembly

5.2b . . . 2nd gear . . .

5.2c . . . and 2nd gear bush

5.3a 1st/2nd synchro sleeve . . .

5.3b . . . and hub

3

5.4a Remove 1st gear . . .

5.4a . . . the needle thrust bearing . . .

5.4c . . . and the bearing circlip

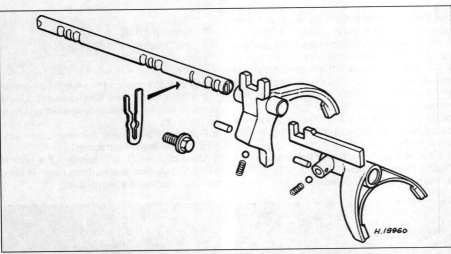

6.1a 1st/2nd and 3rd/4th selector fork and shaft assembly

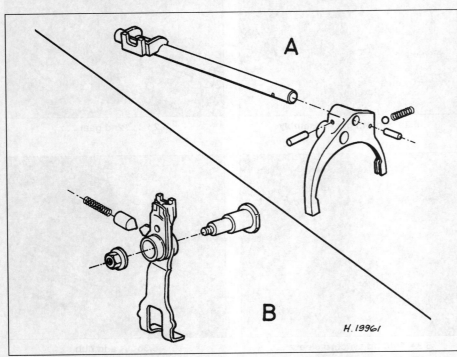

6.1b 5th gear selector shaft and fork (A) and reverse selector assembly (B)

4 Remove 1st gear and the needle thrust bearing and circlip (**see illustrations**).

5 Press or drive the shaft out of the pinion end bearing, protecting the end of the shaft.

6 Before commencing reassembly, make sure that the shaft is free from burrs or wear marks. Lubricate all parts as they are fitted.

7 Fit the pinion end bearing to the shaft, using a piece of tube to drive or press it home and fit a new circlip.

8 Fit the needle thrust bearing.

9 Refit 1st gear.

10 Refit the 1st/2nd synchro unit, observing the mating marks made when dismantling. The chamfer on the external teeth must face *towards* 1st gear on BE1 gearboxes, and *away from* 1st gear on BE3 gearboxes (**see illustration 8.39c**).

11 Fit 2nd gear and its bush.

12 Fit the 3rd/4th gear assembly, making sure it is the right way round.

13 Fit the rear bearing, with the circlip groove nearest the tail of the shaft.

14 Fit the 5th gear with its boss towards the bearing.

15 Fit a new nut to the output shaft but do not tighten it yet. Assembly of the output shaft is now complete.

6 Selector mechanism - dismantling and reassembly

1 An unusual feature of the gearbox is the location of the detent balls and springs in the selector forks, and not in the gearbox casing as is more usual (**see illustrations**).

2 The springs and balls are retained in the forks by spring pins and can be removed after tapping out the pins. If the springs are weak, renew them.

3 The 5th selector fork is retained on its selector shaft by a spring pin.

4 The 1st/2nd and 3rd/4th forks can be removed from the shaft by rotating them to disengage the detent balls, then sliding them from the shaft.

5 If the ends of the selector fork fingers are worn, renew them.

6 Similarly, renew the selector shafts if they show signs of wear.

7 Reassembly is a reversal of removal.

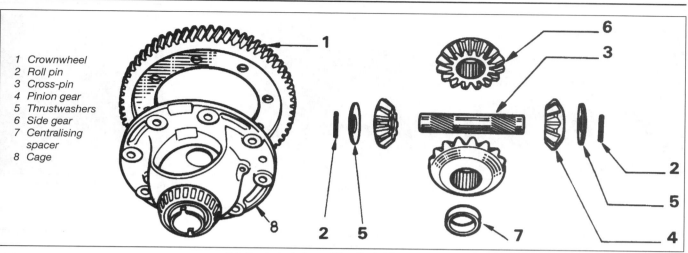

1 Crownwheel
2 Roll pin
3 Cross-pin
4 Pinion gear
5 Thrustwashers
6 Side gear
7 Centralising spacer
8 Cage

7.1 **Exploded view of the final drive assembly**

7 Final drive - dismantling and reassembly

1 Unbolt the crownwheel from the final drive cage (**see illustration**).
2 Remove the side gears by pushing them around inside the cage until they can be lifted out (**see illustration**).

7.2 **Removing the side gears**

3 Drive out the roll pins which secure the cross-pin in the cage.
4 Extract the cross-pin and remove the pinion gears and thrustwashers (**see illustration**).
5 If necessary, remove the bearings using a press or bearing puller.
6 Examine all components for wear and damage and renew as necessary. Lubricate all components before reassembly. If the bearings have been removed, they must be renewed.
7 Fit the new bearings, driving them home using a length of tube and a press.
8 Locate the centralising spacer in the cage, retaining it in position with grease.
9 Fit the side gears.
10 Assemble the pinion gears, thrustwashers and cross-pin to the cage, then secure the cross-pin with new roll pins. Note that the pins are only knocked in by half their length (**see illustration**).
11 Fit the crownwheel with its chamfer toward the cage.
12 Fit and tighten the crownwheel bolts to the specified torque using a diagonal tightening sequence.
13 Refitting of the final drive unit to the gearbox is described in Section 8.

8 Reassembly

1 Fit the centralising dowel to the gearbox casing.
2 Oil the engagement shaft and slide it into the casing.
3 Coat the mating surfaces of the final drive unit with sealant and fit the crownwheel and cage assembly to the gearbox casing (**see illustration**).
4 Fit the final drive unit half-casing but only tighten the bolts finger tight.
5 Fit the extension housing temporarily and nip up the bolts to align the casing halves.
6 Fit a new driveshaft oil seal to the side opposite the extension housing, tapping it home flush with the casing using a suitable size socket or length of tube.
7 If new final drive bearings have been fitted, the final drive unit preload must now be calculated and set as follows.
8 Remove the extension housing and fit a 2.2 mm thick preload shim to the bearing outer race.

3

7.4 **Extracting the cross-pin, pinion gears and thrustwashers**

7.10 **Roll pin correctly located**

8.3 **Crownwheel and cage assembly fitted to casing. Note locating dowel (arrowed)**

8.12 Measure from the joint face to the bearing outer race . . .

8.13 . . . and the joint face and face of the flange

8.17 Fitting the speedometer gear

9 Refit the extension housing, without its O-ring seal.
10 Settle the bearings and races by progressively tightening the extension housing bolts while turning the crownwheel until resistance is felt.
11 Remove the extension housing and preload shim.
12 Using a depth gauge, measure the distance between the casing joint face and the bearing outer race **(see illustration)**. Call this measurement (a).
13 Measure the distance between the joint face and the face of the flange on the extension housing (measurement b) **(see illustration)**.
14 Subtract (b) from (a) and add 0.1 mm to

the result which is the thickness of shim required to set bearing preload.
15 Tighten the final drive housing bolts to the specified torque.
16 Fit the previously calculated preload shim to the bearing outer race.
17 Fit the speedometer gear **(see illustration)**.
18 Oil and fit a new O-ring seal to the extension housing then fit the housing and tighten the bolts **(see illustrations)**.
19 Fit the speedometer drive pinion and lockplate and tighten the bolt.
20 If it has been removed, fit a new selector shaft oil seal, tapping it into its bore in the casing using a suitable size socket.
21 Temporarily fit the release bearing guide

tube without its gasket and only finger tighten the bolts.
22 Fit the input shaft front bearing outer race with the lettering on the rim facing toward the clutch end **(see illustration)**.
23 Position the oil jet in the output shaft bearing gallery **(see illustration)**.
24 Bolt the selector lever spring bracket in position.
25 Ensure the centralising dowels are in position in the main casing.
26 Fit the reverse release spring and plunger **(see illustration)**.
27 Push the plunger down into its bore against the spring and fit the reverse selector lever, tightening the pivot bolt and nut squarely **(see illustrations)**.

8.18a O-ring seal . . .

8.18b . . . and housing being fitted

8.22 Fitting input shaft bearing outer race

8.23 Positioning the oil jet

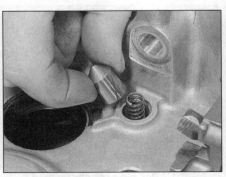

8.26 Fitting reverse release spring and plunger

8.27a Reverse selector lever and pivot bolt (arrowed) . . .

8.27b . . . being tightened

8.28 Screwing in the reversing lamp switch

8.30 Sliding in the selector shaft

28 Screw in the reversing lamp switch, using a new copper sealing washer, and tightening it to the specified torque **(see illustration)**.

29 Assemble the selector lever spring, washers, spacer, interlock key and selector shaft/lever.

30 Slide the shaft into the casing and through the assembled components **(see illustration)**.

31 Tap in a new roll pin to secure the engagement finger to the shaft **(see illustration)**.

32 Fit the swarf collecting magnet to its slot in the casing **(see illustration)**.

33 Pull the selector lever out and down to lock it against the casing.

34 Pull the interlock key upward.

35 Fit a new O-ring seal to the engagement shaft, followed by the washer and spring, then the lever. Secure the lever with a new roll pin **(see illustration)**.

36 Assemble the input and output shafts together with 1st/2nd selector fork and position the assembly in the casing **(see illustration)**.

37 Engage reverse gear.

38 Fit 3rd/4th fork to the input shaft, then fit 1st/2nd-3rd/4th fork shaft **(see illustration)**.

39 Fit the reverse idler gear and shaft, noting that the grooved side of the gear faces up and that the pin must protrude from the shaft by 5.0 mm (0.20 in) **(see illustrations)**. The gear and shaft are positioned differently in the BE3 gearbox **(see illustration)**.

8.31 Engagement finger roll pin (arrowed)

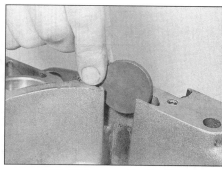

8.32 Fitting swarf collecting magnet

8.35 Tapping in a new roll pin to secure engagement lever

8.36 Fitting input shaft, output shaft and 1st/2nd selector fork

3

8.38 Fitting fork and selector shaft to input shaft

8.39a Fitting reverse idler gear . . .

8.39b . . . and shaft

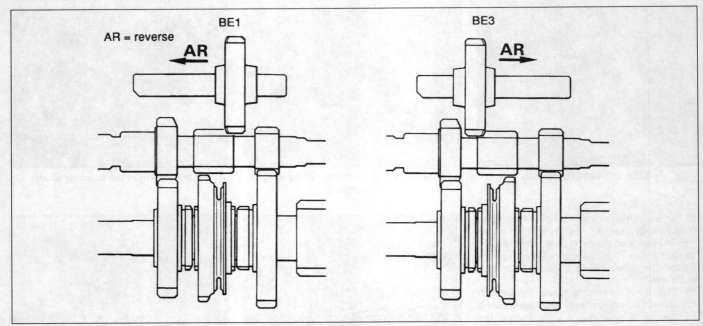

8.39c Position of reverse idler gear and 1st/2nd synchro in the BE3 gearbox

40 Fit 5th gear selector shaft **(see illustration)**.
41 Coat the clutch housing joint face with sealant, then fit the gearbox casing, tightening the bolts to the specified torque **(see illustration)**.

42 Fit the reverse shaft retaining bolt into the side of the casing using a new washer and tighten to the specified torque **(see illustration)**.
43 Fit the reverse shaft locking plate and tighten the bolt **(see illustration)**.
44 Fit a new bearing retaining circlip to the

output shaft bearing, ensuring that it snaps into the groove in the bearing **(see illustration)**. Pull the shaft upward to achieve the fit if necessary.
45 Fit and tighten the bearing retaining bolts and washers **(see illustration)**.

8.40 Fitting 5th gear selector shaft

8.41 Positioning the gearbox casing onto the clutch housing

8.42 Tightening reverse shaft retaining bolt

8.43 Reverse shaft locking plate bolt being tightened

8.44 Bearing retaining circlip

8.45 Tightening bearing retaining bolts

8.46a Fit the spacer . . .

8.46b . . . and bush

8.47a Slide on 5th gear . . .

46 Fit the spacer, flat side up, and 5th gear bush to the input shaft **(see illustrations)**.
47 Slide on 5th gear, synchro-hub and sleeve **(see illustrations)**.
48 Engage 3rd/4th gear, apply thread-locking compound to a new nut then fit and tighten the nut on the output shaft to the specified torque. Stake the nut to the shaft **(see illustrations)**.
49 Remove 5th gear and synchro-hub and sleeve, align the marks made during dismantling and fit the selector fork, refitting the complete assembly to the input shaft.
50 Fit the locking ball to the fork and push it

into its bore with a small screwdriver, then push the assembly down onto the input and selector shafts **(see illustration)**.
51 Engage two gears to lock the gear trains.
52 Apply thread-locking compound to a new input shaft nut, fit and tighten the nut to the specified torque **(see illustration)**, then stake it to the shaft.
53 Line up the holes in the selector fork and shaft and tap in a new roll pin **(see illustration)**.
54 Apply sealant to the joint face of the rear cover, fit the cover and tighten the retaining bolts. Note that the filler/level plug has a different torque setting to the retaining bolts **(see illustrations)**.

8.47b . . . and synchro-hub and sleeve

8.48a Apply thread-locking compound . . .

8.48b . . . and stake the nut to the shaft

8.50 5th gear selector fork with detent ball and spring arrowed

3

8.52 Tightening the input shaft nut

8.53 Tapping in a new roll pin

8.54a Fitting the rear cover . . .

8.54b . . . and filler/level plug

8.61 Measuring the distance from the clutch housing front face to the bearing outer race

8.62 Measuring the distance between the guide tube flange and front face

55 The input shaft bearing adjustment shim thickness must now be calculated as follows.
56 Remove the clutch release bearing guide tube.
57 Fit a preload shim (any size) to the outer race of the input shaft bearing.
58 Refit the release bearing guide tube without its gasket.

59 Tighten the guide tube retaining bolts progressively while turning the input shaft, until the shaft becomes difficult to turn. If the shaft does not become difficult to turn even with the guide tube bolts fully tightened, repeat the procedure using a thicker preload shim.
60 Remove the guide tube and shim.
61 Using a depth gauge, measure the distance between the front face of the clutch housing and the input shaft bearing outer race **(see illustration)**. Call this measurement (a).
62 Measure the distance between the release bearing guide tube flange and front face of the guide tube, measurement (b) **(see illustration)**.
63 Add 0.3 mm (0.012 in) to the difference between these two measurements (a - b) to allow for the thickness of the gasket, then select a shim that will give a final clearance of 0.08 mm + 0.04 mm (0.003 in + 0.001 in).
64 Fit a new oil seal into the release bearing guide tube.
65 Fit the selected shim over the input shaft and onto the front face of the bearing **(see illustration)**.
66 Fit the release bearing tube using a new gasket and tighten the bolts to the specified torque **(see illustration)**.
67 Fit the clutch release arm and fork.
68 Renew the driveshaft oil seals.
69 Do not fill the gearbox with oil until it has been refitted and the driveshafts inserted.

8.65 Fitting a shim over the input shaft

8.66 Fitting the release bearing guide tube

Chapter 4
Citroën/Peugeot MA gearbox

Contents

Specifications

General

Type	Four or five forward speeds, all synchromesh, one reverse gear
Designation	MA4 (4-speed) or MA5 (5-speed)

Gear ratios (typical)

Citroën AX

	MA4	MA5 (petrol)	MA5 (diesel)
1st	3.42 : 1	3.42 : 1	3.42 : 1
2nd	1.81 : 1	1.95 : 1	1.81 : 1
3rd	1.13 : 1	1.36 : 1	1.28 : 1
4th	0.81 : 1	1.05 : 1	0.98 : 1
5th	-	0.85 : 1	0.77 : 1
Reverse	3.58 : 1	3.58 : 1	3.58 : 1
Final drive	3.59 : 1	3.44 : 1	3.94 : 1

Citroën ZX

1st	3.42 : 1
2nd	1.81 : 1
3rd	1.28 : 1
4th	0.98 : 1
5th	0.77 : 1
Reverse	3.58 : 1
Final drive	4.29 : 1

Peugeot 106

	MA4	MA5
1st	3.42 : 1	3.42 : 1
2nd	1.81 : 1	1.95 : 1
3rd	1.13 : 1	1.36 : 1
4th	0.81 : 1	1.05 : 1
5th	-	0.85 : 1
Reverse	3.58 : 1	3.58 : 1
Final drive	4.29 : 1	4.29 : 1

Peugeot 205

	MA4	MA5
1st	3.42 : 1	3.42 : 1
2nd	1.81 : 1	1.81 : 1
3rd	1.13 : 1	1.28 : 1
4th	0.81 : 1	0.98 : 1
5th	-	0.77 : 1
Reverse	3.58 : 1	3.58 : 1
Final drive	3.77 : 1	3.94 : 1

Peugeot 306

1st	3.42 : 1
2nd	1.81 : 1
3rd	1.28 : 1
4th	0.98 : 1
5th	0.77 : 1
Reverse	3.58 : 1
Final drive	4.06 : 1

4

Lubrication

Oil capacity (drain and refill)	2.0 litres (3.5 pints)	
Lubrication type/specification	See *Recommended lubricants and fluids*	

Torque wrench settings

	Nm	lbf ft
Bearing half-rings	18	13
Drain and filler plugs	25	18
Gearbox housing to clutch/final drive housing	18	13
Gearbox to engine	45	33
Intermediate plate to clutch/final drive housing	50	37
Output shaft nut (five-speed gearbox)	140	103
Pressed-steel housing	18	13

1 General description

This gearbox is mounted on the left-hand side of the engine, and may be removed separately, leaving the engine in the car. It has either four or five forward gears depending on the model, all with synchromesh, and one reverse gear.

All the synchromesh units are located on the output shaft, and the differential unit is located in the main gearbox casing **(see illustrations)**.

There are no specified oil change requirements for the MA gearbox, but regular oil level checks should be carried out **(see illustrations)**. Make sure that all topping-up is made using only the specified grade of oil.

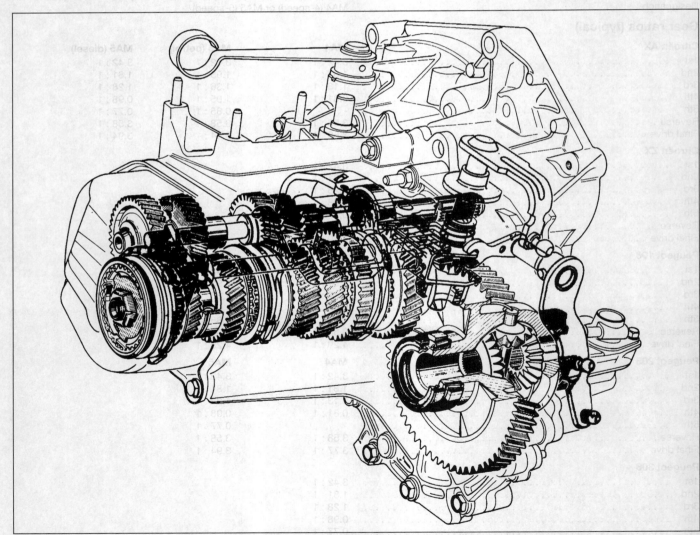

1.2a Cutaway view of the MA 5-speed gearbox

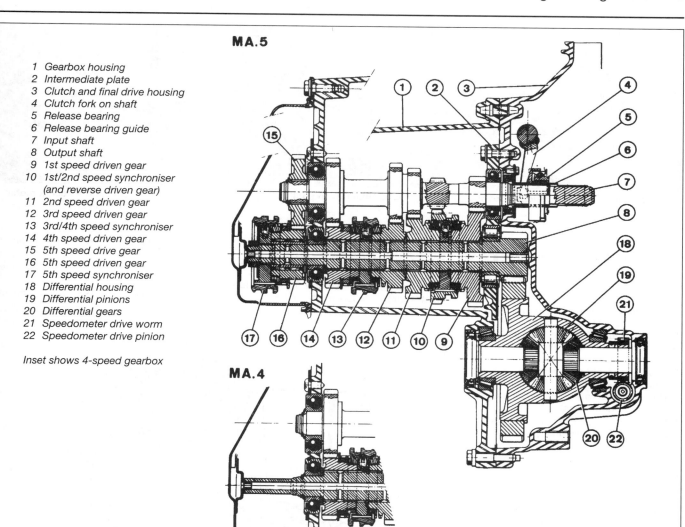

MA.5

1 Gearbox housing
2 Intermediate plate
3 Clutch and final drive housing
4 Clutch fork on shaft
5 Release bearing
6 Release bearing guide
7 Input shaft
8 Output shaft
9 1st speed driven gear
10 1st/2nd speed synchroniser
   (and reverse driven gear)
11 2nd speed driven gear
12 3rd speed driven gear
13 3rd/4th speed synchroniser
14 4th speed driven gear
15 5th speed drive gear
16 5th speed driven gear
17 5th speed synchroniser
18 Differential housing
19 Differential pinions
20 Differential gears
21 Speedometer drive worm
22 Speedometer drive pinion

Inset shows 4-speed gearbox

MA.4

1.2b Cross-section of the MA gearbox

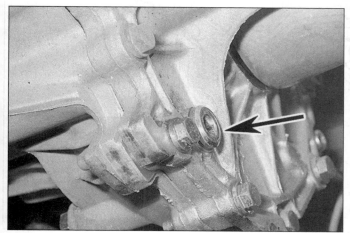

1.3a Gearbox drain plug (arrowed)

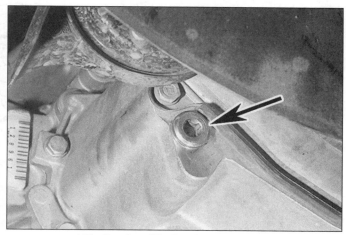

1.3b Gearbox filler/level plug (arrowed)

4

2.2 Removing the clutch release bearing

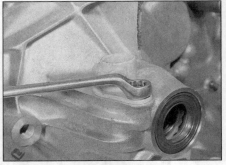

2.4a Unscrew the bolt . . .

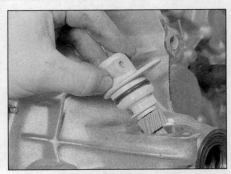

2.4b . . . and remove the speedometer drive pinion

2 Dismantling into assemblies

1 With the unit removed from the car, clean all exterior surfaces and wipe dry.
2 Pull the clutch release bearing from the guide sleeve, and release the spring clips from the fork ends **(see illustration)**.
3 Position the gearbox with the clutch end downwards.
4 Unbolt and remove the speedometer drive pinion **(see illustrations)**.
5 Unbolt the pressed-steel housing. Remove the rubber gasket **(see illustrations)**.

5-speed gearbox only

6 Drive the pin from the 5th speed selector fork.
7 Engage both reverse and 5th gears **(see illustration)**, then loosen the nut on the end of the output shaft. Return the gears to neutral.
8 Remove the nut and lockwasher **(see illustrations)**.
9 On models up to late 1991, remove the 5th

2.5a Unscrew the bolt

2.5b . . . and remove the pressed-steel housing

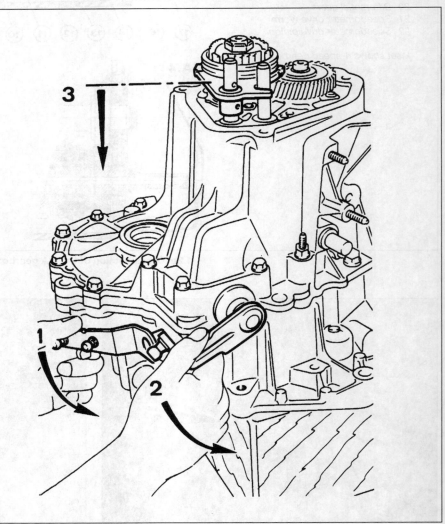

2.7 Sequence for selecting reverse and 5th gears

2.8a Remove the 5th synchro nut . . .

2.8b . . . and lockwasher

synchro unit together with its selector fork, making sure that the sleeve remains central on the hub to avoid loss of the internal balls and springs (see illustration). On models from late 1991, mark the selector sleeve in relation to the hub. Cover the sleeve with a cloth, to retain the internal balls and springs. Remove the 5th speed sleeve together with the selector fork. Using a suitable three-legged puller, remove the synchro hub with the 5th speed driven gear (see illustration). Separate the hub, synchro ring and gear.

10 On models up to late 1991, remove from the output shaft the 5th synchro ring, followed by the 5th speed driven gear, needle bearing, sleeve, and thrustwasher (see illustrations). On models from late 1991, remove from the output shaft the needle bearing, sleeve and thrustwasher.

11 Extract the circlip from the end of the input shaft, followed by the special washer,

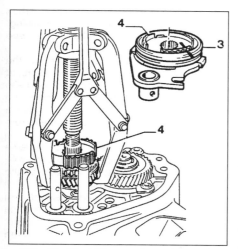

2.9b Modified 5th speed synchromesh assembly

Mark the synchro sleeve (3) in relation to the hub (4)

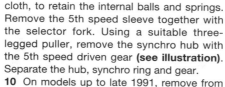

2.9a Removing the 5th synchro unit and selector fork

2.10a Removing the 5th synchro ring . . .

2.10b . . . 5th speed driven gear. . .

2.10c . . . needle bearing. . .

2.10d . . . sleeve . . .

2.10e . . . and thrustwasher

4

2.11 Removing the special washer from the input shaft

2.12 Removing the 5th speed drive gear

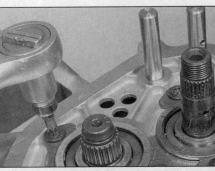

2.13a Unscrew the Torx screws . . .

2.13b . . . and extract the bearing half-rings

2.14 Unscrewing a gearbox housing bolt

noting that the convex side is uppermost (see illustration).

12 Using a suitable puller if necessary, pull the 5th speed drive gear from the splines on the input shaft (see illustration).

4 and 5-speed gearboxes

13 Unscrew the Torx screws and extract the half-rings from the grooves in the shaft bearings, noting their locations (see illustrations).

14 Unscrew the bolts securing the gearbox housing to the clutch/final drive housing, noting the location of the bolts (see illustration).

15 Lift the gearbox housing from the clutch/final drive housing (see illustration), at the same time guiding the selector fork shafts through the housing. Do not prise the housings apart with a screwdriver; use a wooden or hide mallet to release them from the sealant.

16 Remove the plastic ring from the reverse idler gear shaft, then remove the shaft from the clutch/final drive housing and remove the idler gear (see illustrations).

17 Press down on the reverse selector arm directly over the shaft, and at the same time extract the shaft from the intermediate plate. Remove the reverse selector arm (see illustrations).

18 Lift the gate lever to the 1st/2nd position, and support with a block of wood.

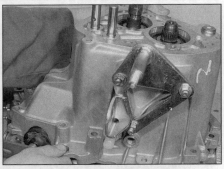

2.15 Lifting the gearbox housing from the clutch/final drive housing

2.16a Removing the plastic ring . . .

2.16b . . . reverse idler gear shaft . . .

2.16c . . . and reverse idler gear

2.17a Removing the reverse selector shaft . . .

2.17b . . . and arm

2.20 Removing the selector shaft

2.21 Removing the neutral return spring and plastic cups

19 Using a suitable pin punch, drive out the pin securing the selector finger to the selector shaft. Recover the pin, and return the gate lever to neutral.

20 Pull out the selector shaft, and remove the rubber boot from it **(see illustration)**.

21 Prise out the neutral return spring, together with the two plastic cups **(see illustration)**.

22 Lift the gate lever, and at the same time remove the interlocking key and selector finger **(see illustrations)**.

23 Tie the two selector fork shafts together as an aid to reassembly.

24 Using both hands, lift the input and output shafts, together with the selector fork shafts, directly from the clutch/final drive housing **(see illustration)**. Separate the input shaft from the output shaft, and disengage the selector forks from the synchro units on the output shaft.

25 Unscrew the bolts and remove the intermediate plate from the clutch/final drive housing **(see illustration)**. Adhesive is used on assembly, so some difficulty may be experienced, but do not lever directly on the mating faces.

26 Remove the reverse locking plunger and spring, using a magnet if available **(see illustrations)**.

27 Lift out the differential unit **(see illustration)**.

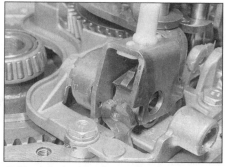

2.22a Interlocking key and selector finger assembly

2.22b Interlocking key and selector finger separated

2.24 Lifting input and output shafts with selector fork shafts from the clutch/final drive housing

2.25 Removing the intermediate plate

2.26a Removing the reverse locking plunger . . .

2.26b . . . and spring

2.27 Lifting out the differential unit

4

28 The gearbox is now dismantled into its major assemblies.

Gearbox casing - modifications

29 From approximately June 1991, an oil deflector has been fitted to the gearbox casing, to improve the lubrication of the 3rd/4th speed synchroniser assembly **(see illustration)**. Note that the new gearbox casings are interchangeable with the older components, but an oil deflector cannot be fitted to an earlier gearbox.

3 Examination and renovation

1 Clean all components, and examine them thoroughly for wear and damage. Circlips, locking pins, gaskets and oil seals should all be renewed as a matter of course. Read through the reassembly sub-section, and obtain the necessary adhesive and sealants required.

4 Clutch/final drive housing - dismantling and reassembly

1 Using a suitable punch, drive out the locking pin and remove the gate lever from the shaft **(see illustration)**.

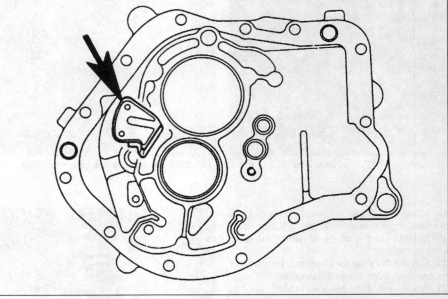

2.29 Oil deflector (arrowed) fitted to gearbox casing

2 Withdraw the shaft, and prise the oil seal from the housing.
3 Prise out the driveshaft and input shaft oil seals **(see illustrations)**.
4 If necessary, drive out the location dowels.
5 If necessary, drive out the right-hand final drive bearing outer track, using a punch through the cut-outs provided **(see illustration)**.
6 Unbolt the clutch release bearing guide sleeve **(see illustration)**.
7 Clean all the components.
8 Commence reassembly by refitting the clutch release bearing guide sleeve, together with a new input shaft seal. Apply jointing compound to the threads, then insert and tighten the bolts. Smear a little oil on the seal.
9 Using a metal tube, drive the right-hand final drive bearing outer track fully into the housing.
10 Drive in the location dowels.
11 Oil the new driveshaft oil seal, and drive it into the housing using a block of wood.
12 Oil the new gate lever shaft oil seal, and drive it into the housing. Oil the shaft and refit it.
13 Locate the gate lever on the shaft towards the final drive, align the holes, and drive in the new locking pin.

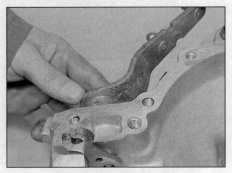

4.1 Removing the gate lever

4.3a Prising out the driveshaft oil seal . . .

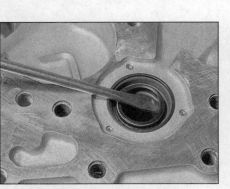

4.3b . . . and input shaft oil seal

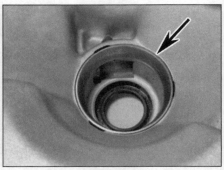

4.5 Right-hand final drive bearing outer track (arrowed)

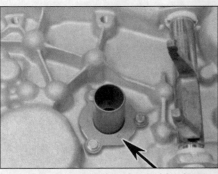

4.6 Clutch release bearing guide sleeve (arrowed)

5 Gearbox housing - dismantling and reassembly

1 Prise out the driveshaft oil seal.
2 If necessary, drive out the left-hand final drive bearing outer track using a punch through the cut-outs provided **(see illustration)**.
3 Using a metal tube, drive the new outer track fully into the housing.
4 Oil the new driveshaft oil seal, and drive it into the housing using a block of wood.

6 Input shaft - dismantling and reassembly

1 On the 4-speed gearbox, extract the circlip with circlip pliers, and remove the washer.
2 On 4 and 5-speed gearboxes, pull the bearing from the 4th speed end of the input shaft using a suitable puller. Similarly pull the bearing from the 1st speed end. Note that the re-use of removed bearings is not recommended.

5.2 Left-hand final drive bearing outer track

3 To reassemble, drive the bearing on the 1st speed end of the shaft using a length of metal tube on the inner track. Similarly drive the bearing on the 4th speed end, but note that the groove in the outer track must be towards the end of the shaft **(see illustration)**.
4 Locate the washer over the end of the shaft on the 4-speed gearbox. Rest the circlip on the tapered end of the shaft, and use a socket to drive it into the groove. Check that the circlip is seated correctly by squeezing it with pliers.

6.3 Input shaft and bearings assembled

7 Output shaft - dismantling and reassembly

1 On the 4-speed gearbox, extract the circlip with circlip pliers, and remove the washer.
2 On 4 and 5-speed gearboxes, pull the bearing from the shaft using a suitable puller if necessary.
3 Remove the thrustwasher, followed by 4th gear, the 4th synchro ring, the 3rd/4th synchro unit, and the 3rd synchro ring **(see illustrations)**. Keep the synchro unit sleeve central on the hub.

7.3a Removing the thrustwasher . . .

7.3b . . . 4th gear . . .

7.3c . . . 4th synchro ring . . .

7.3d . . . 3rd/4th synchro unit. . .

7.3e . . . and the 3rd synchro ring

4

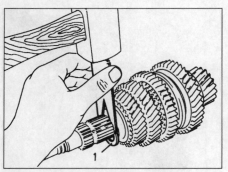

7.4a Forked tool for removing C-clips (1) from the output shaft

7.4b Removing the C-clip

4 Tap out the C-clip using a screwdriver or a forked tool **(see illustrations)**.

5 Remove the 3rd gear, the C-clip, the 2nd gear, 2nd synchro ring, 1st/2nd synchro unit, 1st synchro ring, the C-clip, 1st gear, and the final C-clip **(see illustrations)**. Keep the synchro unit sleeve central on the hub.

6 Remove the final bearing using a suitable puller, or by supporting the bearing in a vice and driving the output shaft through it. Note that the re-use of removed bearings is not recommended.

7 To reassemble, drive the bearing onto the output shaft using a length of metal tube on the inner track. Do not support the shaft on the plastic lubrication disc.

7.5a Remove the 3rd gear. . .

7.5b . . . C-clip . . .

7.5c . . . 2nd gear . . .

7.5d . . . 2nd synchro ring . . .

7.5e . . . 1st/2nd synchro unit . . .

7.5f . . . 1st synchro ring . . .

7.5g . . . C-clip. . .

7.5h . . . 1st gear . . .

7.5l . . . and the final C-clip (arrowed)

7.8 Inserting a C-clip

7.14 Driving the bearing onto the input shaft

8 Press the C-clip into its groove, followed by 1st gear and the next C-clip **(see illustration)**.
9 Fit the 1st synchro ring, then lower the 1st/2nd synchro unit onto the splines with the selector groove downwards, at the same time aligning the projections on the 1st synchro ring with the rockers on the synchro unit.
10 Fit the 2nd synchro ring, aligning the projections as described in paragraph 9.
11 Fit the 2nd gear, the C-clip, 3rd gear, and the C-clip.
12 Fit the 3rd synchro ring, 3rd/4th synchro unit, and the 4th synchro ring as described in paragraph 9.
13 Fit the 4th gear and thrustwasher.
14 Locate the bearing on the shaft, with the groove towards the end of the shaft. Drive the bearing onto the shaft using a length of metal tube on the inner track **(see illustration)**. Do not support the shaft on the plastic lubrication disc.
15 On the 4-speed gearbox, locate the washer on the end of the shaft. Rest the circlip on the tapered end of the shaft, and use a socket to drive it into the groove. Check that the circlip is seated correctly by squeezing it with pliers.

8 Differential bearings - removal and refitting

1 Lever off the speedometer drive worm **(see illustration)**.
2 Pull the bearings from both sides of the differential unit using a suitable puller. Identify them for location if they are to be re-used.
3 Drive the new bearings into position using a length of metal tube on their inner tracks.
4 Press the speedometer drive worm into position.

9 Selector fork shafts - dismantling and reassembly

1 Support the 3rd/4th selector fork shaft in a soft jawed vice, then drive out the roll pin using a suitable punch. Slide off the selector fork, noting which way round it is fitted.
2 Similarly drive out the roll pin, and remove the 1st/2nd selector fork and the reverse control relay from the other shaft.
3 Reassembly is a reversal of dismantling, but use new roll pins **(see illustrations)**.

8.1 Speedometer drive worm (arrowed)

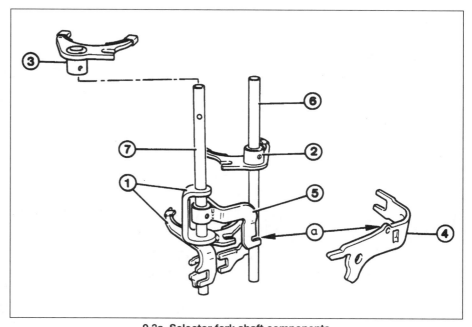

9.3a Selector fork shaft components

1	1st/2nd selector fork	5	Reverse control relay
2	3rd/4th selector fork	6	3rd/4th selector fork shaft
3	5th selector fork	7	5th selector fork/reverse control relay shaft
4	Reverse selector arm		
		a	Reverse selector arm-to-relay stud

4

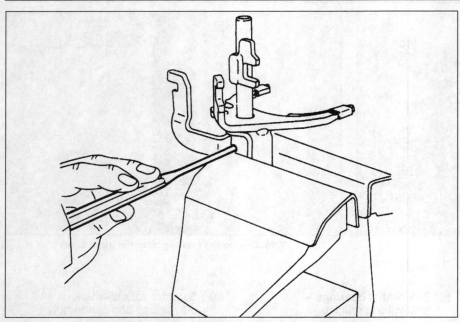

9.3b Driving the roll pin from the reverse control relay

10 Synchro units - dismantling and reassembly

Note: *From early 1993 onwards, the synchro hub assemblies were modified to improve gearchange action. Note that these modified synchro hub assemblies cannot be dismantled without the use of the special service tools. The modified synchro-hubs can be installed in earlier gearbox units at overhaul. Refer to a dealer for further information.*

1 Mark the hub and the outer sleeve in relation to each other, to ensure correct reassembly.

2 Wrap the unit in a cloth, then slide the sleeve from the hub. Recover the three balls, three springs, and three rockers **(see illustration)**.

3 To reassemble the units, first insert the hub in the sleeve. The rocker slots in the hub and sleeve must be in alignment.

4 Pull out the hub until the rockers, springs and balls can be inserted, then press in the balls and push the hub fully into the sleeve. A large worm drive clip, piston ring compressor, or three narrow strips of metal may be used to press in the balls.

11 Reassembly

1 With the clutch/final drive housing on the bench, lower the differential unit into position.

4 From May 1988, the reverse selector components have been modified.

5 The later components can be identified from the modifications shown **(see illustration)**.

6 The early components are no longer available, and are not interchangeable with the later components. If any of the relevant components are renewed on a gearbox fitted with the early components, the other associated components must also be renewed as a set.

7 Note that if the later components are fitted to an early gearbox, a later-type modified breather and cap *must* be fitted, to avoid possible fouling of the selector components.

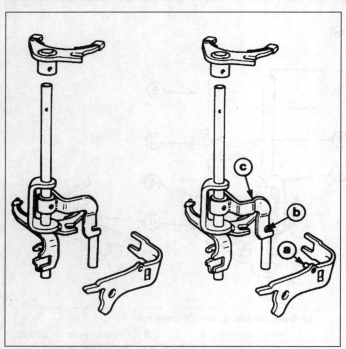

9.5 Modifications (a, b and c) to reverse selector components

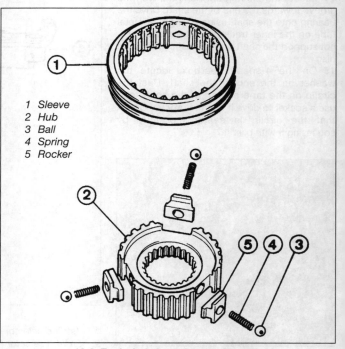

1 Sleeve
2 Hub
3 Ball
4 Spring
5 Rocker

10.2 Exploded view of a synchro unit

11.3a Applying adhesive to the intermediate plate

11.3b Guiding the gate lever through the intermediate plate

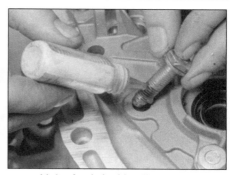

11.4a Apply locking fluid to the intermediate plate bolt threads . . .

11.4b . . . and tighten the bolts to the specified torque

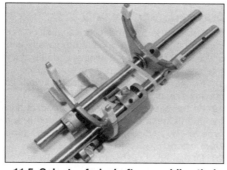

11.5 Selector fork shaft assemblies tied together with a plastic strap

11.6 Shafts and selector forks assembled in the clutch/final drive housing

2 Insert the reverse locking spring and plunger.

3 Apply Loctite Autoform 549 adhesive to the contact area on the intermediate plate, then lower the plate onto the clutch/final drive housing, at the same time guiding the gate lever through the hole provided **(see illustrations)**.

4 Apply locking fluid to the intermediate plate bolt threads. Insert the bolts and progressively tighten them to the specified torque **(see illustrations)**. Clean the excess adhesive from the bearing locations.

5 Tie the two selector fork shaft assemblies together **(see illustration)**.

6 Engage the selector forks in the synchro unit grooves, and mesh the input and output

shaft assemblies together. Using both hands, lower the complete assembly into the clutch/final drive housing **(see illustration)**.

7 Locate the selector finger within the interlocking key **(see illustration)**, then lift the gate lever and insert the key assembly in the clutch/final drive housing. Make sure that the selector finger engages the fork gates, and that the gate lever engages the outer plate of the interlocking key.

8 Engage the plastic cups with the neutral return spring, and insert them between the interlocking key and intermediate plate **(see illustrations)**.

9 Fit the rubber boot on the selector shaft. Insert the shaft through the intermediate plate, interlocking key and selector finger, align the

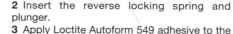

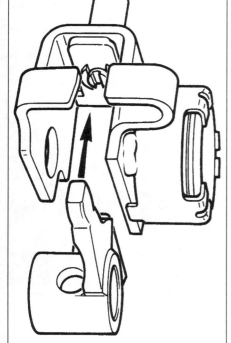

11.7 Locating the selector finger in the interlocking key

11.8a Neutral return spring and plastic cups (arrowed)

11.8b Neutral return spring showing gate lever (arrowed) engaged with interlocking key

4

11.9a Insert the locking pin. . .

11.9b . . . and drive it through the selector shaft

11.13 Applying jointing compound to the clutch/final drive housing

holes and drive in the locking pin (see illustrations).

10 Insert the reverse selector arm in the intermediate plate, press down on it to depress the plunger, and insert the shaft. Make sure that the stud on the arm enters the cut-out on the control relay.

11 Engage the reverse idler gear with the selector arm, with the projecting shoulder uppermost, and insert the shaft, cut-out end downwards. Turn the shaft until the cut-out drops in the recess.

12 Fit the plastic ring on the shaft.

13 Apply a thin, even, coat of a silicone-based jointing compound to the mating face of the clutch/final drive housing (see illustration).

14 Lower the gearbox housing onto the clutch/final drive housing, at the same time guiding the input and output shaft bearings and selector fork shafts through their holes.

15 Insert the bolts in their previously-noted locations, and tighten them evenly to the specified torque.

16 Fit the retaining half-rings in the bearing grooves with the chamfers uppermost, then insert and tighten the bolts.

5-speed gearbox only

17 Locate the 5th speed drive gear on the input shaft splines, support the opposite end of the shaft on a block of wood, and fully drive the gear on the splines using a metal tube.

18 Fit the washer on the input shaft, with its convex side uppermost.

19 Fit the circlip using a suitable socket and hammer. Check that it is fully entered in the groove by squeezing with pliers (see illustration).

20 Fit the thrustwasher to the output shaft (oil groove uppermost) followed by the sleeve, needle bearing, 5th speed driven gear and the 5th synchro ring.

21 On models up to late 1991, engage the selector fork with the 5th synchro unit, then lower them onto the output shaft and selector fork shafts. Make sure that the projections on the synchro ring are aligned with the rockers in the synchro unit. On models from late 1991, coat the internal splines of the 5th synchro hub with Loctite (part No 9733.10 or 9734.41), then engage the selector fork with the 5th synchro unit, and lower them onto the output shaft and selector fork shafts. Make sure that

the projections on the synchro ring are aligned with the rockers in the synchro unit

22 On models up to late 1991, fit the special lockwasher and nut (finger-tight). On models from late 1991, fit the special lockwasher, then coat the threads of a **new** nut with Loctite, and fit the nut to the end of the shaft finger-tight.

23 Engage both reverse and 5th speed gears (see illustration 2.7). Tighten the nut to the specified torque, then return the gears to neutral (see illustration).

24 Align the holes in the 5th speed selector fork and shaft, and drive in the locking pin (see illustration).

4 and 5-speed gearboxes

25 Fit the dry rubber gasket to the pressed-steel housing. Locate the housing on the gearbox housing, insert the bolts and tighten them to the specified torque.

26 Refit the speedometer drive pinion. Insert and tighten the bolt.

27 Apply a little grease to the guide sleeve, then refit the clutch release bearing and engage the spring clips with the fork ends.

11.19 Squeezing circlip into groove in input shaft

11.23 Tightening the 5th synchro nut

11.24 Driving in the 5th selector fork locking pin

Chapter 5
Ford B & N gearboxes

Contents

Specifications

General

Type	Four or five forward speeds and reverse, synchromesh on all forward speeds, constant four-wheel-drive on 4x4 models
Designation	B (4-speed) or N (5-speed)

Ratios (typical)

	B	N
1st	3.65 : 1	3.65 : 1*
2nd	1.97 : 1	1.97 : 1**
3rd	1.37 : 1	1.37 : 1
4th	1.00 : 1	1.00 : 1
5th	-	0.82 : 1
Reverse	3.66 : 1	3.66 : 1
Final drive	3.38 : 1	3.62 : 1

* Transit: 3.90 : 1
** Transit petrol: 2.28 : 1; diesel: 2.87 : 1

Lubrication

Capacity (approx):	
B	1.46 litres (2.6 pints)
N:	
Four cylinder:	
Up to 1987	1.9 litres (3.3 pints)
From 1987	1.25 litres (2.2 pints)
V6 except 4x4 models	1.9 litres (3.3 pints)
4x4 models	1.25 litres (2.2 pints)
Transfer box	0.5 litre (0.9 pints)
Lubricant type/specification	See *Recommended lubricants and fluids*

5

Torque wrench settings

	Nm	lbf ft
5th gear collar nut	120 to 150	89 to 111
5th gear lockplate	21 to 26	15 to 19
Clutch guide sleeve	9 to 11	7 to 8
Clutch housing to engine	40 to 51	30 to 38
Clutch housing to gearbox casing	70 to 90	52 to 66
Countershaft cluster spigot	14 to 19	10 to 14
Crossmember	20 to 25	15 to 18
Extension housing	45 to 49	33 to 36
Filler plug:		
Except 4x4	33 to 41	24 to 30
4x4	40 to 60	30 to 44
Gear lever to extension housing	21 to 26	15 to 19
Gearbox cover	9 to 11	7 to 8
Insulator to crossmember		
Except 4x4	16 to 20	12 to 15
4x4	20 to 26	15 to 19
Insulator to gearbox (except 4x4)	50 to 57	37 to 42
Insulator to transfer box (4x4)	40 to 50	30 to 37
Reversing light switch	1 to 2	0.7 to 1.5
Selector interlock	17 to 19	13 to 14
Transfer box housing central bolt	50 to 70	37 to 52
Transfer box housing outer bolts	21 to 28	15 to 21
Transfer box to gearbox	45 to 49	33 to 36

1 General description

The manual gearbox fitted is either a four-speed (type B) or five-speed (type N). 4x4 models are fitted with a modified five-speed (type N) gearbox with a transfer box instead of the rear extension housing.

The gearbox construction is conventional. Drive from the clutch is transmitted to the input shaft which runs in line with the mainshaft **(see illustrations)**. The input shaft and mainshaft forward gears are in constant mesh with the countershaft gear cluster, and

selection of gears is by sliding the synchromesh sleeves, which link the appropriate mainshaft gear to the mainshaft. Drive in 4th gear in direct (ie the input shaft is locked to the mainshaft). Reverse gear is obtained by sliding an idler gear into mesh with two spur-cut gears on the mainshaft and countershaft. All forward gear teeth are

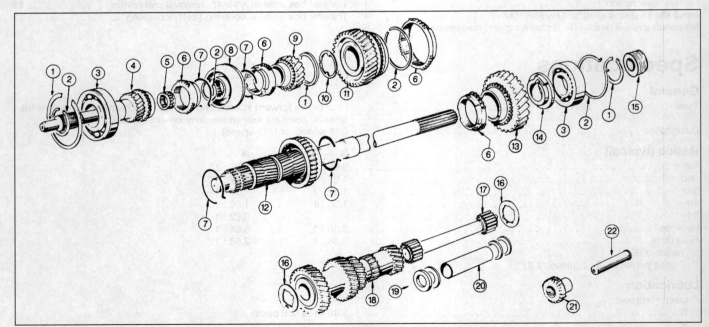

1.2a Exploded view of type B gearbox gear assemblies

1 Circlip	7 Retaining spring	13 1st gear	18 Countershaft gear cluster
2 Circlip	8 Synchroniser hub	14 Oil scoop ring	19 Spacer
3 Grooved ball bearing	9 3rd gear	15 Speedometer drivegear	20 Spacer tube
4 Input shaft	10 Thrust half washers	16 Thrust washer	21 Reverse gear idler
5 Needle roller bearing	11 2nd gear	17 Needle rollers	22 Idler shaft
6 Synchroniser ring	12 Mainshaft with synchroniser		

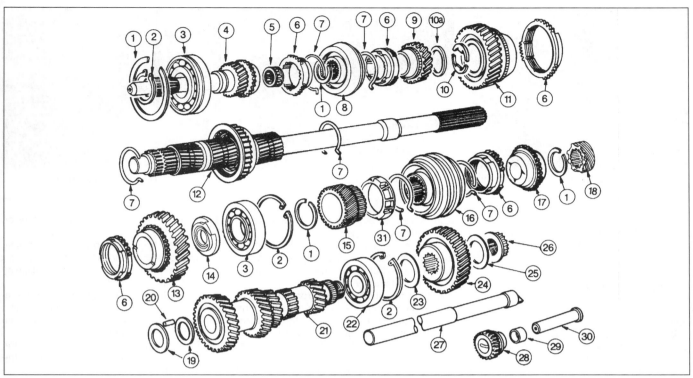

1.2b Exploded view of type N gearbox gear assemblies

1 *Circlip*	9 *3rd gear*	16 *5th gear synchroniser*	24 *5th gear (countershaft*
2 *Circlip*	10 *Thrust half washers*	17 *5th gear synchroniser*	*gear cluster)*
3 *Ball bearing*	10a *Thrust washer circlip*	*hub*	25 *Washer*
4 *Input shaft*	11 *2nd gear*	18 *Speedometer drivegear*	26 *Twelve-sided nut*
5 *Needle roller bearing*	12 *Mainshaft with*	19 *Spacer*	27 *Countershaft*
6 *Synchroniser ring*	*synchroniser*	20 *Needle rollers*	28 *Reverse idler gear*
7 *Retaining spring*	13 *1st gear*	21 *Countershaft gear cluster*	29 *Bush*
8 *3rd/4th gear*	14 *Oil scoop ring*	22 *Roller bearing*	30 *Idler shaft*
synchroniser	15 *5th gear*	23 *Washer*	31 *Blocker bar retainer*

helically cut to reduce noise and improve wear characteristics.

The transfer box on 4x4 models incorporates a centre differential **(see illustration)**. Drive from the gearbox mainshaft is transmitted to the differential gear pivot shafts, and is then split to the rear wheels via an outer ring, and to the front wheels via an inner sun gear shaft. Due to the take-off diameters from the differential gears, 66% torque is transmitted to the rear wheels and 34% torque to the front wheels. Drive from the inner sun gear shaft to the front wheels is via a silent chain and specially cut chain wheels, front propeller shaft, final drive unit, and driveshafts. A viscous coupling is fitted between the front and rear drive outputs to improve traction, by limiting any speed difference between the front and rear wheels.

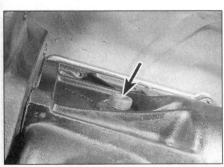

1.2c Oil filler/level plug location location (arrowed) - type N gearbox
No drain plug is fitted

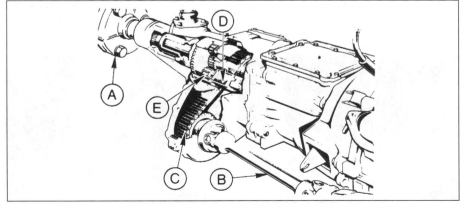

1.3 Cutaway view of the transfer box fitted to 4x4 models

A *Rear propeller shaft*	C *Drive chain*	E *Epicyclic centre*
B *Front propeller shaft*	D *Viscous coupling*	*differential*

5

2.4 Extension housing rear cover removal

2.7 Selector locking pin and spring

2.8 Blanking plug removal

2 Dismantling into assemblies
- type B gearbox

1 Clean the exterior of the gearbox with paraffin and wipe dry.
2 Remove the clutch release bearing and arm.
3 Where applicable unbolt the clutch bellhousing from the front of the gearbox.
4 Working through the gear lever aperture, use a screwdriver or small drift to tap out the extension housing rear cover (see illustration).
5 Unscrew the bolts and remove the top cover and gasket.
6 Invert the gearbox and allow the oil to drain, then turn it upright again.
7 Using a screwdriver, unscrew the selector locking mechanism plug then extract the spring and locking pin if necessary using a pen magnet (see illustration).
8 Extract the blanking plug from the rear of the gearbox casing and, using a suitable drift through the hole, drive out the selector locking plate roll pin (see illustration).
9 Drive the roll pin from the selector boss, then withdraw the selector shaft through the selector forks and out of the rear extension housing (see illustration).
10 Note the location of the components then withdraw the selector forks, selector locking plate and selector boss (see illustrations).
11 Unscrew the bolts securing the extension housing to the main gearbox casing.
12 Release the extension housing complete with mainshaft from the main casing, then turn the extension housing so that the cut-away reveals the countershaft.
13 Invert the gearbox and use a soft metal drift to tap the countershaft rearwards until it can be removed from the rear of the main casing (see illustration).
14 Turn the gearbox upright and allow the countershaft gear cluster to move to the bottom of the main casing.
15 Withdraw the extension housing complete with mainshaft from the main casing (see illustration).
16 Remove the input shaft needle roller

2.9a Removing the selector boss roll pin

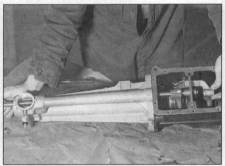
2.9b Withdrawing the selector shaft

2.10a Removing the selector locking plate and selector boss . . .

2.10b . . . and the selector forks

2.13 Removing the countershaft

2.15 Withdrawing the extension housing and mainshaft

2.17a Unscrew the bolts . . .

2.17b . . . and remove the clutch release bearing guide sleeve . . .

2.17c . . . and O-ring

bearing from the end of the mainshaft or from the centre of the input shaft.

17 Unscrew the bolts and withdraw the clutch release bearing guide sleeve from the front of the main casing. Note that the cut-out on the sleeve faces to the bottom of the casing. Remove the O-ring **(see illustrations)**.

18 Using a soft metal drift from inside the main casing, drive out the input shaft and bearing.

19 Remove the countershaft gear cluster, together with the thrustwashers, keeping them identified for location **(see illustration)**. Take care not to lose the needle roller bearings and spacers from inside the gear cluster.

20 Insert an suitable bolt into the reverse gear idler shaft, and using a nut, washer and socket pull out the idler shaft **(see illustrations)**. Note the fitted position of the reverse idler gear, then remove it **(see illustration)**.

21 Extract the circlip and withdraw the reverse relay lever from the pivot pin. Also disengage the return spring.

22 Prise out the speedometer drivegear cover from the extension housing and withdraw the drive pinion.

23 Squeeze the ends of the mainshaft bearing circlip together and extract it from the extension housing. Then using a soft-faced mallet drive the mainshaft from the extension housing **(see illustration)**.

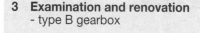

3 Examination and renovation
- type B gearbox

1 Thoroughly clean the interior of the gearbox, and check for dropped needle rollers and roll pins.

2 Carefully clean and then examine all the component parts for general wear, distortion, slackness of fit, and damage to machined faces and threads.

3 Examine the gears for excessive wear and chipping of the teeth. Renew them as necessary.

4 Examine the countershaft for signs of wear, where the needle rollers bear. If a small ridge

can be felt at either end of the shaft it will be necessary to renew it. Renew the thrustwashers at each end.

5 The four synchroniser rings should be renewed as a matter of course.

6 The needle roller bearing and cage, located between the nose of the mainshaft and the annulus in the rear of the input shaft, is also liable to wear, and should be renewed as a matter of course.

7 Examine the condition of the two ball-bearing assemblies, one on the input shaft and one on the mainshaft. Check them for noisy operation, looseness between the inner and outer races, and for general wear. Normally they should be renewed on a gearbox that is being rebuilt.

2.19 Removing the countershaft gear cluster

2.20a Reverse idler shaft removal

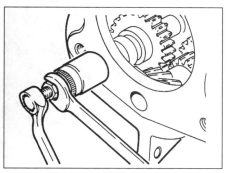

2.20b Method of removing the reverse gear idler shaft on the type B gearbox

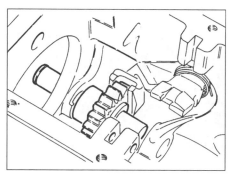

2.20c Reverse idler gear on the type B gearbox

2.23 Separating the mainshaft from the extension housing

5

4.1 Extract the circlip from the input

4.3 . . . and remove the bearing

4.5 Using a metal tube to fit the input shaft bearing

8 If either of the synchroniser units is worn, it will be necessary to buy a complete assembly as the parts are not sold individually. Also check the blocker bars for wear.

9 Examine the ends of the selector forks where they rub against the channels in the periphery of the synchroniser units. If possible compare the selector forks with new units to help determine the wear that has occurred. Renew them if worn.

10 If the bearing bush in the extension is badly worn it is best to have the bearing pulled out and a new one fitted. **Note:** *This*

can be done with the mainshaft assembly still located in the extension housing.
11 The oil seals in the extension housing and clutch release bearing guide sleeve should be renewed as a matter of course. Drive out the old seal with the aid of a drift or screwdriver. It will be found that the seal comes out quite easily. With a piece of wood or suitably-sized tube to spread the load evenly, carefully tap a new seal into place ensuring that it enters the bore squarely.

4 Input shaft - dismantling and reassembly

1 Extract the small circlip from the input shaft **(see illustration)**.
2 Locate the bearing outer track on top of an open vice, then using a soft-faced mallet, drive the input shaft down through the bearing.
3 Remove the bearing from the input shaft noting that the groove in the outer track is towards the front splined end of the shaft **(see illustration)**.
4 Place the input shaft on a block of wood

and lightly grease the bearing location shoulder.
5 Locate the new bearing on the input shaft with the circlip groove facing the correct way. Then using a metal tube on the inner track drive the bearing fully home **(see illustration)**.
6 Refit the small circlip.

5 Mainshaft (type B gearbox) - dismantling and reassembly

1 Remove the 4th gear synchroniser ring from the 3rd/4th synchroniser unit.
2 Extract the circlip and slide the 3rd/4th synchroniser unit, together with the 3rd gear, from the front of the mainshaft, using a two-legged puller where necessary. Remove the 3rd gear synchroniser ring **(see illustrations)**.
3 Remove the outer ring from the 2nd gear then extract the thrustwasher halves.
4 Slide the 2nd gear from the front of the mainshaft and remove the 2nd gear synchroniser ring and thrust ring where, applicable **(see illustration)**.
5 Mark the 1st/2nd synchroniser unit hub and sleeve in relation to each other and note the location of the selector fork groove. Then slide

5.2a Remove the circlip . . .

5.2b . . . and withdraw the 3rd/4th synchroniser unit, 3rd synchroniser ring, and 3rd gear

5.4 2nd gear and synchroniser ring removal

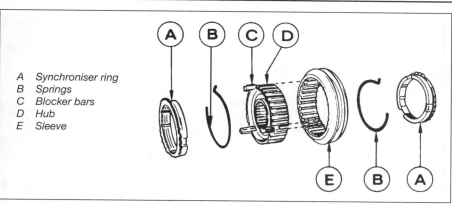

A *Synchroniser ring*
B *Springs*
C *Blocker bars*
D *Hub*
E *Sleeve*

5.5 Exploded view of a synchroniser unit

5.6 Removing the mainshaft bearing retaining circlip

5.10a Assembling the 1st/2nd synchroniser unit

the sleeve forward from the hub and remove the blocker bars and springs **(see illustration)**.

6 Extract the circlip retaining the mainshaft bearing. Then using a suitable puller, remove 1st gear complete with the oil scoop ring, mainshaft bearing and speedometer drivegear **(see illustration)**. Alternatively, support the 1st gear and press the mainshaft downwards.

7 Remove the 1st gear synchroniser ring.

8 If necessary the 3rd/4th synchroniser unit may be dismantled, but first mark the hub and sleeve in relation to each other. Slide the sleeve from the hub and remove the blocker bars and springs. Note that the 1st/2nd synchroniser hub cannot be removed from the mainshaft.

9 Clean all the components in paraffin, wipe dry and examine them for wear and damage. Obtain new components as necessary. During reassembly lubricate the components with gearbox oil and where new parts are being fitted lightly grease contact surfaces.

10 Commence reassembly by assembling the synchroniser units. Slide the sleeves on the hubs in their previously noted positions then insert the blocker bars and fit the springs **(see illustrations)**.

11 Fit the 1st gear synchroniser ring to the

1st/2nd synchroniser unit with the blocker bars located in the slots.

12 Slide the 1st gear and oil scoop ring (with the oil groove towards 1st gear) into the mainshaft.

13 If a new mainshaft bearing or extension housing is being fitted, the thickness of the retaining circlip in the extension housing must be determined at this stage. Using vernier calipers measure the width of the bearing outer track (B) then measure the total width of the bearing location in the extension housing (A) - the difference (ie A minus B) represents the thickness of the retaining circlip.

14 Fit the small circlip, if applicable, then loosely locate the bearing retaining circlip as determined from paragraph 13 on the mainshaft.

15 Smear a little grease on the mainshaft, then fit the bearing and drive it fully home using a metal tube on the inner track. Fit the circlip.

16 Locate the speedometer drivegear on the mainshaft and use a metal tube to tap it into position **(see illustration)**.

17 Fit the 2nd gear synchroniser ring to the 1st/2nd synchroniser unit with the blocker bars located in the slots. Fit the thrust ring where applicable.

18 Slide the 2nd gear onto the front of the mainshaft and retain with the thrustwasher halves and outer ring.

19 Slide the 3rd gear onto the front of the mainshaft then locate the synchroniser ring on the gear cone.

20 Locate the 3rd/4th synchroniser unit on the mainshaft splines with the long side of the hub facing the front. Tap the unit fully home using a metal tube then fit the circlip. Make sure that the slots in the 3rd gear synchroniser ring are aligned with the blocker bars as the synchroniser unit is being fitted.

21 Fit the 4th gear synchroniser ring to the 3rd/4th synchroniser unit with the blocker bars located in the slots.

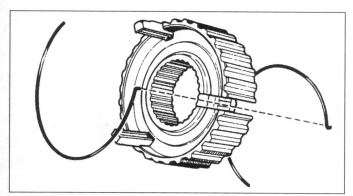

5.10b Correct assembly of the synchroniser springs

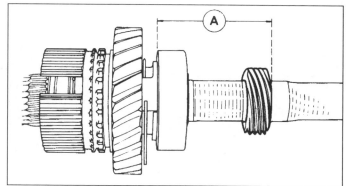

5.16 Speedometer drivegear fitting dimension on the type B gearbox

A = 49.25 mm (1.939 in)

5

6.1 Fitting the mainshaft to the extension housing

6.2 Fitting the mainshaft bearing circlip to the extension housing

6 Reassembly - type B gearbox

1 Immerse the extension housing in hot water for several minutes. Then remove it and quickly insert the mainshaft and push the bearing fully home. If necessary place the extension housing on the edge of the bench and use a soft-faced mallet to drive the mainshaft home (see illustration).

2 Using long nose pliers and a screwdriver refit the bearing circlip (see illustration).

3 Apply a little grease to the extension housing mating face and fit a new gasket (see illustration).

4 Insert the speedometer drive pinion in the extension housing, smear a little sealer on the cover then tap the cover into the housing.

5 Fit the reverse relay lever and return spring onto the pivot pin in the main casing, and fit the circlip.

6 Position the reverse idler gear in the main casing with the long shoulder facing the rear and engaged with the relay lever. Slide in the idler shaft and tap fully home with a soft-faced mallet.

7 Smear grease inside the ends of the countershaft gear cluster, then fit the spacers and needle roller bearings (see illustration). Make sure that the central spacer tube is fitted with thin spacers either side followed by 19 needle rollers and thick spacers on each side. Note that the long needle rollers must be fitted to the rear of the gear cluster. Make sure that there is sufficient grease to hold the needle rollers in position during the subsequent operation, and if available fit a dummy shaft of a length slightly less than the gear cluster.

8 Stick the thrustwashers on the inner faces of the main casing with the location tabs correctly positioned.

9 Lower the gear cluster to the bottom of the main casing keeping the thrustwashers in position.

10 Insert the input shaft fully into the main casing using a soft metal drift if necessary.

11 Fit the clutch release bearing guide sleeve together with a new O-ring. Check that the cut-out on the sleeve faces the bottom of the casing then apply sealer to the bolt threads. Insert them, and tighten to the specified torque in diagonal sequence.

12 Oil the needle roller bearing and locate it in the centre of the input shaft.

13 Insert the mainshaft, together with the extension housing, into the main casing so that the front of the mainshaft enters the needle roller bearing in the centre of the input shaft. Turn the extension housing so that the cutaway reveals the countershaft bore.

14 While keeping the thrustwashers in place, invert the gearbox so that the countershaft gear cluster meshes with the mainshaft and input shaft.

15 Line up the thrustwashers and insert the countershaft from the rear of the main casing. Using a soft metal drift drive the countershaft into the main casing until flush. The flat on the rear end of the countershaft must be horizontal (see illustration).

16 Fully insert the extension housing and make sure that the 4th gear synchroniser ring is correctly aligned with the synchroniser unit.

17 Apply sealer to the bolt threads then insert them and tighten to the specified torque in diagonal sequence.

18 Locate the selector locking plate in the main casing and retain with the roll pin.

19 Coat the new blanking plug with sealer and tap it into the rear of the casing.

20 Fit the selector forks and selector boss, then insert the selector shaft from the rear and guide it through the selector components.

21 Align the holes then drive the roll pin into the selector boss and selector shaft.

6.3 Locating a new gasket on the extension housing

6.7 Fitting the outer spacer to the countershaft gear cluster needle rollers

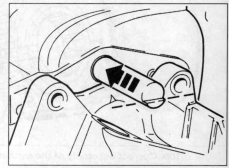

6.15 Countershaft flat alignment on the type B gearbox

7.3 Reversing light switch removal

7.4a Clutch bellhousing bolts (arrowed)

7.4b Clutch bellhousing removal

22 Insert the selector locking pin and spring, apply sealer to the plug threads, then insert and tighten the plug.
23 Fit the gearbox top cover together with a new gasket and tighten the bolts to the specified torque in diagonal sequence.
24 Fit the extension housing rear cover using a little sealer, and stake it in several places to secure.
25 Where applicable fit the clutch bellhousing to the front of the gearbox, apply sealer to the bolt threads, then insert the bolts and tighten them to the specified torque in diagonal sequence.
26 Fit the clutch release bearing and arm.

7 Dismantling into assemblies
- type N gearbox

Note: *On 4x4 models, disregard paragraphs 8 to 13 inclusive and instead remove the transfer box assembly as described in Section 11.*

1 Clean the exterior of the gearbox with paraffin and wipe dry.
2 Remove the clutch release bearing and arm.
3 Unscrew and remove the reversing light switch (see illustration).

4 Unbolt the clutch bellhousing from the front of the gearbox. Remove the gasket (see illustrations).
5 Unscrew the bolts and withdraw the clutch release bearing guide sleeve and gasket from the front of the gearbox (see illustrations).
6 Unscrew the bolts and remove the top cover and gasket (see illustrations).
7 Invert the gearbox and allow the oil to drain, then turn it upright again.
8 Unscrew the bolts and lift the 5th gear locking plate from the extension housing (see illustration).
9 Extract the 5th gear locking spring and pin

7.5a Removing the clutch release bearing guide sleeve . . .

7.5b . . . and gasket

7.6a Remove the bolts . . .

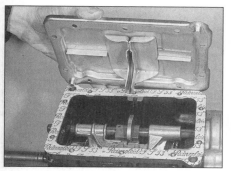

7.6b . . . top cover . . .

7.6c . . . and gasket

7.8 Removing the 5th gear locking plate

5

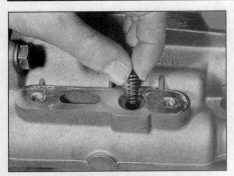

7.9a Extracting the 5th gear locking spring . . .

7.9b . . . and pin

7.10 Extension housing rear cover removal

7.11a Drive out the roll pin . . .

7.11b . . . and remove the selector rod connector

from the extension housing **(see illustrations)**. Use a screw to remove the pin.

10 Working through the gear lever aperture, use a screwdriver or small drift to tap out the extension housing rear cover **(see illustration)**.

11 Select reverse gear and pull the selector shaft fully to the rear. Support the shaft with a piece of wood then drive out the roll pin and withdraw the connector from the rear of the selector rod **(see illustrations)**.

12 Unbolt and remove the extension housing from the rear of the gearbox. If necessary tap the housing with a soft-faced mallet to release it from the dowels. Remove the gasket **(see illustrations)**.

13 Prise the cover from the extension housing and withdraw the speedometer drivegear **(see illustration)**.

14 Select neutral then, using an Allen key, unscrew the selector locking mechanism plug from the side of the main casing then extract the spring and locking pin if necessary using a pen magnet **(see illustrations)**.

15 Drive the roll pin from the selector boss and selector shaft.

16 If necessary the selector shaft centralising spring and 5th gear locking control may be removed. Using a small screwdriver push out the pin and plug and

7.11c Selector rod connector

7.12a Removing the extension housing . . .

7.12b . . . and gasket

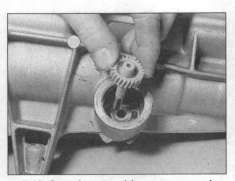

7.13 Speedometer drivegear removal

7.14a Unscrew the plug . . .

7.14b . . . and remove the selector locking spring and pin

7.16a Insert a small screwdriver . . .

7.16b . . . and push out the plug . . .

slide the control from the selector shaft **(see illustrations)**.

17 Note the location of the selector components then withdraw the selector shaft from the rear of the gearbox and remove the selector boss and locking plate. 1st/2nd and 3rd/4th selector forks, and 5th gear selector fork and sleeve. Note that the roll pin hole in the selector boss is towards the front **(see illustrations)**.

18 Extract the circlip and pull the 5th gear synchroniser unit from the main casing leaving it loose on the mainshaft **(see illustrations)**.

7.16c . . . and pin from the selector shaft centralising spring and 5th gear locking control

7.17a Removing the selector boss and locking plate. . .

7.17b . . . 1st/2nd selector fork . . .

7.17c . . . 3rd/4th selector fork . . .

7.17d . . . 5th gear interlock sleeve . . .

7.17e . . . and the 5th gear selector fork

7.18a Extract the circlip . . .

7.18b . . . and remove the 5th gear synchroniser dog hub . . .

5

7.18c . . . and 5th gear synchroniser unit

7.19 Removing the 5th driven gear

7.21 5th driving gear retaining nut removal

7.22a Removing the washer from the 5th driving gear

7.22b Pull the 5th driving gear from the splines with a puller . . .

19 Slide the 5th driven gear from the synchroniser unit hub **(see illustration)**.
20 Select 3rd gear and either 1st or 2nd gear by pushing the respective synchroniser sleeves - this will lock the mainshaft and countershaft gear cluster.
21 Unscrew and remove the 5th driving gear retaining nut while an assistant holds the gearbox stationary **(see illustration)**. The nut is tightened to a high torque setting and an additional extension bar may be required.
22 Remove the washer and pull the 5th driving gear from the countershaft gear cluster using a two-legged puller and socket in contact with the cluster. Remove the spacer ring **(see illustrations)**. Select neutral.
23 Extract the circlip retaining the countershaft gear cluster bearing in the intermediate housing **(see illustration)**.
24 Using a soft-faced mallet tap the intermediate housing free of the main casing and pull the intermediate housing rearwards as far as possible. Using a screwdriver inserted between the intermediate housing and main casing, prise the bearing from the shoulder on the countershaft gear cluster and remove it from the intermediate housing **(see illustration)**.
25 On June 1986-on models (build code GU), unbolt the spigot from the front of the casing then drive it out from the roller bearing by inserting a soft metal drift through the countershaft gear cluster **(see illustration)**.

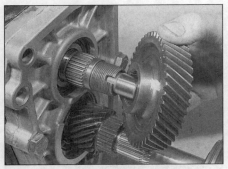

7.22c . . . and remove the gear from the countershaft gear cluster

7.22d Spacer ring removal

7.23 Removing the countershaft gear cluster bearing retaining circlip

7.24 Using a screwdriver to remove the countershaft gear cluster bearing from the intermediate housing

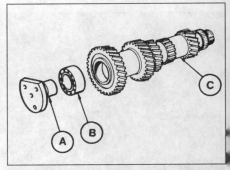

7.25 Spigot (A) and roller bearing (B) fitted to the gear cluster (C) on the type N gearbox from June 1986

7.27 Input shaft removal

7.28a Removing the 4th gear synchroniser ring

7.28b Removing the input shaft needle roller bearing

Remove the drift and lower the gear cluster to the bottom of the casing.

26 On pre-June 1986 models, using a soft metal drift from the front of the main casing, drive the countershaft rearwards sufficiently to allow the gear cluster to be lowered to the bottom of the casing.

27 Ease the input shaft from the front of the casing, if necessary using a small drift inside the gearbox to move the bearing slightly forwards, then using levers beneath the bearing circlip **(see illustration)**.

28 Remove the 4th gear synchroniser ring. Remove the input shaft needle roller bearing from the end of the mainshaft or from the centre of the input shaft **(see illustrations)**.

29 Remove the mainshaft and intermediate housing from the main casing. Remove the gasket **(see illustrations)**.

30 Withdraw the countershaft, where applicable, and gear cluster from the main casing **(see illustrations)**.

31 Insert a suitable bolt into the reverse gear idler shaft, and using a nut, washer and socket pull out the idler shaft. Note the fitted position of the reverse idler gear then remove it **(see illustrations)**.

32 Remove the guide from the reverse relay lever then extract the circlip and remove the relay lever and spring from the pivot **(see illustrations)**.

33 Remove the magnetic disc from the

7.29a Removing the mainshaft and intermediate housing

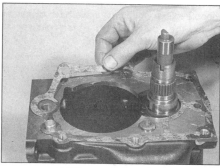

7.29b . . . and gasket

7.30a Countershaft and gear cluster removal

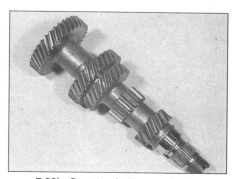

7.30b Countershaft gear cluster

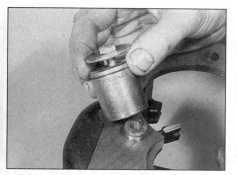

7.31a Method of removing the reverse gear idler shaft

7.31b Reverse idler gear removal

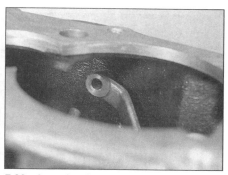

7.32a Location for reverse idler gear guide in the relay lever

5

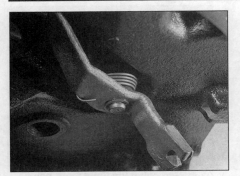

7.32b Reverse relay lever and spring

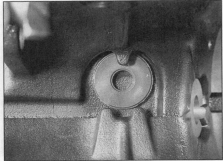

7.33 Magnetic disc location in the bottom of the main casing

8.1a Oil seal removal from the clutch release bearing guide sleeve

bottom of the main casing. Also remove any needle rollers which may have been displaced from the countershaft gear cluster, if applicable **(see illustration)**.

8 Examination and renovation - type N gearbox

1 The procedure is basically as given in Section 3, however there are five synchroniser rings, no countershaft gear cluster thrustwashers, two ball-bearings and either one or two roller bearings **(see illustrations)**.

2 On June 1986-on models (build code GU) if the roller bearing is difficult to remove from the end of the countershaft gear cluster, break the bearing cage and remove the rollers, then use Ford tool 16-025 or a similar tool to extract the outer track. Drive the new bearing into position until flush with the cluster end face, making sure that the lettering faces outwards and using a suitable metal tube on the outer track only.

9 Mainshaft (type N gearbox) - dismantling and reassembly

1 Extract the circlip and slide the 3rd/4th

synchroniser unit, together with the 3rd gear, from the front of the mainshaft, using a two-legged puller where necessary. Separate the gear and unit, then remove the 3rd gear synchroniser ring **(see illustrations)**.

2 Remove the outer ring from the 2nd gear then extract the thrustwasher halves **(see illustrations)**.

3 Slide the 2nd gear from the front of the mainshaft and remove the 2nd gear synchroniser ring **(see illustrations)**.

4 Mark the 1st/2nd synchroniser unit hub and sleeve in relation to each other and note the location of the selector fork groove, then slide the sleeve forward from the hub and remove

8.1b Fitting a new oil seal to the clutch release bearing guide sleeve

8.1c Location of the speedometer drivegear oil seal in the extension housing (except 4x4)

8.1d Rear view of the extension housing, showing the mainshaft oil seal and bush (except 4x4)

9.1a Extract the circlip . . .

9.1b . . . and remove the 3rd/4th synchroniser and ring . . .

9.1c . . . and 3rd gear

9.2a 2nd gear thrust washers and retaining ring location

9.2b Removing the outer retaining ring . . .

9.2c . . . and thrust washer halves

the blocker bars and springs. Note that the synchroniser hub cannot be removed from the mainshaft (see illustrations).

5 Using a suitable puller, pull the speedometer drivegear off the rear of the mainshaft (see illustration).

6 Remove the 5th gear synchroniser unit and 5th driven gear from the mainshaft.

7 Extract the circlip retaining the mainshaft bearing, then support the intermediate housing on blocks of wood and drive the mainshaft through the bearing with a soft-faced mallet (see illustrations).

8 Remove the oil scoop ring, 1st gear, and 1st gear synchroniser ring (see illustrations).

9.3a Removing the 2nd gear . . .

9.3b . . . and synchroniser ring

9.4a Removing the 1st/2nd synchroniser sleeve . . .

9.4b . . . and blocker bars

9.5 Speedometer drivegear removal

9.7a Mainshaft bearing circlip removal

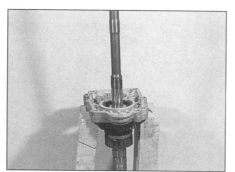

9.7b Method of driving the mainshaft through the intermediate housing and bearing

9.8a Removing the oil scoop ring and 1st gear

5

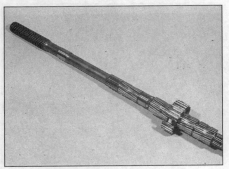

9.8b The dismantled mainshaft

9.9 Extracting the bearing retaining circlip from the intermediate housing

9.12 Intermediate housing and mainshaft bearing

9 If necessary extract the circlip and drive the ball-bearing from the intermediate housing using a metal tube **(see illustration)**. Also the synchroniser units may be dismantled, but first mark the hub and sleeve in relation to each other. Slide the sleeve from the hub and remove the blocker bars and springs.

10 Clean all the components in paraffin, wipe dry and examine them for wear and damage. Obtain new components as necessary. During reassembly lubricate the components with gearbox oil and where new parts are being fitted lightly grease contact surfaces.

11 Commence reassembly by assembling the synchroniser units. Slide the sleeves on the hubs in their previously noted positions, then insert the blocker bars and fit the springs **(see illustration 5.10b)**.

12 Support the intermediate housing then, using a metal tube on the outer track, drive in the new bearing and fit the circlip **(see illustration)**.

13 Fit the blocker bar spring to the rear of the 1st/2nd synchroniser hub, followed by the 1st gear synchroniser ring **(see illustration)**.

14 Slide the 1st gear and oil scoop ring (with the oil groove towards 1st gear) onto the mainshaft.

15 Using a metal tube on the mainshaft bearing inner track, drive the intermediate housing onto the mainshaft and fit the circlip **(see illustration)**. Make sure the large circlip is towards the rear of the mainshaft.

16 Locate the 5th driven gear and 5th gear synchroniser with the circlip, loose on the mainshaft. Tap the speedometer drivegear

lightly onto its shoulder; its final position will be determined later **(see illustration)**.

17 Fit the 1st/2nd synchroniser sleeve to the hub in its previously noted position with the selector groove facing forward then insert the blocker bars and fit the springs **(see illustration 5.10b)**.

18 Fit the 2nd gear synchroniser ring to the 1st/2nd synchroniser unit with the blocker bars located in the slots.

19 Slide the 2nd gear onto the front of the mainshaft and retain with the thrustwasher halves and outer ring **(see illustration)**.

20 Slide the 3rd gear onto the front of the mainshaft, then locate the synchroniser ring on the gear cone.

21 Locate the 3rd/4th synchroniser unit on the mainshaft splines with the long side of the hub facing the front **(see illustration)**. Tap the unit fully home using a metal tube, then fit the circlip. Make sure that the slots in the 3rd gear synchroniser ring are aligned with the blocker bars as the synchroniser unit is being fitted.

10 Reassembly - type N gearbox

Note: *On 4x4 models, disregard paragraphs 24 to 31 inclusive, and instead refit the transfer box assembly as described in Section 11.*

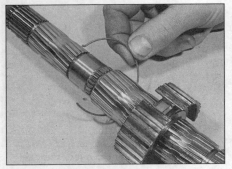

9.13 Fitting the blocker bar spring to the rear of the 1st/2nd synchroniser hub

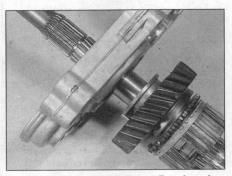

9.15 Assembling the intermediate housing and bearing to the mainshaft

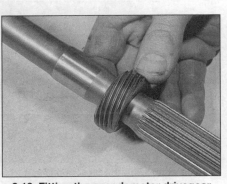

9.16 Fitting the speedometer drivegear

9.19 Location hole for 2nd gear thrust washer halves (arrowed)

9.21 Fitting the 3rd/4th synchroniser unit

10.4a Inserting the spacers in the countershaft gear cluster . . .

10.4b . . . followed by the needle rollers . . .

10.4c . . . and outer spacers

1 Locate the magnetic disc in the bottom of the main casing.

2 Fit the reverse relay lever and spring onto the pivot and retain with the circlip. Fit the guide to the lever.

3 Position the reverse idler gear in the main casing with the long shoulder facing the rear and engaged with the relay lever. Slide in the idler shaft and tap fully home with a soft-faced mallet.

4 Where applicable, smear grease inside the end of the countershaft gear cluster then fit the spacers and needle roller bearings - there are 21 needle rollers. Make sure that there is sufficient grease to hold the needle rollers in position during the subsequent operation (see

illustrations). Note that on early models the countershaft bearing bore was 33 mm (1.3 in) long; on later models it is 25.75 mm (1.01 in) long, and the needle rollers are correspondingly shorter. When rebuilding an old pattern gearbox, use the new shorter rollers and insert two extra spacers behind them (see illustration).

5 Where applicable, insert the countershaft in the gear cluster until the front end is flush with the front gear on the cluster (see illustration).

6 Locate the gear cluster in the bottom of the main casing.

7 Position a new gasket on the main casing then fit the mainshaft and intermediate housing, and temporarily secure with two bolts.

8 Fit the input shaft needle roller bearing to the end of the mainshaft, or in the centre of the input shaft (see illustration).

9 Fit the 4th gear synchroniser ring to the 3rd/4th synchroniser unit with the cut-outs over the blocker bars, then fit the input shaft assembly and tap the bearing fully into the casing up to the retaining circlip (see illustration).

10 Invert the gearbox so that the countershaft gear cluster meshes with the input shaft and mainshaft gears.

11 On pre-June 1986 models, using a soft metal drift, drive the countershaft into

10.5 Countershaft inserted in the gear cluster

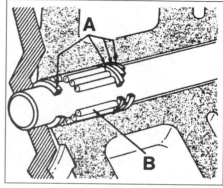

10.4d Shorter countershaft rollers require extra spacers when fitted to early type N gearbox

A Spacers   B Rollers

the main casing until flush at the front face - the flat on the rear end of the countershaft must be horizontal (see illustration).

12 On June 1986-on models, apply sealing compound to the mating face of the spigot, insert it into the countershaft gear cluster front roller bearing, then insert and tighten the bolts. Tap the cluster onto the spigot as it is being fitted.

13 Using a metal tube, tap the countershaft gear cluster bearing into the intermediate

10.8 Fitting the input shaft needle roller bearing on the mainshaft

10.9 Fitting the input shaft

10.11 Correct position of countershaft before driving into the main casing

10.13 Countershaft gear cluster bearing being fitted to the intermediate housing

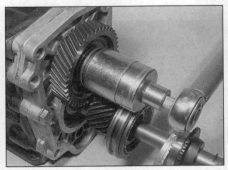

10.15a Tightening the 5th driving gear nut

10.15b Using a chisel to peen the nut collar

10.15c 5th driving gear nut locked to the countershaft gear cluster

10.17a Fitting the spacer to the 5th gear synchroniser unit

housing and secure with the circlip (see illustration).

14 Fit the spacer ring then, using a metal tube, tap the 5th driving gear onto the splines of the countershaft gear cluster.

15 Fit the thrustwasher and retaining nut. Select 3rd gear and either 1st or 2nd gear by pushing the respective synchroniser sleeves. While an assistant holds the gearbox stationary, tighten the nut to the specified torque, then lock it by peening the collar on the nut into the slot in the gear cluster (see illustrations).

16 Select neutral, then slide the 5th driven gear into mesh with the driving gear.

17 Slide the 5th gear synchroniser unit complete with spacer onto the 5th driven gear. Then, using a metal tube, drive the dog hub and 5th synchroniser ring onto the mainshaft splines, while guiding the synchroniser ring onto the blocker bars. Fit the circlip (see illustrations).

18 Tap the speedometer drivegear into its correct position on the mainshaft - the distance between the gear and the 5th gear dog hub circlip should be 123.0 to 124.0 mm (4.85 to 4.89 in) (see illustration).

19 Locate the 5th gear selector fork in its synchroniser sleeve and locate the interlock sleeve in the groove (short shoulder to front), then insert the selector shaft through the sleeve and selector fork into the main casing (see illustration).

10.17b Fitting the 5th gear synchroniser unit to 5th driven gear

10.17c Fitting the 5th gear synchroniser ring and dog hub to the mainshaft

10.17d Fitting the circlip to the dog hub

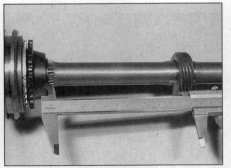

10.18 Checking the distance between the circlip and speedometer drivegear

10.19 Selector shaft and components assembled on the bench to show relative positions

10.22 Driving the roll pin into the selector boss

10.24 Fitting the speedometer drivegear cover (except 4x4)

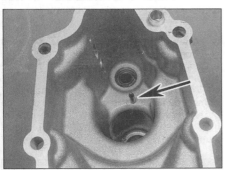

10.26 Location of the selector shaft centralising spring pin (except 4x4)

20 Locate the 1st/2nd and 3rd/4th selector forks in their respective synchroniser sleeves, position the selector boss and locking plate, and insert the selector shaft through the components into the front of the main casing. The roll pin hole in the selector boss must be towards the front.

21 If removed, refit the selector shaft centralising spring and 5th gear locking control by inserting the pin and plug.

22 Align the holes then drive the roll pin into the selector boss and selector shaft (see illustration).

23 Insert the selector locking pin and spring, apply sealer to the plug threads, then insert and tighten the plug using an Allen-key.

24 Fit the speedometer drivegear to the rear extension housing. Apply a little sealer to the cover, then press it into the housing (see illustration).

25 Remove the temporarily fitted bolts from the intermediate housing, then select 4th gear.

26 Stick a new gasket to the extension housing with grease, and fit the housing to the intermediate housing. Take care not to damage the rear oil seal, and make sure that the selector shaft centralising spring locates on the pin (see illustration).

27 Insert the bolts and tighten them to the specified torque in diagonal sequence (see illustration). Before inserting the three bolts which go right through the main casing, apply sealer to their threads.

28 Select reverse gear and locate the connector on the rear of the selector rod. Support the rod with a piece of wood then drive in the roll pin. Select neutral.

29 Press the rear cover into the extension housing.

30 Check that the 5th gear interlock sleeve is correctly aligned, then insert the 5th gear locking pin and spring.

31 Apply some sealer to the 5th gear locking plate, locate it on the extension housing, and insert and tighten the bolts to the specified torque (see illustration).

32 Fit the gearbox top cover together with a new gasket, and tighten the bolts to the specified torque in diagonal sequence.

33 Fit the clutch release bearing guide sleeve (oil slot downwards) together with a new gasket, and tighten the bolts to the specified torque in diagonal sequence. Where necessary apply sealer to the bolt threads.

34 Fit the clutch bellhousing to the front of the gearbox together with a new gasket. Apply sealer to the bolt threads, then insert the bolts and tighten them to the specified torque in diagonal sequence.

35 Insert and tighten the reversing light switch in the extension housing.

36 Fit the clutch release bearing and arm.

11 Transfer box assembly (4x4) - removal and refitting

Note: *The transfer box assembly may be removed from the rear of the gearbox with the gearbox remaining in position. However, considering the relative inaccessibility of some of the components, it is recommended that the gearbox is first removed from the car.*

1 Unscrew the transfer box oil filler plug, then tilt the gearbox and drain the oil into a suitable container.

2 Working through the gear lever aperture, use a screwdriver or small drift to tap out the transfer box housing rear cover (see illustration).

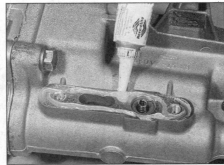

10.27 Tightening the extension housing bolts (except 4x4)

10.31 Applying sealer to the 5th gear locking plate location

11.2 Transfer box housing rear cover

5

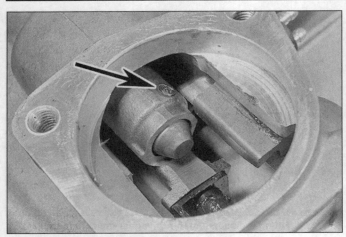

11.3a Drive out the roll pin (arrowed) . . .

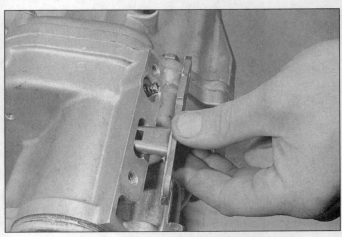

11.3b . . . and withdraw the gear lever connector

3 Select 3rd gear then support the selector shaft with a piece of wood, drive out the roll pin, and withdraw the gear lever connector through the rear aperture **(see illustrations)**.
4 Unscrew the bolts and lift the 5th gear locking plate from the transfer box housing **(see illustrations)**.
5 Extract the 5th gear locking spring and

pin from the transfer box housing **(see illustration)**. Use a screw to remove the pin.
6 Unbolt the transfer box assembly from the gearbox intermediate housing. Lightly tap the transfer box housing to separate it from the intermediate housing, then withdraw the assembly over the mainshaft.
7 Remove the gasket.

8 Slide the mainshaft-to-sun gear shaft oil seal from the mainshaft.
9 Clean all traces of the old gasket from the housing faces.
10 Wrap adhesive tape over the mainshaft splines, then slide on the new oil seal until the outer edge of the oil seal is 23 mm (0.9 in) from the 5th synchroniser hub **(see illustrations)**.

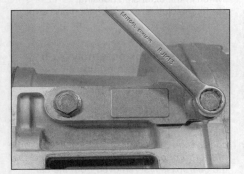

11.4a Unscrew the bolts . . .

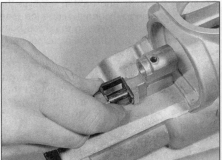

11.4b . . . and remove the 5th gear locking plate

11.5 5th gear locking spring and pin removal

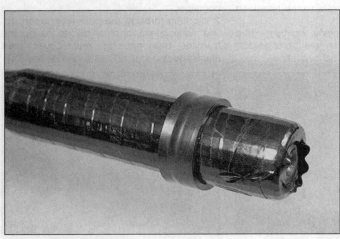

11.10a Wrap adhesive over the mainshaft splines before sliding on the oil seal

11.10b Checking the oil seal position on the mainshaft

11.11 Shift sleeve guide pin in the selector shaft (arrowed)

11.12 Intermediate housing with gasket fitted

11.14 Inserting the transfer box-to-main casing bolts

11 Centralise the shift sleeve guide pin within the selector shaft **(see illustration)**.
12 Position a new gasket on the gearbox intermediate housing **(see illustration)**.
13 With the clutch bellhousing on the bench, lower the transfer box assembly onto the intermediate housing.
14 Apply sealant to the bolt threads, then insert them and tighten progressively to the specified torque **(see illustration)**.
15 Refit the gear lever connector and drive the roll pin into the selector shaft.
16 Press the rear cover into the transfer box housing and secure by staking around the perimeter.
17 Insert the 5th gear locking spring and pin,

and refit the locking plate. Before tightening the bolts, temporarily refit the gear lever and push it fully to the right in neutral. Tighten the bolts and remove the gear lever.
18 After refitting the gearbox, fill the transfer box with oil **(see illustration)**.

12 Transfer box assembly (4x4) - dismantling and reassembly

1 Clean the exterior of the assembly and wipe dry.
2 Using a drift, drive out the dowel pins from the front and rear housings **(see illustration)**.

3 Unscrew the housing bolts, including the central one by the oil filler hole **(see illustration)**.
4 Place the assembly upright on the bench with the rear housing uppermost.
5 Withdraw the rear housing upwards, while tapping the driving chain wheel with a soft metal drift through the oil filler hole, to keep it in its normal position **(see illustration)**.
6 Remove the endfloat shim from the output shaft or from the epicyclic centre stub **(see illustration)**.
7 Remove the magnetic disc from the front housing **(see illustration)**.
8 Mark the driver disc in relation to the ring gear, then slide them from the epicyclic centre

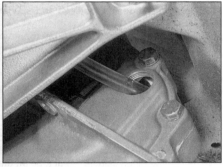

11.18 Topping-up the 4x4 transfer box

12.2 Driving out the dowel pins

12.3 Removing the housing bolts

12.5 Separating the rear housing from the front housing

12.6 Endfloat shim (arrowed) located on the input shaft

12.7 Magnetic disc location

5

12.8 Removing the ring gear and driver disc

12.9 Epicyclic centre differential removal

12.11 Removing the viscous coupling, driven chain wheel and driving chain from the front housing

12.12a Removing the circlip retaining the spring and lock dog

12.12b Spring and lock dog location

12.13a Removing the gearshift sleeve . . .

12.13b . . . and spacer

12.14a Extract the outer circlip (arrowed) . . .

12.14b . . . and withdraw the output shaft

12.16 Using a puller to remove a bearing from the driven chain wheel

differential and viscous coupling **(see illustration)**.

9 Slide the epicyclic centre differential off the front-wheel-drive sun gear shaft **(see illustration)**.

10 Mark the outer edge of the driving chain so that it can be refitted the same way round.

11 Simultaneously remove the viscous coupling, driven chain wheel and driving chain from the front housing **(see illustration)**, then separate them on the bench.

12 Extract the circlip and remove the spring and lock dog from the front housing spigot. Note that the spring ends locate over the return post and the lock dog slot locates over the pin on the gearshift sleeve **(see illustrations)**.

13 Remove the gearshift sleeve and spacer **(see illustration)**.

14 Extract the outer circlip from the rear housing and withdraw the output shaft and bearing **(see illustrations)**.

15 Clean all the components and examine them for wear and damage. Spin the bearing outer tracks and check them for excessive noise or play. Obtain new oil seals.

16 To renew the bearings on the driven chain wheel, use a suitable puller to pull off the old bearings **(see illustration)**, then press or drive on the new bearings using a metal tube on the inner tracks.

17 To renew the bearing on the front-wheel-

12.17a Removing the bearing from the sun gear shaft

12.17b Locate the new bearing on the sun gear shaft . . .

12.17c . . . and press into position with a long bolt and socket

drive sun gear shaft, use a suitable puller to pull off the old bearing **(see illustrations)**. The new bearing may be driven on using a metal tube on the inner track, or alternatively a long bolt inserted through the shaft may be used, together with spacers and a socket located on the inner track **(see illustration)**.

18 With the bearing removed as described in paragraph 17, if necessary slide off the drive chain wheel and extract the front-wheel-drive sun gear shaft by tapping the latter on a block of wood **(see illustrations)**.

19 The viscous coupling is a sealed assembly, and no attempt must be made to dismantle it.

20 Insert the sun gear shaft into the viscous coupling, and press on the drive chain wheel with the protruding collar facing away from the coupling **(see illustration)**.

21 To renew the output shaft bearing, extract the circlip and use a suitable puller to pull off the old bearing **(see illustrations)**. Drive on the new bearing using a metal tube on the inner track.

22 Check that the oil guide ring is correctly located on the output shaft. Carefully tap it off and renew it if it is damaged **(see illustration)**.

23 Refit the circlip to the output shaft.

24 Prise out one of the sun gear shaft oil seals from the front housing, then drive out the remaining oil seal using a drift. Press the new oil seals into position, noting that the rear seal has a metal insert which must face rearwards **(see illustrations)**.

12.18a Removing the drive chain wheel

12.18b Removing the sun gear shaft from the viscous coupling

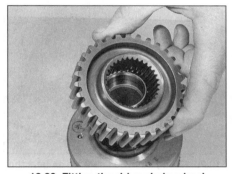

12.20 Fitting the drive chain wheel

12.21a Extract the circlip . . .

12.21b . . . and remove the output shaft bearing with a puller

12.22 Removing the oil guide ring

12..24a Sun gear shaft front oil seal in the front housing

5

12.24b Sun gear shaft rear oil seal removal from the front housing

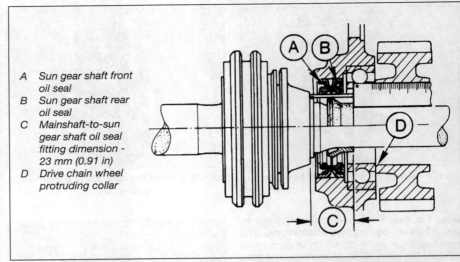

A Sun gear shaft front oil seal
B Sun gear shaft rear oil seal
C Mainshaft-to-sun gear shaft oil seal fitting dimension - 23 mm (0.91 in)
D Drive chain wheel protruding collar

12.24c Cross-section of oil seals between transfer box and main gearbox on 4x4 models

25 Prise the front propeller shaft oil seal from the front housing and drive in the new one using a metal tube or suitable socket **(see illustration)**.

26 Prise the oil seal from the gearshift sleeve and drive in the new seal, using a 20 mm diameter metal tube or socket **(see illustration)**.

27 Prise the gearshift sleeve oil seal from the front housing, and drive in the new seal using a metal tube or socket **(see illustration)**.

28 Prise the selector shaft oil seal from the rear housing and drive in the new seal **(see illustration)**.

29 Prise the oil seal from the rear of the rear housing. Check the rear bush, and if necessary renew it **(see illustrations)**. Ford tool 16-011 may be used to remove the bush, and a metal tube used to drive in the new bush. Similarly drive in the new oil seal.

30 Commence reassembly by inserting the output shaft and bearing into the rear housing. Fit the outer circlip in its groove.

31 Locate the gearshift sleeve and spacer in the front housing oil seal, with the housing on the bench.

32 Fit the lock dog and spring on the

12.25 Fitting a new front propeller shaft oil seal to the front housing

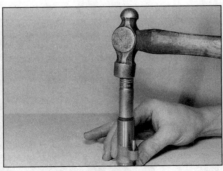

12.26 Fitting a new oil seal to the gearshift sleeve

12.27 Fitting a new gearshift sleeve oil seal to the front housing

12.28 Selector shaft oil seal (arrowed) in the rear housing

12.29a Rear oil seal removal from the rear housing

12.29b Rear bush (arrowed) in the rear housing

12.33 Viscous coupling, driven chain wheel and driving chain - fitted to the front housing

12.38a Measuring distance 'A' in the rear housing

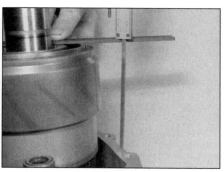

12.38b Measuring distance 'B' in the front housing

front housing spigot and secure with the circlip.

33 Engage the viscous coupling and driven chain wheel with the driving chain, then lower them into the front housing **(see illustration)**. Make sure that the plain bore end of the driven chain wheel faces the oil seal, and that the previously made mark on the driving chain is uppermost.

34 Slide the epicyclic centre differential into the splines of the front-wheel-drive sun gear shaft.

35 Fit the ring gear over the differential gears and engage it with the viscous coupling splines.

36 Fit the driver disc in the end of the ring gear.

37 Fit the magnetic disc in its location inside the front housing.

38 Before refitting the rear housing, check the correct thickness of the endfloat shim as follows. Measure the distance (A)

between the output shaft bearing inner circlip and the rear housing mating surface **(see illustration)**. Then measure the distance (B) between the ground surface of the driver disc and the front housing mating surface **(see illustration)**. The difference between the two measurements (A minus B), less a further 0.4 to 0.6 mm (0.016 to 0.024 in) for the end clearance, is the thickness of the endfloat shim.

39 Apply some grease to the endfloat shim and stick it against the output shaft bearing inner circlip.

40 Apply sealant to the mating surfaces of the front and rear housings.

41 Lower the rear housing onto the front housing, then tap in the dowel pins until centralised.

42 Insert the bolts and tighten them progressively to the specified torque. Note that the central bolt must be tightened more than the outer bolts.

13 Transfer box viscous coupling (4x4) - checking

1 Apply the handbrake and select neutral.

2 Jack up one of the front wheels and support the car on an axle stand. The remaining three wheels must be on the ground.

3 Remove the wheel cap and fit a socket on the driveshaft nut.

4 Using a torque wrench, turn the wheel clockwise approximately half a turn, taking approximately one second to complete the movement. The turning torque must be 70 ± 30 Nm (52 ± 22 lbf ft).

5 A low reading indicates a possible leak of fluid from the viscous coupling, or a deterioration of the fluid. A high reading indicates a partial seizure.

6 Renew the viscous coupling if the correct turning torque cannot be obtained.

5

Notes

Chapter 6
Ford J & K gearboxes

Contents

Specifications

General

Type .... Four or five forward speeds and reverse. Synchromesh on all forward speeds

Designation .... J (4-speed) or K (5-speed)

Gear ratios (typical)

Fiesta 1983 to 1989

Four-speed gearbox:

	1.0	1.1
1st	3.58 : 1	3. 58 : 1
2nd	2.04 : 1	2.04 : 1
3rd	1.35 : 1	1.30 : 1
4th (E)	0.96 : 1	0.88 : 1
Reverse	3.77 : 1	3.77 : 1
Final drive	4.06 : 1	3.58 : 1

Five-speed gearbox:

	1.0	1.1, 1.3, 1.6
1st	3.58 : 1	3.58 : 1
2nd	2.04 : 1	2.04 : 1
3rd	1.35 : 1	1.35 : 1
4th	0.95 : 1	0.95 : 1
5th	0.76 : 1	0.76 : 1
Reverse	3.62 : 1	3.62 : 1
Final drive	4.29 : 1	3.84 : 1

Fiesta 1989 to 1995

Four-speed gearbox:

1st	3.58 : 1
2nd	2.04 : 1
3rd	1.32 : 1
4th (E)	0.95 : 1
Reverse	3.77 : 1
Final drive	4.06 : 1

Five-speed gearbox:

	1.1, 1.4*	1.4, 1.6
1st	3.58 : 1	3.15 : 1
2nd	2.04 : 1	1.91 : 1
3rd	1.32 : 1	1.28 : 1
4th	0.95 : 1	0.95 : 1
5th	0.76 : 1	0.76 : 1
Reverse	3.62 : 1	3.62 : 1
Final drive	4.06 : 1	4.06 : 1 (not fuel injected - 3.82 : 1)

Escort 1980 to 1990

Four-speed gearbox:

	1.1 (3 + E)	1.1, 1.3, 1.4	1.6
1st	3.58 : 1	3. 58 : 1	3.15 : 1
2nd	2.04 : 1	2.04 : 1	1.91 : 1
3rd	1.30 : 1	1.35 : 1	1.28 : 1
4th (E)	0.88 : 1	0.95 : 1	0.95 : 1
Reverse	3.77 : 1	3.77 : 1	3.62 : 1
Final drive	3.58 : 1	3.84 : 1	3.58 : 1 (XR3 - 3.84 : 1)

6

Gear ratios (typical)

Escort 1980 to 1990 (continued)

Five-speed gearbox:	1.1, 1.3 (CVH), 1.4	1.3 (OHV), 1.6
1st	3.58 : 1	3.15 : 1
2nd	2.04 : 1	1.91 : 1
3rd	1.35 : 1	1.28 : 1
4th	0.95 : 1	0.95 : 1
5th	0.76 : 1	0.76 : 1
Reverse	3.62 : 1	3.62 : 1
Final drive	3.84 : 1	3.84 : 1 (fuel injected - 4.27 : 1)

Orion 1983 to 1990

Four-speed gearbox:	1.3 (CVH)	1.3 (OHV)	1.4
1st	3.58 : 1	3.15 : 1	3.58 : 1
2nd	2.04 : 1	1.91 : 1	2.04 : 1
3rd	1.35 : 1	1.28 : 1	1.32 : 1
4th (E)	0.95 : 1	0.95 : 1	0.95 : 1
Reverse	3.77 : 1	3.62 : 1	3.77 : 1
Final drive	3.84 : 1	3.84 : 1	3.84 : 1

Five-speed gearbox:	1.3 (CVH)	1.3 (OHV), 1.6
1st	3.58 : 1	3.15 : 1
2nd	2.04 : 1	1.91 : 1
3rd	1.35 : 1	1.28 : 1
4th	0.95 : 1	0.95 : 1
5th	0.76 : 1	0.76 : 1
Reverse	3.61 : 1	3.62 : 1
Final drive	3.84 : 1	3.58 : 1 (fuel injected - 3.84 : 1)

With controlled catalytic converter

Overhaul data

Snap-ring thicknesses (mainshaft and input shaft bearings)	1.86 to 1.89 mm (0.0733 to 0.0745 in)
	1.94 to 1.97 mm (0.0764 to 0.0776 in)
	2.01 to 2.04 mm (0.0792 to 0.0804 in)

Lubrication

Capacity:	
Four-speed	2.8 litres (4.9 pints)
Five-speed	3.1 litres (5.5 pints)
Lubricant type/specification	See *Recommended lubricants and fluids*
Grease specification (assembly only - see text):	
Four-speed gearbox	To Ford specification SM1C-1020-B
Five-speed gearbox:	
Gears, contact and thrust faces, and synchroniser cones	Molybdenum disulphide paste to Ford specification SM1 C-4505-A
5th gear on input shaft	Ford grease type ESEA-M1C-1014-A
Selector shaft locking assembly sealer	Anaerobic retaining and sealing compound to Ford specification S-M4G-4645-AA or AB

Torque wrench settings

	Nm	lbf ft
5th gear housing cover (five-speed)	8 to 11	6 to 8
5th gear housing to main housing (five-speed)	12 to 15	9 to 11
5th gear selector pin clamp bolt (five-speed)	14 to 20	10 to 15
Anti-roll bar clamp bolts	45 to 56	33 to 41
Clutch housing cover plate	35 to 45	26 to 33
Crownwheel to differential case:		
Saloon and Estate	98 to 128	72 to 94
RS Turbo	80 to 100	59 to 74
Van	75 to 90	55 to 66
Front and rear gearbox mounting bolts (pre-1986 models)	52 to 64	38 to 47
Front gearbox mounting bracket to gearbox (pre-1986 models)	41 to 51	30 to 38
Gearbox assembly to engine	35 to 45	26 to 33
Gearbox housing cover bolts (four-speed)	12 to 15	9 to 11
Gearbox mountings to gearbox (1986 models onwards)	80 to 100	59 to 74
Gearbox support crossmember to body (1986 models onwards)	52	38
Gearchange housing to floor (1984 models onwards)	5 to 7	4 to 5
Gearchange housing to floor (pre-1984 models)	13 to 17	10 to 13
Gearchange rod clamp bolt	14 to 17	10 to 13
Gearchange stabiliser to gearbox	50 to 60	37 to 44
Lower arm balljoint pinch-bolt	48 to 60	35 to 44

Torque wrench settings (continued)

	Nm	lbf ft
Lower arm mounting pivot bolt	51 to 64	38 to 47
Oil filler plug	23 to 30	17 to 22
Reversing light switch	23 to 30	17 to 22
Selector shaft locking mechanism cap nut	30	22
Small housing-to-large housing bolts	21 to 27	15 to 20
Starter motor bolts	35 to 45	26 to 33

1 General description

The manual gearbox may be of four or five-speed type depending on model, year of manufacture and/or options fitted. Both gearbox types are basically the same except that the five-speed version incorporates a modified selector mechanism, and an additional gear and synchro-hub contained in a housing attached to the side of the main gearbox casing **(see illustrations)**. Both gearbox types use synchromesh gear engagement on all forward gears.

The mainshaft and input shaft carry the constant mesh gear cluster assemblies and are supported on ball and roller bearings. The short splined end of the input shaft eliminates the need for additional support from a crankshaft spigot bearing.

The synchromesh gear engagement is by sliding keys which act against baulk rings

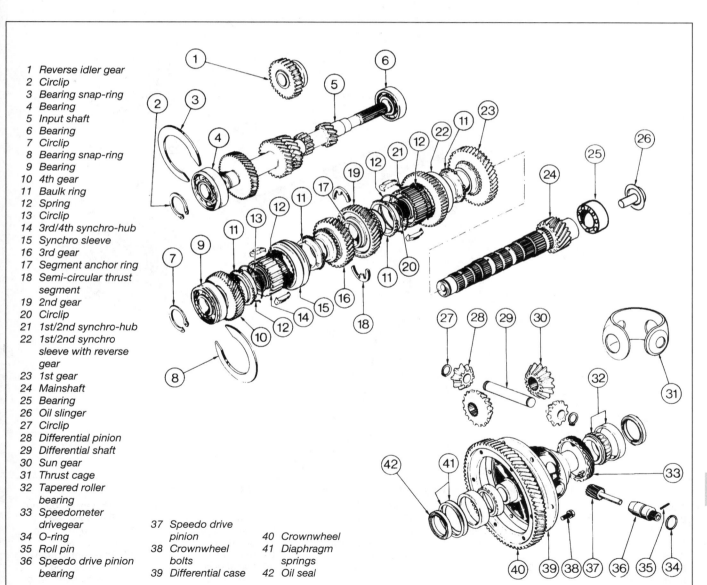

1 Reverse idler gear
2 Circlip
3 Bearing snap-ring
4 Bearing
5 Input shaft
6 Bearing
7 Circlip
8 Bearing snap-ring
9 Bearing
10 4th gear
11 Baulk ring
12 Spring
13 Circlip
14 3rd/4th synchro-hub
15 Synchro sleeve
16 3rd gear
17 Segment anchor ring
18 Semi-circular thrust segment
19 2nd gear
20 Circlip
21 1st/2nd synchro-hub
22 1st/2nd synchro sleeve with reverse gear
23 1st gear
24 Mainshaft
25 Bearing
26 Oil slinger
27 Circlip
28 Differential pinion
29 Differential shaft
30 Sun gear
31 Thrust cage
32 Tapered roller bearing
33 Speedometer drivegear
34 O-ring
35 Roll pin
36 Speedo drive pinion bearing
37 Speedo drive pinion
38 Crownwheel bolts
39 Differential case
40 Crownwheel
41 Diaphragm springs
42 Oil seal

1.1a Exploded view of the gear assemblies and associated components - type J gearbox

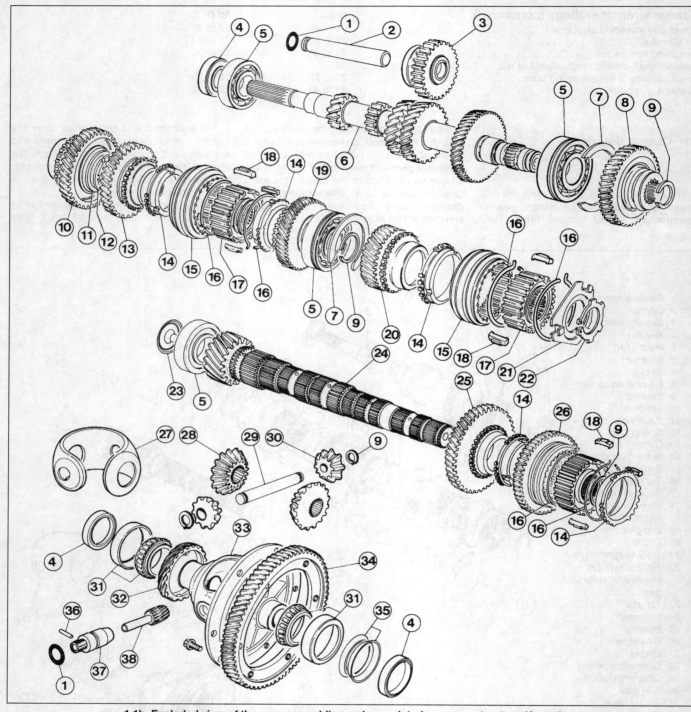

1.1b Exploded view of the gear assemblies and associated components - type K gearbox

1 O-ring	9 Circlip	18 Sliding key	26 1st/2nd synchro sleeve with reverse gear
2 Reverse idler gear shaft	10 2nd gear	19 4th gear	27 Thrust cage
3 Reverse idler gear	11 Segment anchor ring	20 5th gear	28 Sun gear
4 Radial oil seal	12 Thrust segment	21 Retaining plate	29 Differential shaft
5 Bearing	13 3rd gear	22 Circlip	30 Planet gear
6 Input shaft	14 Baulk ring	23 Oil slinger	31 Taper roller bearing
7 Snap-ring	15 Synchro sleeve	24 Mainshaft	32 Speedometer drive worm
8 5th gear	16 Retaining spring	25 1st gear	
	17 Synchro hub		

33 Differential housing	
34 Final drive gear	
35 Diaphragm springs	
36 Locking pin	
37 Speedometer drive pinion bearing	
38 Speedometer drive pinion	

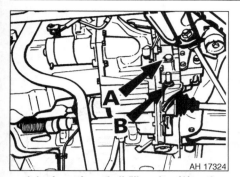

1.1c Location of oil filler plug (A) and selector shaft locking mechanism cap (B)

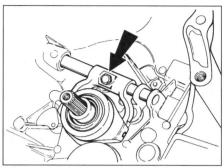

2.2 Clutch release fork locking bolt (arrowed)

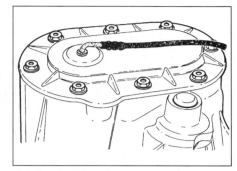

2.4 Gearbox housing cover retaining bolts

under the movement of the synchroniser sleeves. Gear selection is by means of a floor-mounted lever connected by a remote control housing and gearchange rod to the selector shaft in the gearbox. Selector shaft movement is transmitted to the selector forks via the guide shaft and guide levers.

The final drive (differential) unit is integral with the gearbox and is located between the two gearbox housings. On Escort RS Turbo models a viscous coupling type limited slip differential is fitted as standard equipment.

Renewal of the transmission oil is not a service requirement, but if draining is necessary prior to a repair or overhaul task place a suitable container beneath the selector shaft locking mechanism cap located just below the filler cap **(see illustration 1.1c)**. Unscrew the cap nut, remove the spring and interlock pin and allow the oil to drain.

2 Dismantling into assemblies
- type J gearbox

1 With the gearbox removed from the vehicle, clean away external dirt and grease using paraffin and a stiff brush or a water-soluble solvent. Take care not to allow water to enter the gearbox.
2 Unscrew the lockbolt which holds the clutch release fork to the shaft and remove the shaft, followed by the fork and release bearing **(see illustration)**.

3 If not removed for draining, unscrew the selector shaft cap nut, spring and interlock pin.
4 Unbolt and remove the gearbox housing cover **(see illustration)**.
5 Remove the snap-rings from the main and input shaft bearings **(see illustration)**.
6 Unscrew and remove the connecting bolts and lift the smaller housing from the gearbox **(see illustration)**. If it is stuck, tap it off carefully with a plastic-headed mallet.
7 Extract the swarf collecting magnet and clean it **(see illustration)**. Take care not to drop the magnet or it will shatter.
8 Withdraw the selector shaft, noting that the longer portion of smaller diameter is at the bottom as the shaft is withdrawn **(see illustration)**.
9 Remove the selector shaft coil spring, the

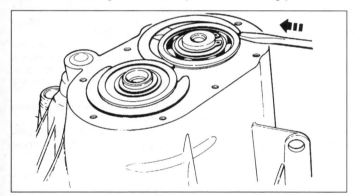

2.5 Removing the mainshaft and input shaft bearing snap-rings

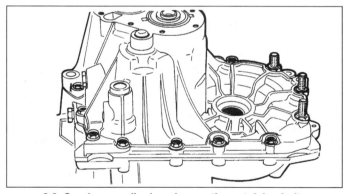

2.6 Gearbox smaller housing section retaining bolts

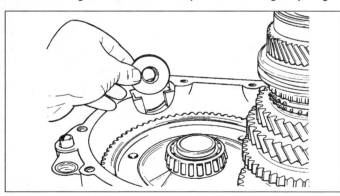

2.7 Removing the swarf collecting magnet

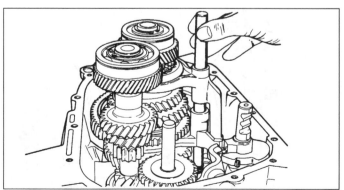

2.8 Selector shaft removal

6

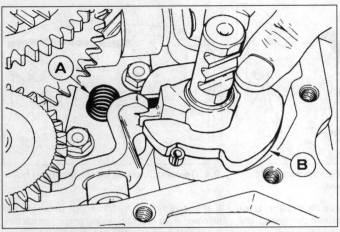

2.9 Selector shaft coil spring (A) and shift locking plate (B)

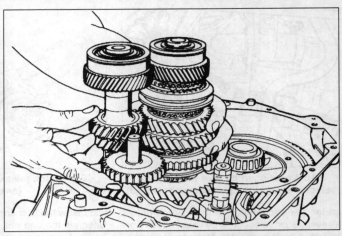

2.10 Removing the mainshaft, input shaft and reverse gear assemblies

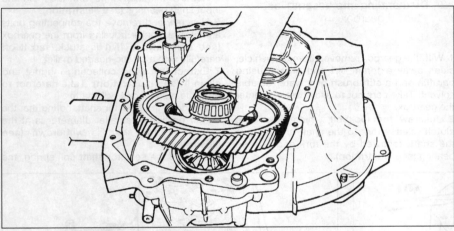

2.11 Withdrawing the differential

selector forks and the shift locking plate **(see illustration)**. Note the roll pin located in the locking plate cut-out.

10 Withdraw the mainshaft, the input shaft and reverse gear as one assembly from the gearbox housing **(see illustration)**.

11 Lift the differential assembly from the housing **(see illustration)**.

12 The gearbox is now dismantled into its major assemblies.

3 Dismantling into assemblies - type K gearbox

1 With the gearbox removed from the vehicle, clean away external dirt and grease using paraffin and a stiff brush, or a water-soluble grease solvent. Take care not to allow water to enter the gearbox.

2 Drain off any residual oil in the gearbox through a driveshaft opening.

3 Unscrew the lockbolt which holds the clutch release fork to the shaft and remove the shaft, followed by the fork and release bearing **(see illustration 2.2)**.

4 If not removed for draining, unscrew the selector shaft cap nut, spring and interlock pin. Now remove the additional 5th gear selector shaft cap nut, spring and interlock pin.

5 Unbolt and remove the gearbox housing cover **(see illustration)**.

6 Unscrew the clamp bolt and lift the 5th gear selector pin assembly off the shaft rod **(see illustration)**.

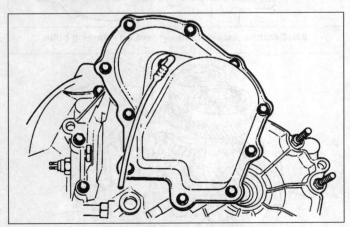

3.5 Gearbox housing cover retaining bolts

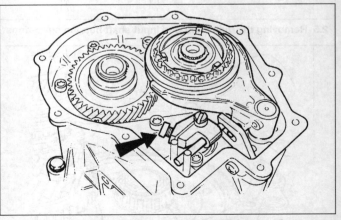

3.6 5th gear selector pin clamp bolt (arrowed)

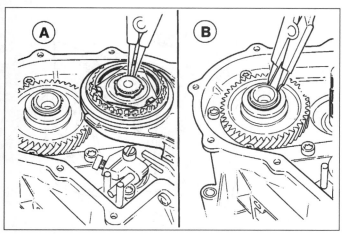

3.7 Removing 5th gear retaining snap-ring (A) and input shaft circlip (B)

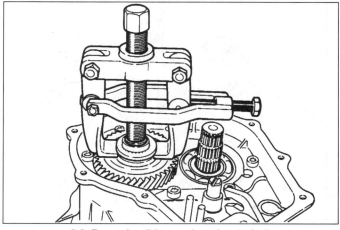

3.8 Removing 5th gear from input shaft

7 Using circlip pliers, extract the 5th gear retaining snap-ring, then lift off the 5th gear, complete with synchro assembly and selector fork from the mainshaft **(see illustration)**.

8 Extract the circlip securing the 5th gear driving gear to the input shaft. Using a two-legged puller, draw the gear off the input shaft **(see illustration)**. *Do not re-use the old circlip when reassembling; a new one must be obtained.*

9 Unscrew the nine socket-headed bolts securing the 5th gear housing to the main housing and carefully lift it off.

10 Remove the snap-rings from the main and input shaft bearings **(see illustration)**.

11 Unscrew and remove the connecting bolts and gearbox mounting bolts, then lift the smaller housing from the gearbox housing **(see illustration)**. If it is stuck, tap it off carefully with a plastic-headed mallet.

12 Extract the swarf-collecting magnet and clean it. Take care not to drop the magnet or it will shatter.

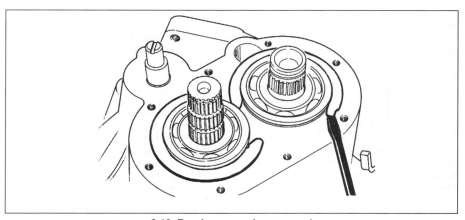

3.10 Bearing snap-ring removal

13 Release the circlips from the selector shaft guide sleeve and 1st/2nd gear selector fork **(see illustration)**. Carefully withdraw the guide sleeve.

14 Lift out the complete mainshaft assembly, together with the input shaft, selector forks and reverse gear as a complete unit from the gearbox housing **(see illustration overleaf)**.

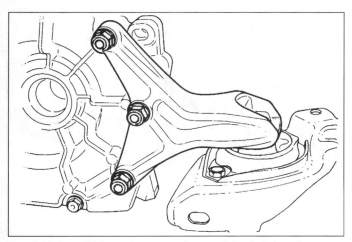

3.11 Pre-1986 gearbox mounting retaining bolt locations

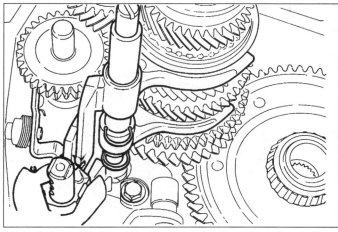

3.13 Selector shaft guide sleeve and 1st/2nd gear selector fork circlip locations

6

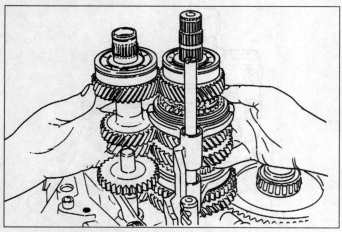

3.14 Removing mainshaft, input shaft and reverse gear assemblies

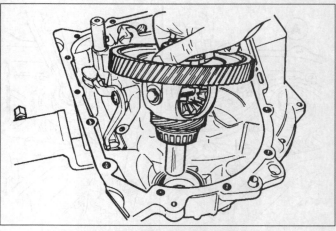

3.16 Removing the differential

15 Remove the selector shaft and the shaft locking plate.
16 Finally lift the differential assembly from the housing **(see illustration)**.
17 The gearbox is now dismantled into its major assemblies, which can be further dismantled if necessary, as described in Sections 6 to 9, but note the following differences when overhauling the mainshaft.
18 If overhauling the 5th gear synchroniser unit, note that the sliding keys are secured by means of a retaining plate. When assembling the unit, proceed as described for the other synchro units (Section 7), but ensure that the retaining spring located between the hub and the retaining plate is pressing against the sliding keys **(see illustration)**.
19 When reassembling the mainshaft, fit the 1st/2nd synchro so that the reverse gear teeth on the unit are positioned towards 1st gear, with the selector groove facing 2nd gear **(see illustration)**.
20 Should it be necessary to renew the input shaft or 5th gear, these components are supplied as a matched pair in the form of a repair kit.

4 Examination and renovation - type J gearbox

1 The need for further dismantling will depend upon the reasons for removal of the gearbox in the first place.
2 A common reason for dismantling will be to renew the synchro units. Wear or malfunction in these components will have been obvious when changing gear by the noise, or by the synchro being easily beaten.
3 The renewal of oil seals may be required as evident by drips of oil under the vehicle when stationary.
4 Jumping out of gear may mean renewal of the selector mechanism, forks or synchro sleeves.
5 General noise during operation on the road may be due to worn bearings, shafts or gears and when such general wear occurs, it will probably be more economical to renew the gearbox complete.
6 When dismantling the gear trains, always keep the components strictly in their originally installed order.

5 Examination and renovation - type K gearbox

1 As mentioned in the introduction of this Chapter, the five-speed gearbox is virtually the same as the four-speed type, the main differences being the additional gear and synchro-hub, and a modified selector mechanism.
2 The overhaul procedures described previously for the four-speed gearbox are therefore also applicable to the five-speed unit, but note the following.
3 It is important to note that, during the assembly of the five-speed gearbox, the sub-assembly components should be lubricated with the special greases as shown in the Specifications.
4 The limited slip differential is a sealed assembly and cannot be dismantled for repair or overhaul. It is possible to renew the crownwheel using the procedure described in Section 9, but if any other repair is necessary a new unit must be obtained.
5 When referring to other Sections for

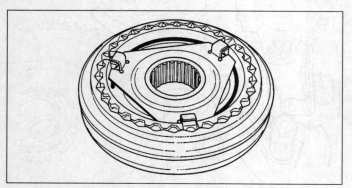

3.18 5th gear synchro unit

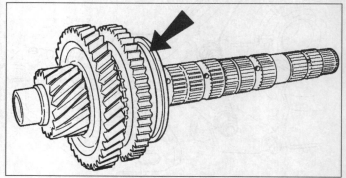

3.19 Correct location of 1st/2nd synchro unit with selector groove positioned as shown (arrowed)

6.1 Breaking the mainshaft bearing plastic cage

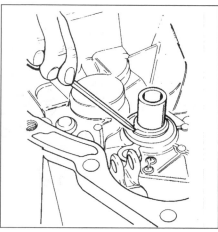

6.3 Input shaft oil seal removal

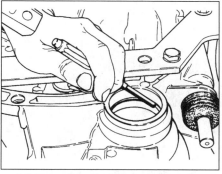

6.5 Removing the differential bearing track

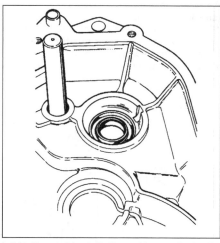

6.7 Correct installation of input shaft oil seal

overhaul procedures, it should be noted that all photos are of the four-speed gearbox. Due to the close resemblance of the two gearboxes, the photos shown can also be used in most instances for pictorial guidance when working on the five-speed gearbox.

6 Gearbox housing and selector mechanism - dismantling and reassembly

1 To remove the mainshaft bearing, break the plastic roller cage with a screwdriver. Extract the rollers and the cage, the oil slinger and retainers **(see illustration)**. Remove the bearing outer track.
2 When fitting the new bearing, also renew the oil slinger.
3 When renewing the input shaft oil seal, drive the oil seal out by applying the drift inside the bellhousing **(see illustration)**.

4 The constant velocity joint (differential) oil seals should be renewed at time of major overhaul.
5 The differential bearing tracks can be removed, using a drift inserted from the large housing section **(see illustration)**.
6 The differential bearing outer track and the diaphragm adjustment springs can be driven out of the smaller housing section using a suitable drift such as a piece of tubing.
7 Refit the input shaft oil seal so that its lips are as shown **(see illustration)**. Apply grease to all the oil seal lips and check that the lip retaining spring has not been displaced during installation of the seal.
8 When installing the differential diaphragm springs and bearing track to the smaller housing section, note that the spring convex faces are towards each other **(see illustration)**. Stake the track with a light blow from a punch **(see illustration)**. This is only to

hold the track during assembly of the remainder of the gearbox.
9 If the selector mechanism is worn, sloppy or damaged, dismantle it by extracting the

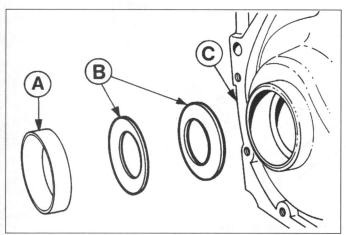

6.8a Differential bearing diaphragm springs

A Bearing track   B Diaphragm springs   C Small housing section

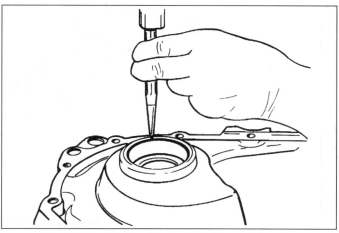

6.8b Staking the bearing track in the small housing section

6

6.9a Reverse selector lever circlip

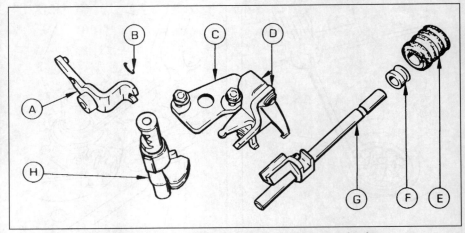

6.9b Exploded view of the four-speed selector mechanism

circlip and taking off the reverse selector lever **(see illustrations)**.
10 Remove the guide lever retaining plate and the guide shaft **(see illustration)**. Two bolts hold these components in place.
11 Extract the two circlips and detach the

A	Reverse selector lever	D	Guide levers	G	Selector shaft with dog
B	Circlip	E	Gaiter	H	Guide shaft with dog
C	Guide lever retaining plate	F	Oil seal		

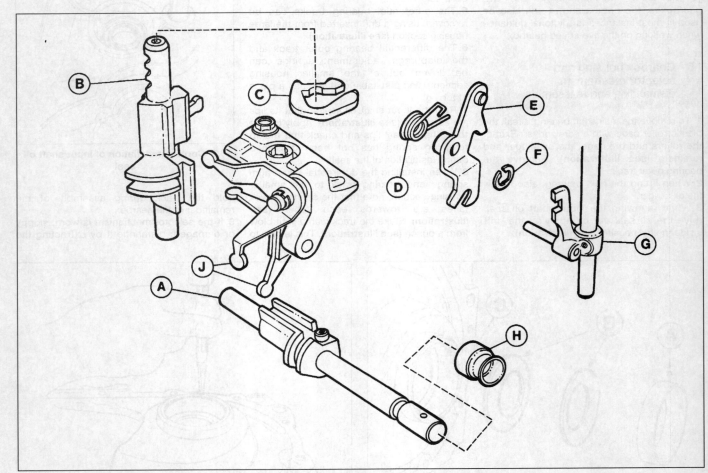

6.9c Exploded view of the five-speed selector mechanism

A	Selector shaft with dog	D	Reverse gear selector lever spring	G	5th/reverse shift rod
B	Guide shaft with dog	E	Reverse selector lever	H	Oil seal
C	Shift locking plate	F	Circlip	J	Guide levers

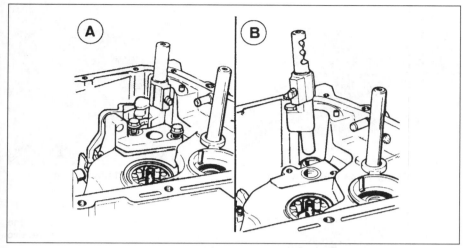

6.10 Selector mechanism dismantling

A Removing retaining plate   B Removing guide shaft

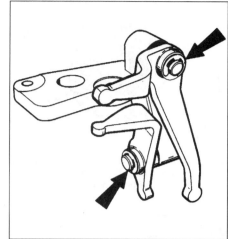

6.11 Guide lever circlip locations

guide lever from the retaining plate **(see illustration)**.

12 To remove the main selector shaft, pull the rubber gaiter up the shaft and then extract the single socket screw which secures the selector dog **(see illustration)**. Withdraw the shaft.

13 The selector shaft plastic bushes and oil seal should be renewed.

14 Reassembly is a reversal of dismantling, but when fitting the rubber gaiter make sure that its drain tube will point downwards when installed in the vehicle. Use new circlips at reassembly.

7 Mainshaft -
dismantling and reassembly

Note: *Refer to Section 3 for additional information if working on a five-speed gearbox.*

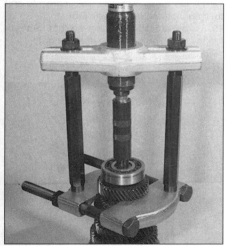

7.2 4th gear and bearing removal from mainshaft

1 Extract the circlip which holds the bearing to the shaft.

2 Using a puller, engaged behind 4th gear, draw off the gear and the bearing from the end of the mainshaft **(see illustration)**.

3 Discard the bearing.

4 Extract the circlip and remove the 3rd/4th synchro with 3rd gear, using hand pressure only.

5 Remove the anchor ring and the two thrust semi-circular segments, then take 2nd gear from the mainshaft.

6 Extract the circlip and take off 1st/2nd synchro unit with 1st gear.

7 The mainshaft is now completely dismantled. Do not attempt to remove the drive pinion gear.

8 The synchro units can be dismantled and new components fitted after extracting the circular retaining springs **(see illustration)**.

9 When reassembling the hub and sleeve,

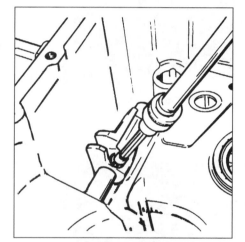

6.12 Removing the selector dog-to-shaft socket screw

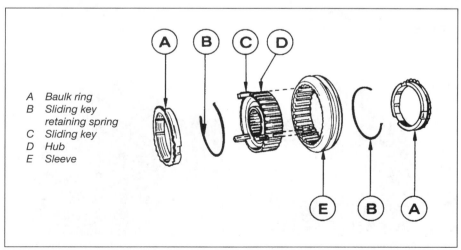

A   Baulk ring
B   Sliding key retaining spring
C   Sliding key
D   Hub
E   Sleeve

7.8 Exploded view of a synchro unit

6

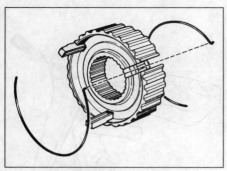

7.10 Fitted direction of sliding key retaining springs

7.12 Fitting 1st gear to mainshaft

7.13 Fitting 1stbaulk ring

7.14 Fitting 1st/2nd synchro unit

7.15 Fitting 1st/2nd synchro unit circlip (arrowed)

align them so that the cut-outs in the components are in alignment, ready to receive the sliding keys.

10 The two springs should have their hooked ends engaged in the same sliding key, but must run in opposing directions **(see illustration)**.

11 The baulk rings should be renewed if they do not 'stick' when pressed and turned onto the gear covers, or if a clearance no longer exists between the baulk ring and the gear when pressed onto its cone.

12 With all worn or damaged components renewed, commence reassembly by oiling the shaft and then sliding 1st gear onto the shaft so that the gear teeth are next to the pinion drivegear **(see illustration)**.

13 Fit 1st synchro baulk ring **(see illustration)**.

14 Fit 1st/2nd synchro so that reverse gear teeth on the unit are furthest from 1st gear **(see illustration)**.

15 Fit the circlip to secure the synchro to the mainshaft **(see illustration)**.

16 Slide on the synchro baulk ring **(see illustration)**.

17 Fit 2nd gear so that the cone is towards the baulk ring **(see illustration)**.

18 Fit the thrust semi-circular segments and their anchor ring **(see illustrations)**.

19 To the shaft fit 3rd gear so that its teeth are towards 2nd gear **(see illustration)**.

7.16 Engaging synchro baulk ring with sliding keys

7.17 Fitting 2nd gear

7.18a Fitting thrust semi-circular segments in position . . .

7.18b . . . and retained by anchor ring

7.19 Fitting 3rd gear

7.20 Locating 3rd synchro baulk ring on synchro unit cone face

7.21 3rd/4th synchro unit fitment with serrated edge towards 3rd gear

7.22 Securing 3rd/4th synchro unit with circlip

20 Fit the baulk ring **(see illustration)**.
21 Slide on 3rd/4th synchro so that its serrated edge is towards 3rd gear **(see illustration)**.
22 Secure the synchro to the mainshaft with the circlip **(see illustration)**.
23 Fit the baulk ring **(see illustration)**.
24 Fit 4th gear **(see illustration)**.
25 Fit the bearing so that its circlip groove is nearer the end of the shaft. Apply pressure only to the bearing centre track, using a press or a hammer and a piece of suitable diameter tubing **(see illustrations)**.
26 Fit the circlip to secure the bearing to the shaft. The mainshaft is now fully assembled **(see illustrations)**.

8 Input shaft - dismantling and reassembly

1 The only components which can be renewed are the two ball-bearing races **(see illustration)**.
2 Remove the securing circlip from the larger bearing and extract both with a two-legged extractor or a press **(see illustrations overleaf)**.
3 When fitting the new bearings, apply pressure to the centre track only, using a press or a piece of suitable diameter tubing

7.23 Engaging 3rd/4th synchro baulk ring with sliding keys

7.24 Fitting 4th gear

7.25a Mainshaft bearing fitment with circlip groove towards end of mainshaft

7.25b Using a tube to drive on mainshaft bearing

7.26a Fitting mainshaft bearing circlip

7.26b Mainshaft fully assembled

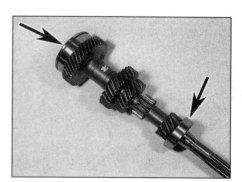

8.1 Input shaft bearings (arrowed)

6

8.2a Input shaft large bearing and retaining circlip (arrowed)

8.2b Input shaft smaller bearing

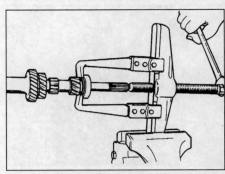

8.2c Removing an input shaft bearing

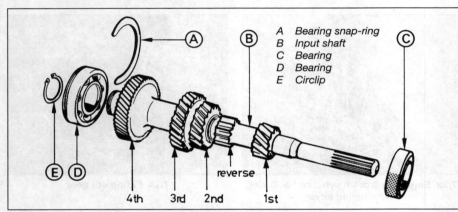

A   Bearing snap-ring
B   Input shaft
C   Bearing
D   Bearing
E   Circlip

reverse

4th   3rd   2nd   1st

8.3 Input shaft components

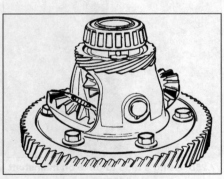

9.1 Removing the sun gears from the differential case

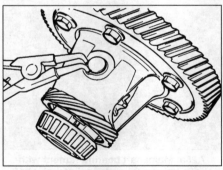

9.2 Extracting differential case shaft circlip

9.3 Differential bearing removal

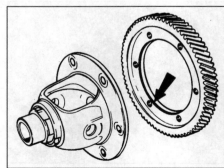

9.6 Crownwheel chamfered edge location - arrowed

and a hammer. When installing the larger bearing, make sure that the circlip groove is nearer the end of the shaft **(see illustration)**.

9 Differential - dismantling and reassembly

Note: *The limited slip differential is a sealed unit and cannot be dismantled for overhaul. It is, however, possible to renew the crownwheel in the same way as for conventional units.*

1 With the differential removed from the gearbox housing, twist both sun gears out of the differential case **(see illustration)**.
2 Extract one of the circlips from the end of the differential shaft, press the shaft out of the differential case and extract the planet gears and the cage **(see illustration)**.
3 The differential tapered roller bearings can be drawn off using a two-legged extractor **(see illustration)**.
4 The crownwheel can be separated from the differential case after removing the six securing bolts. Tap the components apart, using a plastic mallet.
5 If the crownwheel is to be renewed, then the gearbox mainshaft should be renewed at the same time, as the gear teeth are matched and renewal of only one component will give rise to an increase in noise during operation on the road.
6 Reassembly is a reversal of dismantling, but make sure that the deeply chamfered edge of the inside diameter is against the differential case **(see illustration)**. Tighten all bolts to the specified torque.
7 The sun gears should be held in position by inserting dowels or similar so that they will be in correct alignment for eventual installation of the driveshafts.

10 Reassembly - type J gearbox

1 With the larger housing section on the bench, lubricate the differential bearings with

10.1 Inserting differential assembly into the housing

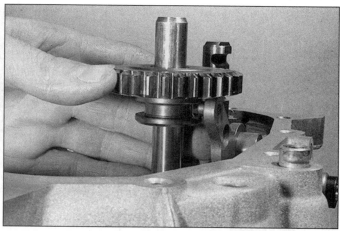

10.2 Engaging reverse idler gear with its shaft and selector lever

gear oil and insert the differential assembly into the housing (see illustration).

2 Slide reverse idler gear onto its shaft, at the same time engaging the selector lever in the groove of the gear which should be pointing downwards (see illustration).

3 In order to make installation of the mainshaft and input shaft easier, lift the reverse idler gear so that its selector lever is held by the reversing lamp switch spring-loaded ball (see illustration).

4 Mesh the gears of the mainshaft and the input shaft and install both gear trains into the gearbox housing simultaneously (see illustration).

5 Lower the reverse idler gear and its selector lever.

6 Fit the shift locking plate (see illustration).

7 Engage 1st/2nd selector fork with the groove in the mainshaft synchro sleeve. This fork has the shorter actuating lever (see illustration).

8 Engage 3rd/4th selector fork with the groove in its synchro sleeve. Make sure that the end of this fork actuating lever is engaged with the shift locking plate (see illustration).

9 Insert the coil spring in the selector shaft hole and pass the shaft downwards through the holes in the forks, make sure that the longer section of the reduced diameter of the rod is pointing downwards (see illustrations).

10 Actuate the appropriate selector fork to engage the correct gear: 4th on early models (approx pre-February 1987) or 2nd on later models. 4th gear is selected by inserting a rod in the hole in the end of the selector shaft

10.3 Reverse idler gear supported in raised position

10.4 Installing mainshaft and input shaft gear trains

10.6 Fitting shift locking plate

10.7 Engaging 1st/2nd selector fork with synchro unit sleeve

10.8 Engaging 3rd/4th selector fork with synchro unit sleeve

10.9a Inserting selector shaft coil springs . . .

6

10.9b . . . followed by the selector shaft

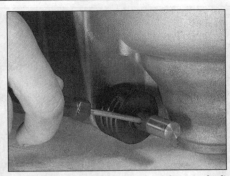

10.10 Using a screwdriver in selector shaft hole to engage 4th gear

10.11 Fitting the magnet

10.12a Locate a new gasket on the housing flange . . .

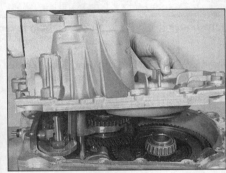

10.12b . . . and fit the smaller housing

which projects from the gearbox casing and turning the shaft fully clockwise to its stop, then pushing the shaft inwards **(see illustration)**. 2nd gear can be selected by turning the selector shaft fully clockwise (3rd/4th) and then gradually rotating it anti-clockwise until the shaft can be pushed inwards into 2nd gear.

11 Insert the magnetic swarf collector in its recess, taking care not to drop it **(see illustration)**.

12 Locate a new gasket on the housing flange, install the smaller housing section and screw in and tighten the bolts to the specified torque **(see illustrations)**.

13 Fit the snap-rings to the ends of the main and input shafts. Cut-outs are provided in the casing so that the bearings can be levered upwards to expose the snap-ring grooves **(see illustrations)**. Snap-rings are available in three thicknesses and the thickest possible ring should be used which will fit into the groove. If any difficulty is experienced in levering up the bearing on the input shaft, push the end of the shaft from within the bellhousing.

14 Tap the snap-rings to rotate them so that they will locate correctly in the cut-outs in the cover gasket which should now be positioned on the end of the housing **(see illustration)**. Fit a new gasket.

15 Fit the housing cover, screw in the bolts and tighten them to the specified torque **(see illustration)**.

10.13a Raising bearing for snap-ring installation

10.13b Fitting the bearing snap-ring

10.14 Bearing snap-rings and cover gasket in position

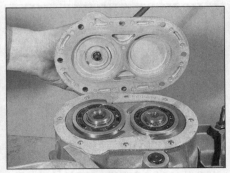

10.15 Fitting gearbox housing cover

10.16 Selector shaft locking mechanism cap nut (arrowed)

10.17a Inserting clutch release shaft . . .

10.17b . . . and securing release fork to the shaft

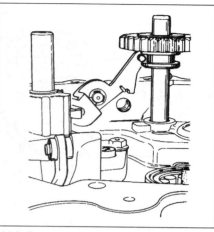

11.2 Reverse selector lever engaged with groove of idler gear

16 Fit the interlock pin, spring and cap nut for the selector shaft locking mechanism **(see illustration)**. The threads should be coated with jointing compound before installation.
17 Refit the clutch release shaft, lever and bearing into the bellhousing **(see illustrations)**.
18 The gearbox is now ready for installation in the vehicle. Wait until it is installed before filling with oil.

11 Reassembly - type K gearbox

1 With the larger housing section on the bench, lubricate the differential bearings with gear oil and insert the differential assembly into the housing.
2 Slide the reverse idler gear onto its shaft, at the same time engaging the selector lever in the groove of the gear which should be pointing downwards **(see illustration)**.
3 Refit the selector shaft and shift locking plate.
4 Refit the mainshaft and input shaft as an assembly complete with selector forks **(see illustration)**. Guide the selector forks past the shift locking plate, noting that the plate must

be turned clockwise to bear against the dowel.
5 Install the selector shaft guide sleeve and secure the 1st/2nd gear selector fork on the guide sleeve using new circlips.
6 Refit the swarf-collecting magnet to its location in the housing.
7 Locate a new gasket on the housing flange and place the small housing section in position. Refit and tighten the retaining bolts to the specified torque. Refit the gearbox mounting bracket.
8 Fit the snap-rings to the ends of the main and input shafts. Cut-outs are provided in the casing so that the bearings can be levered upwards to expose the snap-ring grooves

(see illustration). Snap-rings are available in three thicknesses, and the thickest possible ring should be used which will fit into the groove. If any difficulty is experienced in levering up the bearing on the input shaft, push the end of the shaft from within the bellhousing.
9 Tap the snap-rings to rotate them so that they will locate correctly in the cut-outs in the 5th gear housing gasket, which should now be placed in position **(see illustration)**.

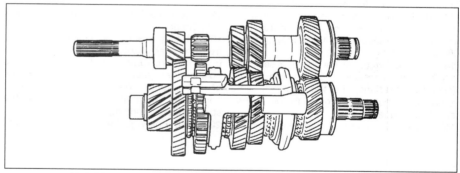

11.4 Mainshaft meshed with input shaft and selector forks fitted

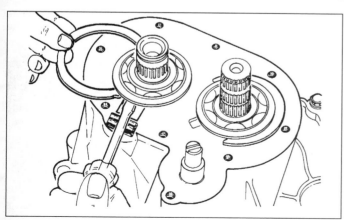

11.8 Fitting mainshaft and input shaft bearing snap-rings

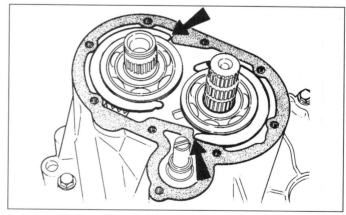

11.9 Correct positioning of bearing snap-rings and cover gasket

6

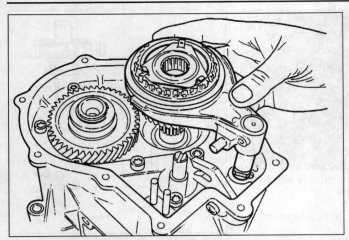

11.13 Fitting 5th gear synchro unit and selector fork

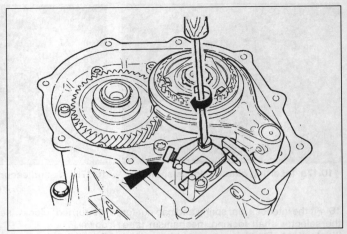

11.19 Turning the shift rod clockwise with a screwdriver prior to tightening selector pin clamp bolt (arrowed)

10 Fit the 5th gear housing and tighten the retaining bolts to the specified torque.

11 Coat the splines of 5th gear and the input shaft with the special grease (see Specifications). Before fitting the 5th gear, check that the marks on the input shaft and gear web are the same colour.

12 Heat 5th gear to approximately 80°C (176°F), and then drift it into place on the input shaft. Fit a new circlip to the input shaft using a tube of suitable diameter as a drift.

13 Fit 5th gear, complete with synchro assembly and selector fork, onto the mainshaft and secure with the snap-ring **(see illustration)**.

14 Coat the threads of the 5th gear selector shaft locking mechanism cap nut with sealer (see Specifications). Fit the interlock pin, spring and cap nut, then tighten the nut to the specified torque.

15 Fit the 1st/4th and reverse gear selector shaft interlock pin, spring and cap nut after first coating the threads of the cap nut with sealer. Tighten the nut to the specified torque.

16 Refit the 5th gear selector pin assembly to the shift rod, but do not tighten the clamp bolt at this stage.

17 Engage 5th gear with the selector shaft by turning the shaft clockwise as far as it will go from the neutral position, and then pulling it fully out.

18 Slide the selector ring and selector fork onto 5th gear.

19 Rotate the shift rod clockwise viewed from the rear of the car as far as the stop, using a screwdriver, and retain it in this position **(see illustration)**. Smear the threads of the clamp bolt with thread locking compound, then fit it and tighten to the specified torque setting.

20 Place a new gasket in position and refit the housing cover, tightening the retaining bolts to the specified torque.

21 At this stage check the operation of the selector mechanism by engaging all the gears with the selector shaft.

22 Refit the clutch release shaft, lever and bearing into the bellhousing.

23 The gearbox is now ready for installation in the vehicle. Wait until it is installed before filling with oil.

24 Use the selector shaft to engage an appropriate gear (for reconnection to the gearchange mechanism): reverse on early models (approx pre-February 1987) or 4th on later models. Reverse can be selected by turning the shaft fully clockwise and then pushing it inwards. 4th gear is selected by turning the shaft fully clockwise (5th/reverse) and then gradually rotating it anticlockwise until it can be pushed inwards into 4th gear.

Chapter 7
Vauxhall F10 gearbox

Contents

Specifications

General

Type	Four or five forward speeds (all synchromesh) and reverse. Final drive integral with main gearbox
Designation	F10/4 (4-speed) and F10/5 (5-speed)

Gear ratios (typical)

Nova/Corsa 1983 to 1993

1st	3.55 : 1
2nd	1.96 : 1
3rd	1.30 : 1
4th	0.89 : 1
5th	0.71 : 1
Reverse	3.18 : 1

Final drive:

	4-speed	5-speed
1.0 litre:		
Up to Februry 1983	3.74 : 1	4.18 : 1
From Februry 1983	3.94 : 1	4.18 : 1
1.2 and 1.3 litre	3.74 : 1	3.94 : 1

Corsa 1993 to 1998

1st	3.55 : 1
2nd	1.96 : 1
3rd	1.30 : 1
4th	0.89 : 1
5th	0.71 : 1
Reverse	3.31 : 1

Final drive:

4-speed	3.94 : 1
5-speed	4.18 : 1 (X 12 SZ engine - 3.74 : 1)

Astra/Kadett 1980 to 1984

	Early models	Later models
1st	3.66 : 1	3.55 : 1
2nd	2.12 : 1	1.96 : 1
3rd	1.43 : 1	1.30 : 1
4th	0.97 : 1	0.89 : 1
5th	-	0.71 : 1
Reverse	3.18 : 1	3.18 : 1
Final drive:		
Saloon and Hatchback	4.18 : 1	3.94 : 1
Estate	4.29 : 1 (1.2 - 4.53 : 1)	4.18 : 1

7

Gear ratios (typical) (continued)

Astra/Kadett/Belmont 1984 to 1990

1st	. . . .	3.55 : 1	
2nd	. . . .	1.96 : 1	
3rd	. . . .	1.30 : 1	
4th	. . . .	0.89 : 1	
5th	. . . .	0.71 : 1	
Reverse	. . . .	3.18 : 1	
Final drive:		**4-speed**	**5-speed**
Hatchback	. . . .	3.94 : 1	4.18 : 1
Van and Estate	. . . .	4.18 : 1	4.18 : 1

Cavalier/Ascona 1981 to 1988

		Early models	Later models
1st	. . . .	3.64 : 1	3.55 : 1
2nd	. . . .	2.21 : 1	1.96 : 1
3rd	. . . .	1.43 : 1	1.30 : 1
4th	. . . .	0.97 : 1	0.89 : 1
5th	. . . .	-	0.71 : 1
Reverse	. . . .	3.18 : 1	3.18 : 1
Final drive	. . . .	4.18 : 1	4.29 : 1

Cavalier/Vectra 1988 to 1994

1st	. . . .	3.55 : 1
2nd	. . . .	1.96 : 1
3rd	. . . .	1.30 : 1
4th	. . . .	0.89 : 1
5th	. . . .	0.71 : 1
Reverse	. . . .	3.31 : 1
Final drive	. . . .	4.29 : 1

Lubrication

Capacity:

Nova/Corsa 1983 to 1993:		
Four-speed gearbox	. . . .	1.7 litres (3.0 pints)
Five-speed gearbox	. . . .	1.8 litres (3.1 pints)
Corsa 1993 to 1998	. . . .	1.6 litres (2.8 pints)
Astra/Kadett 1980 to 1984	. . . .	1.7 litres (3.0 pints)
Astra/Kadett/Belmont 1984 to 1990:		
Four-speed gearbox	. . . .	1.7 litres (3.0 pints)
Five-speed gearbox	. . . .	1.8 litres (3.1 pints)
Astra 1991 to 1994	. . . .	1.6 litres (2.8 pints)
Cavalier/Ascona 1981 to 1988:		
Four-speed gearbox	. . . .	1.7 litres (3.0 pints)
Five-speed gearbox	. . . .	1.8 litres (3.1 pints)
Cavalier/Vectra 1988 to 1995	. . . .	1.6 litres (2.8 pints)
Lubricant type/specification	. . . .	See *Recommended lubricants and fluids*

Torque wrench settings

	Nm	lbf ft
Crownwheel to differential	85	63
Differential cover plate to gearbox casing	30	22
End cover shield retaining bolts (F10/5)	15	11
End cover to gearbox casing	22	16
Gearbox bellhousing to engine	75	55
Gearchange remote control housing to underbody	16	12
Interlock pin bridge piece bolts (F10/5)	5	4
Left-hand engine/gearbox mounting retaining bolts	65	48
Rear engine/gearbox mounting bracket bolt	65	48
Release bearing guide tube to gearbox casing	5	4
Reversing lamp switch to gearbox casing	20	15
Selector cover to gearbox casing	15	11
Selector fork bearing support (F10/5)	22	16
Selector interlock pawl bolts (F10/5)	9	7

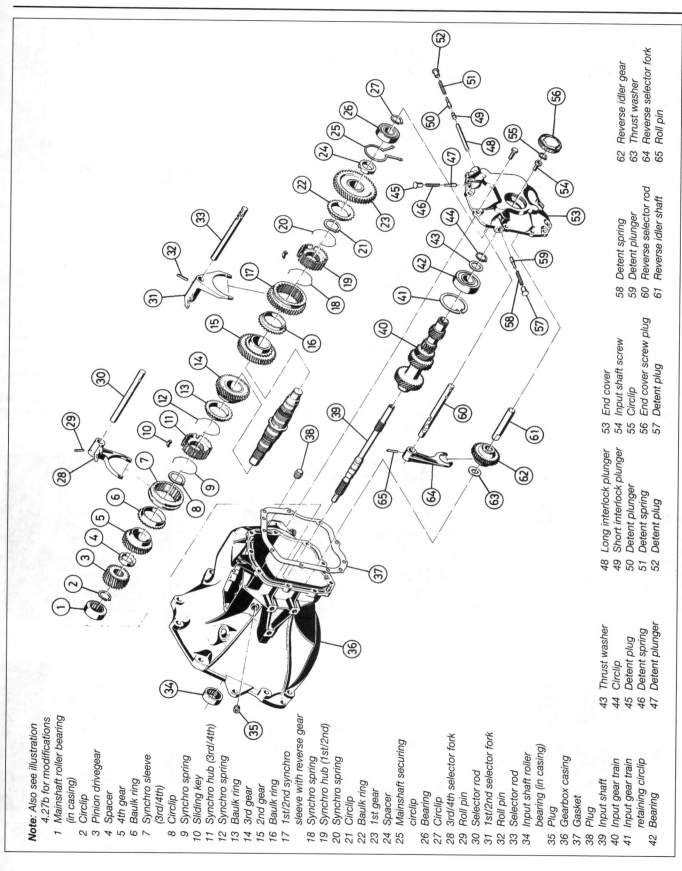

1.1a Exploded view of the gear train assemblies - four-speed gearbox

Note: Also see illustration
4.27b for modifications
1 Mainshaft roller bearing
   (in casing)
2 Circlip
3 Pinion drivegear
4 Spacer
5 4th gear
6 Baulk ring
7 Synchro sleeve
   (3rd/4th)
8 Circlip
9 Synchro spring
10 Sliding key
11 Synchro hub (3rd/4th)
12 Synchro spring
13 Baulk ring
14 3rd gear
15 2nd gear
16 Baulk ring
17 1st/2nd synchro
   sleeve with reverse gear
18 Synchro spring
19 Synchro hub (1st/2nd)
20 Synchro spring
21 Circlip
22 Baulk ring
23 1st gear
24 Spacer
25 Mainshaft securing
   circlip
26 Bearing
27 Circlip
28 3rd/4th selector fork
29 Roll pin
30 Selector rod
31 1st/2nd selector fork
32 Roll pin
33 Selector rod
34 Input shaft roller
   bearing (in casing)
35 Plug
36 Gearbox casing
37 Gasket
38 Plug
39 Input shaft
40 Input gear train
41 Input gear train
   retaining circlip
42 Bearing
43 Thrust washer
44 Circlip
45 Detent plug
46 Detent spring
47 Detent plunger
48 Long interlock plunger
49 Short interlock plunger
50 Detent plunger
51 Detent spring
52 Detent plug
53 End cover
54 Input shaft screw
55 Circlip
56 End cover screw plug
57 Detent plug
58 Detent spring
59 Detent plunger
60 Reverse selector rod
61 Reverse idler shaft
62 Reverse idler gear
63 Thrust washer
64 Reverse selector fork
65 Roll pin

7

1.1b Oil level plug location (arrowed)

1.1c Oil filler plug location (arrowed)

1.3 The differential cover plate must be removed to drain the transmission oil

1 General description

A four- or five-speed manual gearbox may be fitted, depending on engine size and options specified. All types of gearbox have synchromesh on all forward gears **(see illustrations)**.

Drive is transmitted through the gearbox and the integral final drive/differential assembly to the driveshafts. Gear selection is by a floor-mounted lever and a remote control linkage.

Since transmission oil draining and refilling is not specified by Vauxhall as a routine service operation, the transmission is regarded as a sealed unit and therefore has no drain plug. If, for any reason, it is wished to drain the oil, the differential cover plate must be removed **(see illustration)**.

2 Dismantling and reassembly - F10/4 gearbox

This gearbox is very similar to the F16/4 gearbox; refer to Chapter 8, Sections 2 and 4.

3 Dismantling and reassembly - F10/5 gearbox

1 Undo the bolts securing the end cover shield to the end cover.
2 Unbolt and remove the selector cover from the gearbox casing **(see illustrations)**.
3 Unbolt the retaining plate and withdraw the speedometer driven gear **(see illustrations)**.
4 Unscrew and remove the reversing lamp switch **(see illustration)**.
5 Using a screwdriver as a lever, engage 2nd gear by moving the selector fork nearest the end cover **(see illustration)**.

3.2a Undo the retaining bolts . . .

3.2b . . . and remove the selector cover

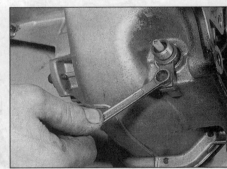

3.3a Unbolt the retaining plate . . .

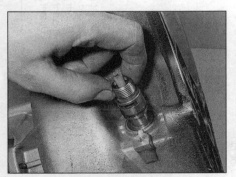

3.3b . . . and withdraw the speedometer driven gear assembly

3.4 Unscrew the reversing lamp switch

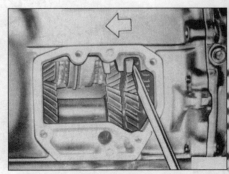

3.5 Using a screwdriver to engage 2nd gear

3.7 Removing the main casing from the end cover

3.8 Selector fork and bearing support socket-headed retaining bolts

6 Unscrew and remove the end cover bolts and nuts.

7 Withdraw the main casing from the end cover and gear trains (see illustration).

8 Using a suitable Allen key undo the two socket-headed bolts and remove the bearing support with selector fork from the end cover (see illustration).

9 Engage 3rd and reverse gear by moving the selector forks.

10 Extract the 5th gear synchroniser retaining circlip and then remove the synchroniser using a two-legged puller. Recover the baulk ring.

11 Lift off the mainshaft 5th gear, needle roller bearing, the two thrustwasher halves and the thrustwasher retaining ring (see illustration).

12 Extract the input shaft 5th gear retaining circlip and then draw off the gear using a large puller. Use a tubular distance piece for the puller centre screw so that it bears against the input gear train and not directly on the input shaft itself.

13 Using an Allen key unscrew the socket-headed screws which secure the 5th gear selector interlock pawl to the end cover (see illustration).

14 Using a forked tool as a lever, extract the four detent plugs from the edge of the end cover. Be prepared to catch the coil spring which will be ejected. Pull out the detent plungers. Renew the detent plugs if they were damaged during removal.

15 Move 5th gear selector rod to its engaged position and also move the 2nd gear selector fork to engage the gear.

16 Again using the Allen key unscrew the socket-headed bolts and remove the interlock pin bridge piece (see illustration).

17 Return all the gears and selector rods to neutral.

18 Drive out the securing roll pin and remove the selector shaft and fork for 3rd/4th gears. Remove the reverse shaft and fork in the same way.

3.11 Mainshaft 5th gear, needle roller bearing and thrustwashers

3.13 Selector interlock pawl retaining bolts - arrowed

3.16 Interlock pin bridge piece retaining bolts (arrowed)

3.18 Removing the 5th gear selector driver

7

3.20a Mainshaft bearing retaining circlip

3.20b Remove the swarf collecting magnet

19 Pull the 5th gear selector driver from the end cover (see illustration).
20 Extract the circlips which retain the mainshaft and input shaft gear trains. Extract the swarf collecting magnet (see illustrations).
21 Remove the gear train assemblies together with the 1st/2nd selector fork and rod simultaneously.

22 Extract the selector rod interlock pins from the end cover.
23 Remove the reverse idler shaft from the end cover. To do this, grip the shaft in the jaws of a vice fitted with soft metal protectors and, using a brass drift, gently tap the cover off the shaft. Take care not to lose the locking ball (see illustrations).
24 Unbolt and remove the pressed-steel

cover from the gearbox casing at the base of the differential (see illustration).
25 Mark the position of the bearing adjuster ring in relation to the gearbox casing (see illustration). Unbolt the ring lock (see illustration).
26 Unscrew the bearing adjuster ring. A piece of flat steel bar will act as a suitable wrench (see illustrations).

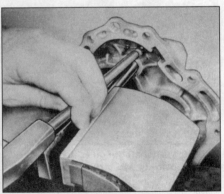

3.23a Tapping the end cover off the reverse idler shaft

3.23b Reverse idler shaft locking ball (arrowed)

3.24 Remove the differential cover plate

3.25a Mark the differential bearing adjuster ring position with a punch . . .

3.25b . . . then unscrew the bolt and remove the ring lock

3.26a Use a flat steel bar to unscrew the adjuster ring . . .

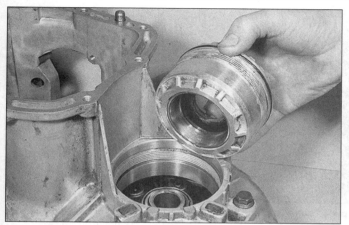

3.26b . . . then remove the adjuster ring from the casing

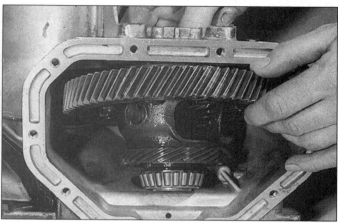

3.27 Withdraw the differential crownwheel assembly

3.28a Using a tube, block of wood and hammer to renew the oil seal and bearing track in the adjuster ring . . .

3.28b . . . and in the gearbox casing

27 Withdraw the differential/crownwheel assembly (see illustration).
28 Renew the oil seals and bearings in the adjuster ring and gearbox casing using a piece of tubing to remove the old components and to install the new (see illustrations).
29 Using a suitable puller, remove the tapered roller bearings from the differential (see illustration).

30 Unbolt the crownwheel and tap it from its register using a brass drift (see illustration).
31 If the crownwheel or pinion gear are to be renewed, they must always be renewed as a matched pair.

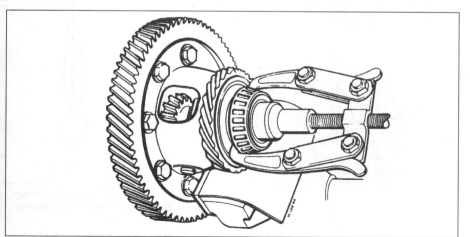

3.29 Differential bearing removal

3.30 Removing the crownwheel retaining bolts

7

3.32 Splitting the speedometer drivegear

3.33 Removing the pinion shaft circlips

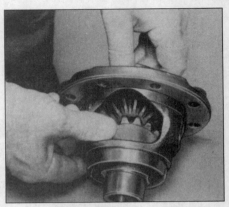

3.35 Differential pinion and side gear removal

32 Split the speedometer drivegear and discard it **(see illustration)**.

33 Extract the circlips from the differential pinion shaft **(see illustration)**.

34 Use a drift to remove the pinion shaft from the differential case.

35 Slide the differential pinions and side gears out of the differential case **(see illustration)**. Remove the spring discs.

36 Overhaul of the selector housing cover, gearbox casing, input shaft, mainshaft and synchronisers are described elsewhere.

37 Liberally lubricate the differential components with the recommended grade of oil.

38 Install the side gears and pinions, the spring discs and the pinion shaft into the differential case.

39 Fit new retaining circlips.

40 If the speedometer drivegear was removed, warm the new gear in hot water at 80°C (176°F) and tap it onto the differential case with a piece of tubing until it snaps into position. Make sure that the lugs on the gear are aligned with the cut-outs in the differential case.

41 Warm the crownwheel to 80°C (176°F) and locate it on the differential case. Use new bolts and tighten them to the specified torque.

42 Fit the tapered roller bearings to the differential case (if removed at dismantling).

43 If not already done, fit the bearing outer tracks to the gearbox casing.

44 Fit new driveshaft seals into the gearbox casing (if not already done) and fill the lips with grease.

45 Lower the differential into the gearbox casing.

46 Fit a new O-ring and oil seal to the bearing adjuster ring **(see illustration)**. Apply grease to the seal lips and to the screw threads **(see illustration)**.

47 Screw the adjuster ring into the gearbox casing, hand tight at this stage.

48 Adjust the bearing in one of the following ways, depending upon whether the original bearings have been refitted or new ones installed.

49 Original bearing: Simply screw in the adjuster ring until the alignment marks made before dismantling are opposite to each other. Should any axial play exist, the ring may be further adjusted to give a turning torque of between 6.1 and 10.3 kgf cm (5.3 and 8.9 lbf in) as described for new bearings in the following paragraph.

50 New bearings: The bearing preload must be adjusted by means of the adjuster ring so

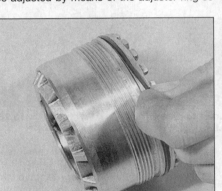

3.46a Fit a new O-ring to the bearing adjuster ring

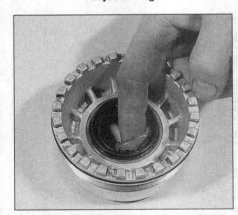

3.46b Fill the space between the oil seal lips with grease

that a torque of 15.3 and 18.3 kgf cm (13.3 to 15.9 lbf in) is required to keep the crownwheel and bearings turning slowly. Unless a special torsion or friction gauge is available push a tapered softwood rod into the splined side gear and then wrap a cord round it and attach it to a spring balance **(see illustration)**. Provided the cord leaves the rod at a point about 25 mm (1.0 in) from the centre point of its cross section, the torque will be fairly

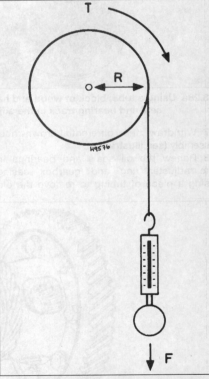

3.50 Calculation of differential turning torque. Do not mix metric and Imperial units

F = Force (kg or lb) read on spring balance
R = Radius (cm or in) of rod
T = F x R (kgf cm or lbf in)

3.52 Refit the differential cover plate using a new gasket

3.56a Locate the short . . .

3.56b . . . and long interlock plungers in the end cover

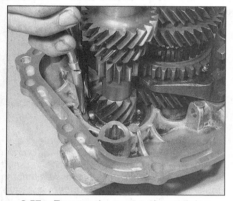

3.57a Engage the gear train retaining circlips in their grooves . . .

3.57b . . . and refit the reverse idler thrustwasher

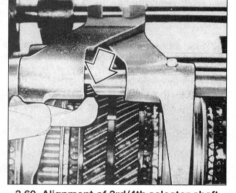

3.60 Alignment of 3rd/4th selector shaft slot with interlock pawl - arrowed

accurately measured on the 'lb' scale. (If using the metric scale a small calculation will be required.) Adjust the ring until the turning torque is within the specified range.

51 Fit the adjuster lock without moving the position of the ring. The ring lock is elongated to make this possible.

52 Use a new gasket and bolt the pressed-steel cover to the gearbox casing **(see illustration)**.

53 Fit the reverse idler shaft to the gearbox end cover, making sure that the locking ball is in position.

54 Pin the 1st/2nd selector fork to its rod, but leave the pin projecting by approximately 2.0 mm (0.08 in).

55 Hold the mainshaft, input shaft and reverse gear trains meshed together, with the 1st/2nd selector fork and rod engaged in the groove of 1st/2nd synchro.

56 Locate the assembly into the end cover. The help of an assistant will facilitate the work. Fit the selector rod interlock plungers **(see illustrations)**.

57 Fit the circlips which retain the mainshaft and input shaft assemblies to the gearbox casing **(see illustration)**. Make sure that they engage positively in their grooves. Fit the thrustwasher to the reverse idler gear **(see illustration)**, also the swarf collecting magnet.

58 Refit the reverse, and 3rd/4th gear selector shafts and forks, and the 5th gear selector driver to the end cover. Secure the forks with the roll pins.

59 Refit the interlock pin bridge piece and secure it in position using new micro-encapsulated socket-headed bolts, tightened to the specified torque.

60 Refit the 5th gear selector interlock pawl to the end cover, noting that the slot in the 3rd/4th selector shaft must align with the pawl **(see illustration)**. Secure the assembly with new socket-headed bolts tightened to the specified torque.

61 Refit the detent plungers and springs and drive in the detent plugs, noting that the long plug is for the 3rd/4th selector shaft **(see illustration)**.

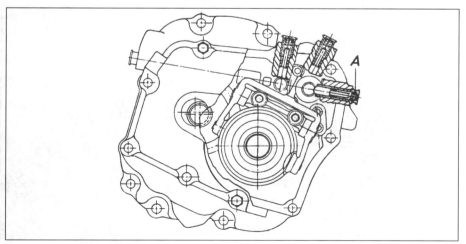

3.61 The long detent plunger (A) is for 3rd/4th selector shaft

7

3.70 Refit the casing to the end cover using a new gasket

4.1 Remove the mainshaft bearing circlip

62 Press the input shaft 5th gear onto the gear train with the longer hub toward the bearing.
63 Refit the retaining circlip.
64 Refit the two thrustwasher halves, retaining ring, needle roller bearing and 5th gear to the mainshaft.
65 Place the baulk ring in position over 5th gear.
66 Heat the 5th gear synchroniser assembly in boiling water and then position it over the mainshaft. Press or drive it into place using a

4.2a Remove the mainshaft bearing . . .

suitable tube, ensuring that the slots in the baulk ring engage with the sliding keys.
67 Refit the retaining circlip.
68 Refit the bearing support and selector fork to the end cover and secure with two new socket-headed bolts tightened to the specified torque.
69 Using a screwdriver, move the sleeve of the appropriate synchro unit to engage 2nd gear.
70 Stick a new gasket, with grease, to the gearbox casing **(see illustration)** and then insert the gear trains with end cover into the casing until the fixing bolts and nuts can be screwed in to the specified torque.
71 Fit the speedometer driven gear and bolt on its retainer plate.
72 Screw in the reversing lamp switch to the specified torque.
73 Set the gearbox in neutral and stick a new selector cover gasket in position.
74 Bolt on the selector cover, tightening the bolts to the specified torque.
75 The gearbox can be filled with oil, provided it is held in the in-vehicle attitude, otherwise wait until it has been refitted to the vehicle.
76 Refit the end cover shield using a new gasket before refilling the gearbox with oil.

4 Examination and renovation

Mainshaft

Note: *An hydraulic press, or suitable heavy-duty puller, may be required to carry out the following procedure. Before pressing the shaft out of a gear, synchro unit, etc, ensure that the lower face of the component is firmly supported. Similarly, if a puller is used, ensure that its claws are securely located on the main body of the component, not solely on the gear teeth. In extreme cases, removal of stubborn components may be aided by gentle heating, bearing in mind that it is not recommended to heat any component above 100°C (212°F).*
1 Extract the retaining circlip from the bearing at the end of the shaft **(see illustration)**.
2 Support the 1st gear and drive the shaft out of the bearing and gear. Note the spacer washer between the bearing and gears **(see illustrations)**.
3 Support 2nd gear and then extract the circlip which secures the 1st/2nd synchro **(see illustration)**.

4.2b . . . and the spacer washer . . .

4.2c . . . followed by 1st gear

4.3 Extract the circlip retaining 1st/2nd synchro unit

4.4 Lift off the baulk ring

4.5 Remove the 1st/2nd synchro unit

4.6 Lift off the next baulk ring

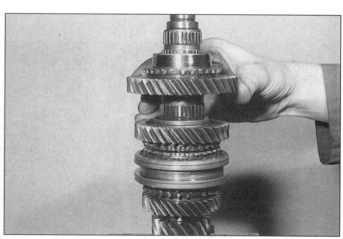

4.7 Remove 2nd gear

4 Take the synchro baulk ring from the shaft **(see illustration)**.
5 Take the 1st/2nd synchro unit from the shaft; if a puller is used, apply pressure behind 2nd gear, and remove 2nd gear, the baulk ring, and the lst/2nd synchro unit as an

assembly. Note the reverse gear teeth on the sleeve **(see illustration)**.
6 Remove the next baulk ring **(see illustration)**.
7 Remove the 2nd gear **(see illustration)**.
8 Now turn your attention to the opposite end

of the mainshaft. Extract the circlip which secures the pinion drivegear to the shaft **(see illustration)**.
9 Remove the pinion drivegear **(see illustration)**.
10 Remove the spacer washer **(see illustration)**.

4.8 At the other end of the mainshaft, extract the pinion retaining circlip

4.9 Remove the pinion drivegear

4.10 Lift off the spacer washer

7

4.11 Remove 4th gear

4.12 Lift off the baulk ring

4.13 Extract the circlip retaining the 3rd/4th synchro unit

4.14 Remove the 3rd/4th synchro unit

4.15 Lift off the next baulk ring followed by 3rd gear

4.21 Use a suitable tube to refit 3rd/4th synchro unit

4.23 Fitting the spacer washer between 4th gear and the pinion drivegear

4.25 Use a suitable tube to refit the 1st/2nd synchro unit, ensuring that the reverse gear teeth are towards 2nd gear

11 Remove 4th gear **(see illustration)**.
12 Remove the baulk ring **(see illustration)**.
13 Extract the circlip which secures the 3rd/4th synchro unit to the mainshaft **(see illustration)**.
14 Remove the 3rd/4th synchro unit **(see illustration)**.
15 Remove the next baulk ring **(see illustration)**.
16 Remove 3rd gear.
17 With the mainshaft completely dismantled, examine the gears for chipped or worn teeth and the shaft for deformation of splines. Renew all circlips.
18 If there has been a history of noisy gear changing or if the synchromesh could be easily beaten during changes, renew the synchro unit complete or overhaul.
19 With all parts clean and oiled, reassemble as follows. Where necessary, tap components onto the shaft using a suitably-sized tubular drift which bears on the component's main body, not solely on the gear teeth.
20 Fit 3rd gear to the shaft's pinion drivegear

end, then place the first baulk ring on the gear's cone.
21 Heating it to 100°C (212°F) if necessary, refit the 3rd/4th synchro unit as noted in paragraph 19 above **(see illustration)**.
22 Fit a new circlip to secure the synchro unit, then refit the remaining baulk ring, followed by 4th gear.
23 Heating them to 100°C (212°F) if necessary, refit the spacer washer and the pinion drivegear **(see illustration)**. Fit a new circlip to secure the pinion drivegear.
24 Fit 2nd gear over the shaft's opposite end, then place the first baulk ring on the gear's cone.
25 Heating it to 100°C (212°F) if necessary and ensuring that the reverse gear teeth are next to 2nd gear, refit the 1st/2nd synchro unit as noted above **(see illustration)**.
26 Fit a new circlip to secure the synchro unit, then refit the remaining baulk ring, followed by 1st gear.
27 Heating it to 100°C (212°F) if necessary, refit the spacer washer, with its grooves

against 1st gear **(see illustration)**. **Note:** Later versions of the F10/4 gearbox had roller bearings in place of the spacer washer **(see illustration)**.
28 Fit a new long-eared circlip, then the bearing; secure the bearing with a new circlip.

Synchro units

29 This gearbox is very similar to the F16 gearbox; refer to Chapter 8, Section 3.

Selector housing cover

30 This gearbox is very similar to the F16 gearbox; refer to Chapter 8, Section 3. Note that only one size of input shaft is available.

Gearbox casing

31 This gearbox is very similar to the F16 gearbox; refer to Chapter 8, Section 3.

Input shaft

32 This gearbox is very similar to the F16 gearbox; refer to Chapter 8, Section 3.

4.27a Refit 1st gear and the spacer washer

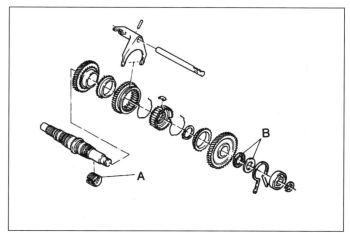

4.27b Additional four-speed gearbox components from April 1986

A Split needle bearing   B Radial needle bearing

7

Notes

Chapter 8
Vauxhall F16 gearbox

Contents

Specifications

General

Type	Four or five forward speeds and one reverse, synchromesh on all forward gears. Integral final drive
Designation	F16/4 (4-speed) and F16/5 (5-speed)

Gear ratios (typical)

Astra/Kadett 1980 to 1984

	F16/4	F16/5	F16/5 sport
1st	3.55 : 1	3.42 : 1	3.42 : 1
2nd	2.16 : 1	1.95 : 1	2.16 : 1
3rd	1.37 : 1	1.28 : 1	1.48 : 1
4th	0.97 : 1	0.89 : 1	1.12 : 1
5th	-	0.71 : 1	0.89 : 1
Reverse	3.33 : 1	3.33 : 1	3.33 : 1
Final drive	3.74 : 1	3.74 : 1	3.94 : 1

Astra/Kadett/Belmont 1984 to 1990

	F16/4	F16/5	F16/5 sport
1st	3.42 : 1	3.42 : 1	3.42 : 1
2nd	1.95 : 1	1.95 : 1	2.16 : 1
3rd	1.28 : 1	1.28 : 1	1.48 : 1
4th	0.89 : 1	0.89 : 1	1.12 : 1
5th	-	0.71 : 1	0.89 : 1
Reverse	3.33 : 1	3.33 : 1	3.33 : 1
Final drive	3.74 : 1	3.94 : 1	3.74 : 1 (2 litre - 3.55 : 1)

Cavalier/Ascona 1981 to 1988

	F16/4	F16/5	F16/5 sport
1st	3.55 : 1	3.42 : 1	3.42 : 1
2nd	2.16 : 1	1.95 : 1	2.16 : 1
3rd	1.37 : 1	1.28 : 1	1.48 : 1
4th	0.97 : 1	0.89 : 1	1.12 : 1
5th	-	0.71 : 1	0.89 : 1
Reverse	3.33 : 1	3.33 : 1	3.33 : 1
Final drive	3.74 : 1	3.74 : 1	3.94 : 1

Cavalier/Vectra 1988 to 1994

	F16/5	F16/5 sport
1st	3.55 : 1	3.55 : 1
2nd	1.95 : 1	2.16 : 1
3rd	1.28 : 1	1.48 : 1
4th	0.89 : 1	1.13 : 1
5th	0.71 : 1	0.89 : 1
Reverse	3.33 : 1	3.33 : 1
Final drive	3.55 : 1	3.55 : 1

8

Lubrication

Lubricant capacity:
  Astra/Kadett 1980 to 1984:
    F16/4 . . . . 2.0 litres (3.5 pints)
    F16/5 . . . . 2.1 litres (3.7 pints)
  Astra/Kadett/Belmont 1984 to 1990:
    F16/4 . . . . 2.0 litres (3.5 pints)
    F16/5 . . . . 2.1 litres (3.7 pints)
  Cavalier/Ascona 1981 to 1988:
    F16/4 . . . . 2.0 litres (3.5 pints)
    F16/5 . . . . 2.1 litres (3.7 pints)
  Cavalier/Vectra 1988 to 1994 . . . . 1.9 litres (3.3 pints)
Lubricant type/specification . . . . See *Recommended lubricants and fluids*

Torque wrench settings

	Nm	lbf ft
Differential bearing flange to casing	25	18
Differential cover to casing	30	22
Differential-to-crownwheel bolts	85	63
End cover to casing	22	16
Gearbox casing to engine	75	55
Input shaft socket screw	15	11
Interlock pin bridge piece screws (5-speed)	5	4
Mounting to body or side-member	75	55
Mounting to casing	65	48
Reversing lamp switch	20	15
Selector cover bolts	15	11
Selector cover screw plug:		
4-speed	50	37
5-speed	30	22
Selector fork/pivot socket screws (5-speed)	22	16
Selector interlock pawl screws (5-speed)	9	7
Selector rod clamp bolt	14	10

1.1a F16/4 gearbox components

1 Bearing outer track
2 Semi-circular thrustwashers
3 Thrust washer retaining ring
4 Needle roller thrustwasher
5 4th gear
6 Baulk ring
7 Synchro sleeve (3rd/4th)
8 Circlip
9 Synchro spring
10 Semi-circular thrustwashers
11 Synchro-hub (3rd/4th)
12 Synchro spring
13 Baulk ring
14 3rd gear
15 2nd gear
16 Baulk ring
17 1st/2nd synchro sleeve with reverse gear
18 Synchro spring
19 Synchro-hub (1st/2nd)
20 Synchro spring
21 Circlip
22 Baulk ring
23 1st gear
24 4th gear needle bearing

25 Mainshaft securing circlip
26 Bearing
27 Circlip
28 3rd/4th selector fork
29 Roll pin
30 Selector rod
31 1st/2nd selector fork
32 Roll pin
33 Selector rod
34 Input shaft roller bearing (in casing)
35 Reversing light switch
36 Gearbox casing
37 Gasket
38 Plug
39 Input shaft
40 Input gear train
41 Input gear train retaining circlip
42 Bearing
43 Thrust washer
44 Circlip
45 Detent plug
46 Detent spring
47 Detent plunger
48 Long interlock plunger

49 Short interlock plunger
50 Detent plunger
51 Detent spring
52 Detent plug
53 End cover
54 Input shaft screw
55 Circlip
56 End cover screw plug
57 Detent plug
58 Detent spring
59 Detent plunger
60 Reverse selector rod
61 Reverse idler shaft
62 Reverse idler gear
63 Thrust washer
64 Reverse selector fork
65 Roll pin
66 Mainshaft with pinion gear
67 3rd gear dual row needle bearing
68 Roller cage
69 Thrust washer retaining ring
70 2nd gear dual row needle bearing
71 1st gear dual row needle bearing
72 Needle bearing

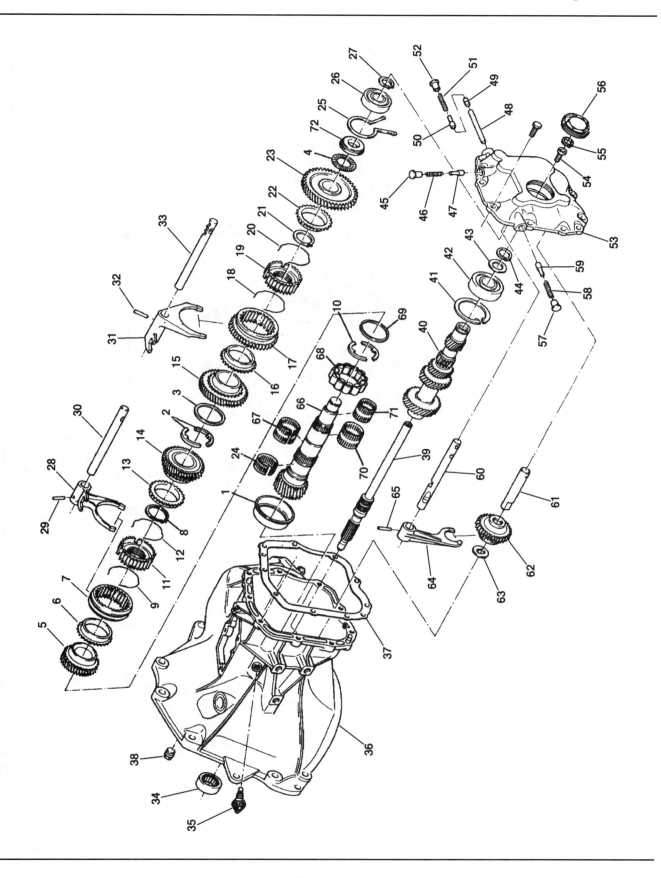

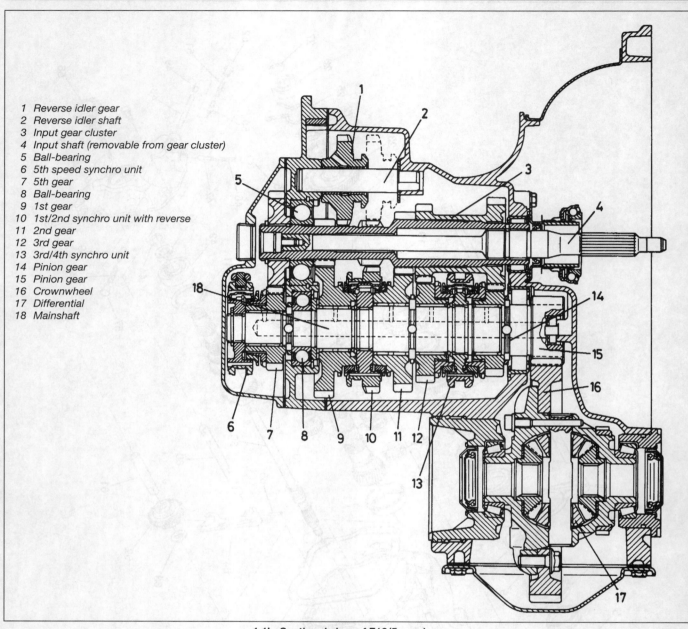

1 Reverse idler gear
2 Reverse idler shaft
3 Input gear cluster
4 Input shaft (removable from gear cluster)
5 Ball-bearing
6 5th speed synchro unit
7 5th gear
8 Ball-bearing
9 1st gear
10 1st/2nd synchro unit with reverse
11 2nd gear
12 3rd gear
13 3rd/4th synchro unit
14 Pinion gear
15 Pinion gear
16 Crownwheel
17 Differential
18 Mainshaft

1.1b Sectional view of F16/5 gearbox

1.1c Typical oil level plug location

1.1d Typical oil filler plug location

1.3 The differential cover plate must be removed to drain the transmission oil

2.2a Undo the retaining bolts . . .

2.2b . . . and remove the selector cover

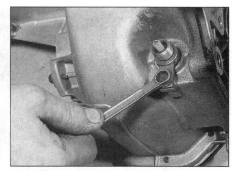

2.3a Unbolt the retaining plate . . .

1 General description

A four- or five-speed manual gearbox may be fitted, depending on engine size and options specified. All types of gearbox have synchromesh on all forward gears **(see illustrations)**.

Drive is transmitted through the gearbox and the integral final drive/differential assembly to the driveshafts. Gear selection is by a floor-mounted lever and a remote control linkage.

Since transmission oil draining and refilling is not specified by Vauxhall as a routine service operation, the transmission is regarded as a sealed unit and therefore has no drain plug. If, for any reason, it is wished to drain the oil, the differential cover plate must be removed **(see illustration)**.

2 Dismantling into assemblies
- F16/4 gearbox

1 With the gearbox removed from the car and on the bench, proceed as follows.
2 Unbolt and remove the selector cover from the gearbox casing **(see illustrations)**.
3 Unbolt the retaining plate and withdraw the speedometer driven gear **(see illustrations)**.

4 Unscrew and remove the reversing lamp switch **(see illustration)**.
5 Using a screwdriver as a lever, engage 2nd gear by moving the selector fork nearest the end cover **(see illustration)**.
6 Unscrew and remove the end cover bolts and nuts.
7 Withdraw the main casing from the end cover and gear trains **(see illustration)**.
8 Prise out the detent plugs from the end cover and extract the springs and detent plungers **(see illustrations)**.
9 Drive out the roll pins which secure the selector forks to the selector rods.
10 Move the synchro sleeve back to the neutral position and then withdraw 3rd/4th and reverse selector forks and their rods from the end cover.

2.3b . . . and withdraw the speedometer driven gear

2.4 Removing the reversing lamp switch

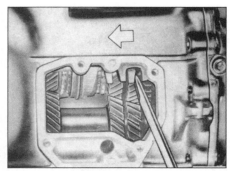

2.5 Using a screwdriver to engage 2nd gear

2.7 Removing the casing from the end cover

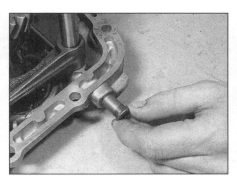

2.8a Removing a detent plug

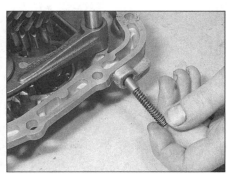

2.8b Detent spring and plunger

8

2.11a Mainshaft bearing retaining circlip

2.11b Removing the swarf-collecting magnet

11 Extract the circlips which retain the mainshaft and input shaft gear trains. Extract the swarf collecting magnet **(see illustrations).**
12 Remove the gear train assemblies, together with the 1st/2nd selector fork and rod.
13 Extract the selector rod interlock pins from the end cover.

14 Remove the reverse idler shaft from the end cover. To do this, grip the shaft in the jaws of a vice fitted with soft metal protectors and using a brass drift, gently tap the cover off the shaft **(see illustration).** Take care not to lose the locking ball **(see illustration).**
15 Unbolt and remove the pressed-

steel cover from the gearbox casing at the base of the differential **(see illustration).**
16 Mark the position of the bearing adjuster ring in relation to the gearbox casing **(see illustration).** Unbolt the ring lock **(see illustration).**
17 Unscrew the bearing adjuster ring. A

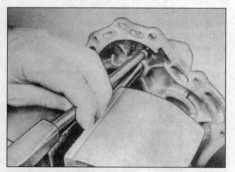

2.14a Tapping the end cover off the reverse idler shaft

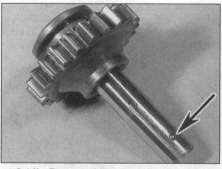

2.14b Reverse idler shaft locking ball (arrowed)

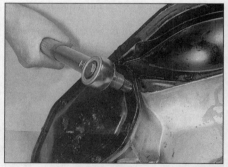

2.15 Removing the differential cover plate

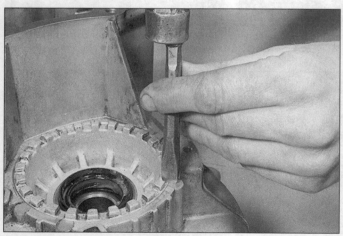

2.16a Marking the position of the differential bearing adjuster ring

2.16b Unbolting the ring lock

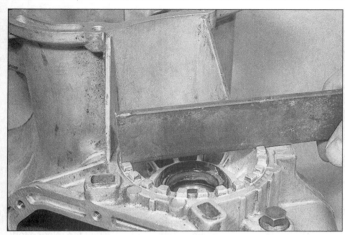

2.17a Unscrewing the adjuster ring with a flat steel bar

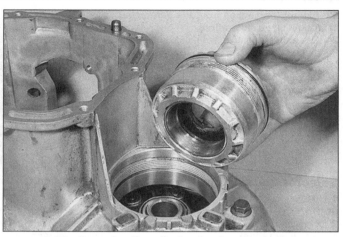

2.17b Removing the adjuster ring from the casing

piece of flat steel bar will act as a suitable wrench **(see illustrations)**.

18 Withdraw the differential/crownwheel assembly **(see illustration)**.

19 Renew the oil seals and bearings in the adjuster ring and gearbox casing using a piece of tubing to remove the old components and to install the new **(see illustrations)**.

20 Using a suitable puller remove the tapered roller bearings from the differential **(see illustration)**.

21 Unbolt the crownwheel and tap it from its register using a brass drift. If the crownwheel or pinion gear are to be renewed, they must always be renewed as a matched pair.

22 Split the speedometer drivegear and discard it **(see illustration)**.

2.18 Removing the differential/crownwheel assembly

2.19a Renewing the oil seal in the adjuster ring . . .

2.19b . . . and in the gearbox casing

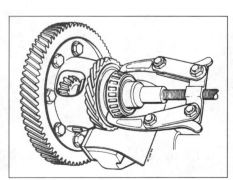

2.20 Differential bearing removal

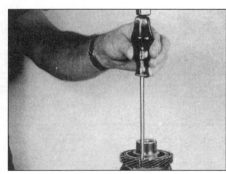

2.22 Splitting the speedometer drivegear

8

23 Extract the circlips from the differential pinion shaft **(see illustration)**.
24 Use a drift to remove the pinion shaft from the differential case.
25 Slide the differential pinions and side gears out of the differential case **(see illustration)**. Remove the spring discs.

2.23 Removing the pinion shaft circlips

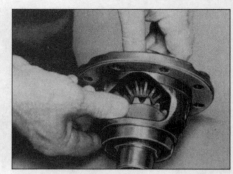

2.25 Differential pinion and side gear removal

3 Examination and renovation
- F16/4 gearbox

Selector housing cover

1 Unscrew and remove the oil filler/breather plug.
2 Remove the circlip from the top of the guide pin **(see illustration)**.
3 Take off the retainer, coil spring and intermediate selector lever **(see illustrations)**.
4 Drive out the retaining pin to release the selector finger from the rod and withdraw both components from the cover.

5 If the universal joint on the selector rod is worn, grind off the rivet to dismantle it and fit new components (if available). A pin and spring clip are available for reassembly.
6 Renew the oil seal in the selector cover.

Gearbox casing

7 Undo the clamp bolt securing the clutch release fork to the release lever pivot shaft. Pull the release lever upwards out of the gearbox casing and withdraw the release fork.
8 Undo the three retaining bolts and remove the release bearing guide tube and input shaft oil seal **(see illustration)**. Recover the O-ring seal.
9 Prise the old seal out of the guide tube and

3.2 Removing the circlip from the guide pin

3.3a Removing the retainer and spring . . .

3.3b . . . Followed by the intermediate selector lever

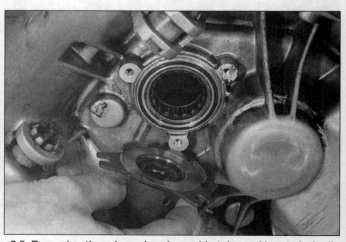

3.8 Removing the release bearing guide tube and input shaft oil seal

3.9 Fitting a new input shaft oil seal

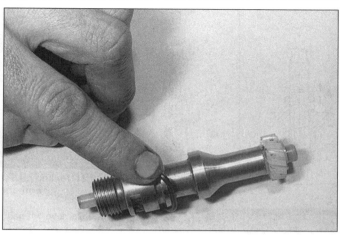

3.11a Speedometer driven gear O-ring . . .

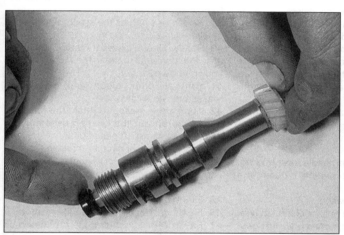

3.11b . . . and small oil seal

3.13 Fit a new O-ring under the release bearing guide tube

tap in a new seal using a tube of suitable diameter **(see illustration).** Fill the space between the lips with general purpose grease.
10 The release lever bushes in the casing can be removed by tapping them out with a suitable drift. Install the new bushes with their

locating tongues engaged in the slots in the casing. Coat the bush inner surfaces with molybdenum disulphide grease.
11 Prise out the speedometer driven gear and its guide. Renew the O-ring and small oil seal before refitting **(see illustrations).**

12 Inspect the roller bearing in the casing and renew if necessary by drifting it out with a tube of suitable diameter. Refit a new bearing in the same way.
13 With a new O-ring in place **(see illustration)**, refit the release bearing guide tube and release lever and fork using the reverse procedure to removal.

Input shaft

14 Support the end of the gear train and tap or press the shaft from it **(see illustration).**
15 Extract the circlip which secures the bearing to the end of the shaft **(see illustration)**. Take off the washer.
16 Using a piece of tubing, drive the gear train out of the bearing.
17 If any of the gears are damaged, the gear train complete will have to be renewed. This will mean that the matching gears on the mainshaft will also have to be renewed.
18 Two sizes of input shaft are available. With the shaft pushed into the gear train by

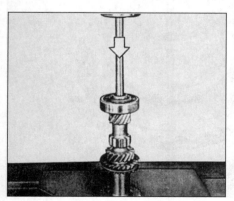

3.14 Pressing the input shaft out of its gear train

3.15 Removing the input shaft bearing retaining circlip

8

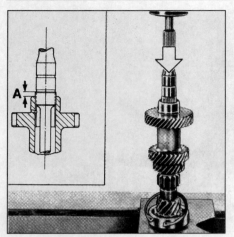

**3.18 Input shaft selection - push shaft into gear train by hand.
For dimension A see text**

hand, measure dimension A **(see illustration)**. If A is greater than 5 mm (0.2 in), renew the gear train. If A is less the zero - ie the shaft is recessed in the gear train - fit a group 2 shaft. If A is between zero and 5 mm (0.2 in), the fit of the shaft in the gear train is satisfactory. Consult a dealer for shaft identification.

19 Reassembly is a reversal of dismantling, but note that the sealed side of the bearing is away from the gear.

20 Remember to locate the gear train securing circlip ready for installation in its gearbox casing groove.

Mainshaft

21 Remove the retaining circlip from the ball-bearing at the end of the shaft. Place the claws of a two-legged puller under the 1st gear and draw the gear and shaft ball-bearing from the mainshaft **(see illustration)**.

22 Extract the circlip, remove the plain thrustwasher and then the needle type thrustwasher.

3.21 Pulling off 1st gear and the bearing from the mainshaft

23 Remove 1st gear baulk ring.

24 Remove the split type needle roller bearing.

25 Extract the circlip.

26 Take off the plain thrustwasher.

27 Place the claws of a puller under 2nd gear and withdraw 1st/2nd synchro unit (with reverse), the baulk ring and 2nd gear all together from the mainshaft. Note that the reverse gear teeth on the synchro sleeve are towards the pinion gear on the end of the shaft.

28 Remove the semi-circular thrustwashers and their retaining ring.

29 Remove 3rd gear.

30 Remove 3rd gear baulk ring.

31 Take off the split type needle roller bearing.

32 Extract the circlip which retains the 3rd/4th synchro unit.

33 Take off the thrustwasher.

34 Place the claws of a puller behind 4th gear and draw off 3rd/4th synchro unit, 4th gear baulk ring and 4th gear all together from the mainshaft.

35 Take off the split type needle roller bearing.

36 Remove the semi-circular thrustwashers with their retaining ring.

3.46 Mainshaft assembled as far as 4th gear baulk ring

37 Remove the roller race from the shaft. The pinion gear cannot be removed.

38 Examine the gears for chipped or worn teeth, and the shaft for deformation of splines. Renew as necessary.

39 Renew or overhaul the synchro units - see below.

49 Renew all circlips as a matter of course, and the bearings unless their condition is known to be perfect.

41 With all parts clean and well oiled, reassemble as follows.

42 Apply thick grease to retain the rollers to their cage and fit the bearing assembly up against the mainshaft pinion gear.

43 Locate the semi-circular thrustwashers so that their keys engage in the holes in the shaft and then fit the retaining ring.

44 Fit the split type needle roller bearing.

45 Fit 4th gear.

46 Fit 4th gear baulk ring **(see illustration)**.

47 Fit 3rd/4th synchro unit, preheated to 100°C (212°F), so that the thin groove in the sleeve is furthest from the shaft pinion **(see illustration)**. Drive the synchro-hub down the shaft using a bearing puller or by applying a length of tubing to the synchro hub.

48 Fit the thrustwasher **(see illustration)**.

3.47 3rd/4th synchro is fitted with thin groove upwards

3.48 Fit the thrustwasher . . .

3.49 . . . and 3rd/4th synchro circlip

3.50 Fitting 3rd gear baulk ring

3.51 3rd gear needle roller bearing

49 Fit the circlip (see illustration).
50 Fit 3rd gear baulk ring (see illustration).
51 Fit the split type needle roller bearing (see illustration).
52 Fit 3rd gear (see illustration).
53 Fit the semi-circular thrustwashers and their retaining ring. Fit the needle roller bearing (see illustrations).
54 Fit 2nd gear (see illustration).
55 Fit 2nd gear baulk ring (see illustration).
56 Fit 1st/2nd synchro, preheated to 100°C (212°F), with reverse gear teeth nearest the pinion gear (see illustration).
57 Fit the plain thrustwasher and circlip (see illustrations).

3.52 Fitting 3rd gear

3.53a Fit the semi-circular thrustwashers . . .

3.53b . . . And their retaining ring

3.53c 2nd gear needle roller bearing

3.54 Fitting 2nd gear

3.55 2nd gear baulk ring

3.56 Fitting 1st/2nd synchro unit - note orientation of reverse gear teeth

3.57a Fit the plain thrustwasher . . .

8

3.57b . . . and the 1st/2nd synchro circlip

3.58a Fit 1st gear baulk ring . . .

3.58b . . . and 1st gear

3.59 Needle roller type thrustwasher

3.60a Fit the plain thrustwasher, step upwards . . .

58 Fit the split needle bearing, 1st gear baulk ring and 1st gear (**see illustrations**).
59 Fit the needle roller thrustwasher (**see illustration**).
60 Preheat the plain thrustwasher to 100°C (212°F) and fit it, step upwards. Place the long-eared circlip on the shaft (**see illustrations**).
61 Fit the ball-bearing to the mainshaft so that the sealed side is visible when fitted, and secure with the circlip (**see illustration**).
62 Locate the long-eared circlip in the thrustwasher step, compress it and fit a retaining clip (**see illustration 5.22**).

Synchro units

63 Components of 1st/2nd and 3rd/4th synchro units are interchangeable.
64 It is not good practice, however, to mix parts which have been in use for a high mileage and which have run-in together.
65 If either the hub or sleeve show signs of wear in their teeth, the individual part may be renewed, but general wear is best rectified by complete renewal of the unit.
66 To dismantle, push the sleeve off the hub, taking care not to allow the sliding keys to fly out.
67 Extract the circular springs and keys.
68 Reassembly is a reversal of dismantling. Make sure that the hooked ends of the springs engage in the same sliding key but run in opposite directions in relation to each other (**see illustrations**).

3.60b . . . And upon it place the long-eared circlip

3.61 Fitting the mainshaft ball-bearing

3.68a Fitting the synchro sleeve to the hub

3.68b Fitting a sliding key in its groove

3.68c Fitting a synchro unit spring

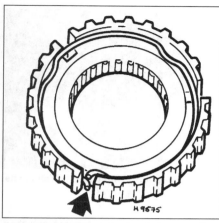

3.68d Synchro spring ends (arrowed) (Sec 15)

69 To check the baulk rings for wear, twist them onto the gear cones. The ring should 'stick' to the cone and show a definite clearance between the ring and the gear shoulder. If these conditions are not met, renew the baulk rings.

4 Reassembly - F16/4 gearbox

1 Liberally lubricate the differential components with the recommended grade of oil.
2 Install the side gears and pinions, the spring discs and the pinion shaft into the differential case.
3 Fit new retaining circlips.
4 If the speedometer drivegear was removed, warm the new gear in hot water at 80°C (176°F) and tap it onto the differential case with a piece of tubing until it snaps into position. Make sure that the lugs on the gear are aligned with the cut-outs in the differential case.
5 Warm the crownwheel to 80°C (176°F) and locate it on the differential case. Use new bolts and tighten them to the specified torque.
6 Fit the tapered roller bearings to the differential case (if removed at dismantling).
7 If not already done, fit the bearing outer tracks to the gearbox casing.
8 Fit new driveshaft seals into the gearbox casing (if not already done) and fill the lips with grease.
9 Lower the differential into the gearbox casing.
10 Fit a new O-ring and oil seal to the bearing adjuster ring (see illustration). Apply grease to the seal lips and to the screw threads (see illustration).
11 Screw the adjuster ring into the gearbox casing, hand tight at this stage.
12 Adjust the bearing in one of the following ways, depending upon whether the original

4.10a Fitting a new O-ring to the bearing adjuster ring

bearings have been refitted or new ones installed.
13 Original bearing: Simply screw in the adjuster ring until the alignment marks made before dismantling are opposite to each other. Should any axial play exist, the ring may be further adjusted to give a turning torque of between 6.1 and 10.3 kgf cm (5.3 and 8.9 lbf in) as described for new bearings in the following paragraph.

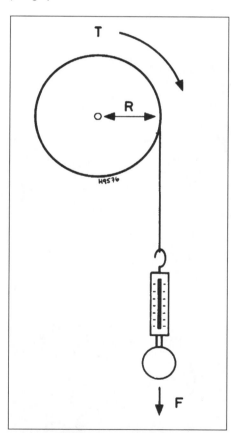

4.14 Calculation of differential turning torque. Do not mix metric and Imperial units

F = Force (kg or lb) read on spring balance
R = Radius (cm or in) of rod
T = F x R (kgf cm or lbf in)

4.10b Fill the space between the oil seal lips with grease

14 New bearings: The bearing preload must be adjusted by means of the adjuster ring so that a torque of 15.3 to 18.3 kgf cm (13.3 to 15.9 lbf in) is required to keep the crownwheel and bearings turning at approximately 1 revolution per second. Unless a special torsion or friction gauge is available, push a softwood rod of suitable diameter into the splined side gear, wrap a cord around it and attach the end of the cord to a spring balance. Pull on the spring balance until the crownwheel is turning at the set speed and note the force required (kg or lb) to achieve this. Multiply the force by the radius of the rod (cm or in) to find the turning torque. Adjust the ring until the turning torque is within the specified range (see illustration).
15 Refit and secure the adjuster lock without moving the position of the adjuster ring. The ring lock fixing hole is elongated to allow this.
16 Refit the differential cover plate, using a new gasket, and tighten the bolts to the specified torque (see illustration).
17 Fit the reverse idler shaft to the gearbox end cover, making sure that the locking ball is in position.
18 Pin the 1st/2nd selector fork to its rod, but leave the pin projecting by approximately 2.0 mm (0.08 in)
19 Hold the mainshaft, input shaft and reverse gear trains meshed together, with the 1st/2nd selector fork and rod engaged in the groove of 1st/2nd synchro.
20 Locate the assembly into the end cover. The help of an assistant will facilitate the work.

4.16 Refitting the differential cover plate, using a new gasket

8

4.20a Locating the short interlock plunger . . .

4.20b . . . and the long interlock plunger

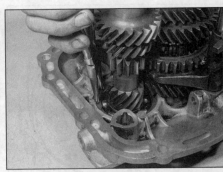

4.21a Engaging the input shaft circlip in its groove

Fit the selector rod interlock plungers **(see illustrations)**.

21 Fit the circlips which retain the mainshaft and input shaft assemblies to the gearbox casing **(see illustration)**. Make sure that they engage positively in their grooves. Fit the thrustwasher to the reverse idler gear **(see illustration)**, also the swarf collecting magnet.

22 Check that the sleeve on 1st/2nd synchro is in neutral, then fit the 3rd/4th and reverse selector forks and rods **(see illustrations)**.

23 Pin the forks to the rods **(see illustration)**. Support the rods when driving in the pins so as not to overload the rods or their guides.

24 Refit the detent plungers and springs. If the sealing plugs are not a really tight fit, oversize ones should be obtained and driven in.

25 Using a screwdriver, move the sleeve of the appropriate synchro unit to engage 2nd gear.

26 Stick a new gasket, with grease, to the gearbox casing **(see illustration)** and then insert the gear trains with end cover into the casing until the fixing bolts and nuts can be screwed in to the specified torque.

27 Fit the speedometer driven gear and bolt on its retainer plate.

28 Screw in the reversing lamp switch to the specified torque.

29 Set the gearbox in neutral and stick a new selector cover gasket in position with a smear of grease.

4.21b Reverse idler gear thrustwasher

4.22a Fitting 3rd/4th selector fork and rod . . .

4.22b . . . and reverse selector fork and rod

4.23 Pinning a fork to its rod

4.26 Fitting a new gasket to the casing

4.31a Removing the oil level plug

4.31b Removing the gearbox breather/filler plug

4.31c Topping-up the gearbox oil

30 Bolt on the selector cover, tightening the bolts to the specified torque.
31 The gearbox can be filled with oil now, provided it is held in the in-vehicle attitude, otherwise wait until it has been refitted to the vehicle **(see illustrations)**.

5 Dismantling into assemblies
- F16/5 gearbox

1 Unbolt the cover plate from the final drive housing and allow the lubricant to drain.
2 Unbolt and remove the cover plate from the flywheel housing.
3 Unbolt and remove the selector housing and peel off the flange gasket.
4 Unbolt and remove the end cover with gasket.
5 Extract the circlip from the end of the input shaft now exposed. This circlip is located deep in the shaft recess and a pair of long-nosed pliers will be needed to extract it.
6 Unscrew and remove the socket-headed screw from the shaft recess. This will require the use of a special key or socket bit which are available from motor accessory shops.

7 Unbolt and remove the gearbox main casing from the intermediate plate.
8 Using an Allen key, unbolt the 5th gear selector fork. It will facilitate removal of the socket-headed screws if 5th gear synchro unit is first moved by hand to its engaged position.
9 Extract the circlip from the end of the mainshaft and then, using a two-legged puller, draw 5th gear and 5th gear synchro unit from the mainshaft. Locate the puller claws under 5th gear.
10 Extract the circlip from the end of the

5.10a Extracting the circlip from the input shaft

5.10b Levering off 5th gear

input shaft and withdraw 5th gear from the shaft. Two tyre levers placed under the gear will remove it quite easily **(see illustrations)**.
11 Using an Allen key, unscrew the socket-headed screws which hold the 5th gear selector interlock pawl to the intermediate plate.
12 Using a forked lever or slide hammer with suitable attachment, withdraw the detent plugs from the edge of the intermediate plate **(see illustrations)**. Be prepared to catch the coil springs which will be ejected. Pull out the detent plungers.

5.12a Levering out a detent plug

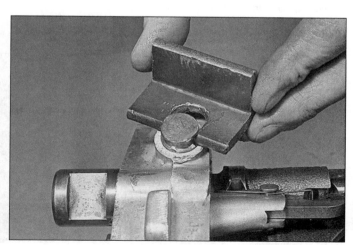

5.12b Detent plug extraction tool suitable for attachment to a slide hammer

8

5.22 Circlip retaining clip

5.23 Expanding the input shaft circlip

13 If you have damaged the detent caps during removal, they should be renewed.

14 Move 5th gear selector rod to its engaged position.

15 Push 2nd gear selector fork to engage the gear.

16 Again using the Allen key, unscrew the socket-headed screws and remove the interlock pin bridge piece.

17 Return all gears to neutral.

18 Drive out the securing roll pin and remove the selector shaft and fork for 3rd/4th gears. Remove reverse selector in a similar way.

19 Withdraw the interlock rod from the intermediate plate.

20 Pull the 5th gear selector driver from the intermediate plate.

21 Drive out the roll pin and remove the 1st/2nd selector rod and fork.

22 Squeeze together the ends of the large circlip which hold the mainshaft bearing into the intermediate plate. A piece of thin rod should be made up to form a retaining clip to keep the circlip contracted **(see illustration)**.

23 Now expand the legs of the circlip which holds the input shaft bearing in the intermediate plate **(see illustration)**.

24 With the help of an assistant, withdraw the gear trains complete with reverse idler gear. The shafts and bearings may require a little gentle tapping with a plastic-faced hammer to eject them from the intermediate plate. Note the thrustwasher on the reverse idler.

25 To remove the differential components, refer to Section 2, paragraph 15 onwards. Note however that the differential pinion shaft is held in the carrier by a screw instead of by circlips.

6 Examination and renovation - F16/5 gearbox

Selector housing cover

1 Refer to Section 3.

Gearbox casing

2 Refer to Section 3.

Input shaft

3 Refer to Section 3.

Mainshaft

4 Refer to Section 3, noting that the ball-bearing is not secured in position with a circlip on 5-speed models.

7 Reassembly - F16/5 gearbox

1 Expand the input shaft circlip in the intermediate plate.

2 With the help of an assistant, mesh the input and output shaft gear train together with the reverse idler gear. The reverse idler selector fork groove must be nearer the pinion gear. Offer the gear trains to the intermediate plate **(see illustration)**.

3 Release the input shaft bearing circlip and remove the mainshaft circlip retaining clip.

4 Refit 1st/2nd selector rod and fork. Secure with a new roll pin, supporting the rod as the pin is driven in. Leave about 2 mm (0.08 in) of the pin protruding **(see illustrations)**.

5 Fit reverse selector rod and fork and drive in a new roll pin **(see illustration)**.

7.2 Offering the gear train to the intermediate plate

7.4a Fitting 1st/2nd selector rod and fork

7.4b Selector fork roll pin

7.5 Remove selector rod and fork

7.7 Passing the selector rod through 3rd/4th fork and 5th driver

7.9 Interlock rod in intermediate plate

7.10a Fitting the interlock pin bridge piece

6 Fit 5th gear selector driver into the intermediate plate.

7 Locate 5th gear selector driver and 3rd/4th selector fork and insert the selector rod through them **(see illustration)**.

8 Fix 3rd/4th selector fork to its rod with a new roll pin.

9 Insert the interlock rod into the hole in the intermediate plate **(see illustration)**.

10 Fit the interlock pin bridge piece. The screws will only be able to be screwed in if 2nd gear and then 5th gear driver are moved to the engaged position **(see illustrations)**. Use new screws and thread locking

compound, and tighten them to the specified torque.

11 Engage the 5th gear interlock pawl in the cut-out of the driver. Using new screws, coated with thread locking compound, secure the pawl to the plate **(see illustrations)**. Tighten the screws to the specified torque.

7.10b Bridge piece fixing screws (arrowed)

7.11a Fitting 5th gear interlock pawl

7.11b Tightening a pawl securing screw

8

7.12 Inserting detent components into the intermediate plate

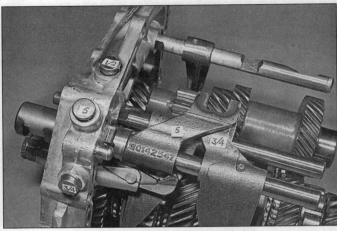

7.13a Detent plug identification

7.13b Reverse detent plug

7.14 Reverse gear thrustwasher

12 Insert the detent plungers and their coil springs in their holes in the intermediate plate **(see illustration)**.

13 Tap in the plugs, noting that the one for 3rd/4th selector is longer than the rest **(see illustrations)**.

14 Locate the thrustwasher (which has the centre hole with flat sides) on the reverse idler shaft. Retain it with thick grease **(see illustration)**.

15 Fit the magnet (clean) into its slot in the intermediate plate **(see illustration)**.

16 Place a new gasket on the gearbox casing flange and lower the gear trains with intermediate plate into the casing **(see illustration)**.

17 Mesh the pinion and crownwheel teeth as the gear trains are lowered.

18 Screw in the securing bolts.

19 If the input shaft was removed, now is the time to refit it into the input shaft gear cluster **(see illustration)**.

20 Fit the 5th gear to the end of the input shaft. Secure it with the circlip **(see illustration)**.

7.15 Fitting the swarf-collecting magnet

7.16 Lowering the gear train into the casing

7.19 Fitting the input shaft

7.20 Fitting 5th gear to the input shaft

7.21a Fit the last two semi-circular thrustwashers . . .

7.21b . . . and their retaining ring

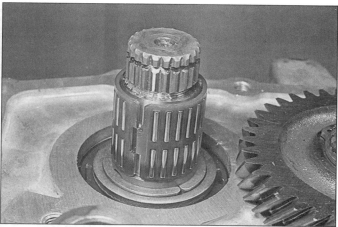

7.22 5th gear mainshaft needle roller bearing

21 To the end of the mainshaft fit the semi-circular thrustwashers and retaining ring **(see illustrations)**.
22 Fit the split type needle roller bearing to the mainshaft **(see illustration)**.
23 Fit 5th gear to the mainshaft **(see illustration)**.

24 Fit 5th gear baulk ring **(see illustration)**.
25 Fit 5th gear synchro unit so that the side where the movable keys are visible is towards 5th gear **(see illustration)**.
26 Fit the retaining circlip **(see illustration)**.
27 Move 5th gear to its engaged position and

fit the selector fork/pivot assembly. Fit new socket-headed screws, using thread locking compound, and tighten them to the specified torque **(see illustration)**.
28 If the gearbox is to be refitted to the engine in the car, the input shaft screw, circlip and end cover plug should not be fitted yet,

7.23 Fitting 5th gear to the mainshaft

7.24 Fitting 5th gear baulk ring

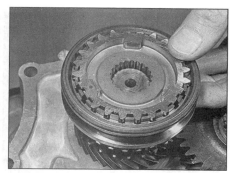

7.25 Fitting 5th gear synchro unit

8

7.26 Fitting the mainshaft circlip

7.27 Tightening a 5th gear selector fork pivot screw

7.29a Input shaft socket-headed screw (arrowed)

7.29b Fitting the circlip to the input shaft recess

as the input shaft must be withdrawn during refitting. If engine and gearbox are both removed, proceed as follows.

29 Fit the screw and the circlip to the end of the input shaft (see illustrations).

30 Using a new gasket bolt on the end cover (see illustration).

31 Screw the threaded plug (if removed) into the end cover (see illustration).

32 Using a new gasket, locate the selector cover so that the selector fingers engage in the dogs (gears in neutral). Insert and tighten the fixing bolts (see illustration).

33 Bolt on the final drive cover plate.

34 Bolt on the flywheel housing cover plate.

35 Check that the selection of all gears is smooth and positive.

36 Fill the gearbox with lubricant after it has been refitted to the vehicle (see illustrations 4.31a, 4.32b and 4.31c).

7.30 Fitting the end cover

7.31 Screw in the end plug

7.32 Fitting the selector cover

Chapter 9
VW 084 & 020 gearboxes

Contents

Specifications

General

Type . . . .   Four or five-speed (all synchromesh) and reverse. Drive to the front
wheels by double CV jointed driveshafts

Designation . . . .   084 (4-speed) and 020 (4-speed or 5-speed)

Lubrication

Capacity:
  084 gearbox:
    All models up to 1992 . . . .   2.2 litres (3.9 pints)
    All models from 1992 . . . .   3.1 litres (5.6 pints)
  020 gearbox:
    4-speed . . . .   1.5 litres (2.6 pints)
    5-speed . . . .   2.0 litres (3.5 pints)
Lubricant type/specification . . . .   See *Recommended lubricants and fluids*

9

Ratios (typical)

Maestro

	4-speed	3+E	5-speed	MG 1600
1st	3.45 : 1	3.45 : 1	3.45 : 1	3.45 : 1
2nd	1.94 : 1	1.75 : 1	1.94 : 1	2.12 : 1
3rd	1.29 : 1	1.06 : 1	1.29 : 1	1.44 : 1
4th	0.91 : 1	0.70 : 1	0.91 : 1	1.13 : 1
5th	-	-	0.71 : 1	0.91 : 1
Reverse	3.17 : 1	3.17 : 1	3.17 : 1	3.17 : 1
Final drive	4.17 : 1	4.17 : 1	3.89 : 1	3.65 : 1

Montego

	4-speed	5-speed
1st	3.45 : 1	3.45 : 1
2nd	1.94 : 1	1.94 : 1
3rd	1.29 : 1	1.29 : 1
4th	0.91 : 1	0.91 : 1
5th	-	0.71 : 1
Reverse	3.17 : 1	3.17 : 1
Final drive	4.25 : 1	3.94 : 1

Golf and Jetta 1974 to 1984

1st	3.45 : 1
2nd	1.94 : 1
3rd	1.29 : 1
4th	0.97 : 1
5th	0.71 : 1
Reverse	3.17 : 1
Final drive	3.89 : 1

Golf and Jetta 1984 to 1992

	084	020 (4-speed)	020 (5-speed)
1st	3.45 : 1	3.45 : 1	3.45 : 1
2nd	1.95 : 1	1.94 : 1	2.11 : 1
3rd	1.25 : 1	1.28 : 1	1.44 : 1
4th	0.89 : 1	0.90 : 1	1.12 : 1
5th	-	-	0.89 : 1
Reverse	3.38 : 1	3.16 : 1	3.16 : 1
Final drive	4.06 : 1	3.66 : 1	3.66 : 1

Golf and Vento from 1992

1st	3.45 : 1
2nd	1.84 : 1
3rd	1.13 : 1
4th	0.81 : 1
Reverse	3.38 : 1
Final drive	4.06 : 1

Polo 1982 to 1990

	1.1	1.3
1st	3.45 : 1	3.45 : 1
2nd	1.95 : 1	1.77 : 1
3rd	1.25 : 1	1.04 : 1
4th	0.89 : 1	0.80 : 1
Reverse	3.38 : 1	3.38 : 1
Final drive	4.27 : 1	4.06 : 1

Scirocco 1974 to 1982

1st	3.45 : 1
2nd	1.94 : 1
3rd	1.29 : 1
4th	0.97 : 1
5th	0.71 : 1
Reverse	3.17 : 1
Final drive	3.89 : 1

Scirocco 1982 to 1990

	4-speed & 4+E	5-speed
1st	3.45 : 1	3.45 : 1
2nd	1.94 : 1	2.12 : 1
3rd	1.29 : 1	1.44 : 1
4th	0.91 : 1	1.13 : 1
5th	0.71 : 1	0.91 : 1
Reverse	3.17 : 1	3.17 : 1
Final drive	3.89 : 1	3.67 : 1

Wear limits

084 gearbox

Synchro ring gap clearance	0.5 mm (0.020 in)
Input and output shaft maximum endfloat	0.5 mm (0.020 in)

020 gearbox

Synchro ring gap clearance	0.5 mm (0.020 in)
Output shaft preload	0.2 mm (0.008 in)
Output shaft preload shims	0.65 mm (0.026 in)
	0.70 mm (0.028 in)
	0.75 mm (0.030 in)
	0.80 mm (0.032 in)
	0.85 mm (0.033 in)
	0.90 mm (0.035 in)
	0.95 mm (0.037 in)
	1.00 mm (0.039 in)
	1.05 mm (0.041 in)
	1.10 mm (0.043 in)
	1.15 mm (0.045 in)
	1.20 mm (0.047 in)
	1.25 mm (0.049 in)
	1.30 mm (0.051 in)
	1.35 mm (0.053 in)
	1.40 mm (0.055 in)

Output shaft turning torque:

New bearings	50 to 150 Ncm
Used bearings	At least 30 Ncm

3rd gear axial play circlips available:

	Thickness
Brown	2.5 mm (0.099 in)
Black	2.6 mm (0.102 in)
Bright	2.7 mm (0.106 in)
Copper	2.8 mm (0.110 in)
Brass	2.9 mm (0.114 in)
Blue	3.0 mm (0.118 in)

Torque wrench settings

084 gearbox

	Nm	lbf ft
Bracket to engine	45	33
Clutch guide sleeve to gearbox	15	11
Clutch housing-to-gearbox bolts	25	18
Drive flange bolt	25	18
Driveshaft to gearbox	45	33
Gear lever stop plate nuts	10	7
Gearbox housing cover bolts	25	18
Gearbox mountings	60	44
Gearbox to engine:		
M12	75	55
M10	45	33
Gearshift housing bolts	15	11
Oil drain plug	25	18
Oil filler plug	25	18
Relay lever bolt	35	26
Selector finger (to inner shift lever)	25	18
Shift rod clip nut	20	15
Shift rod mounting coupling screw (new)	20	15

020 4-speed gearbox

	Nm	lbf ft
Driveshafts to flange	45	33
Gearbox to clutch housing	25	18
Gearbox to engine (M12)	75	55
Input shaft bearing clamp screw nut	15	11
Left console to gearbox	35	26
Left console to subframe	60	44
Output shaft bearing plate bolts	40	30
Peg bolt for selector shaft	20	15
Rear right console to engine	25	18

Torque wrench settings

	Nm	lbf ft
020 4-speed gearbox (continued)		
Selector shaft end cap	50	37
Starter motor to gearbox/engine	60	44
Reverse shaft set screw:		
Hex head type	20	15
Torx head type	30	22
020 5-speed gearbox		
Bearing plate bolts	40	30
First gear synchroniser screw	150	111
Gear lever retaining plate nuts	10	7
Gearbox housing cover bolts	25	18
Gearbox-to-clutch housing bolts	25	18
Oil filler plug	25	18
Reverse shaft securing bolt	20	15
Selector shaft end cap	50	37
Selector shaft lever nut	15	11
Selector shaft securing bolt	20	15

1 General description

This gearbox is type 084 or 020, according to model. It incorporates four or five forward speeds and one reverse speed, with synchromesh engagement on all forward gears. The clutch withdrawal mechanism comprises a release arm and lever located at the outer end of the gearbox and a pushrod located in the input shaft.

Gearshift is by means of a floor-mounted lever connected by a remote control housing and shift rod to the gearbox selector shaft and relay lever.

The differential (final drive) unit is integral with the main gearbox and is located between the main casing and the bearing housing.

Drain and filler/level plugs are screwed into the main gearbox casing (see illustrations).

1.4a Gearbox filler/level plug location (arrowed) - 084 gearbox

1.4b Gearbox drain plug - 084 gearbox

1.4c Using a key to remove the gearbox filler/level plug - 020 gearbox

1.4d Gearbox drain plug - 020 gearbox

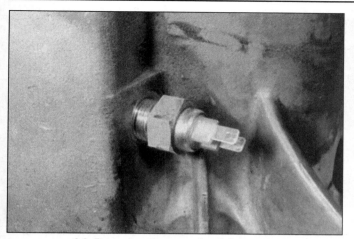

2.3 Removing the reversing light switch

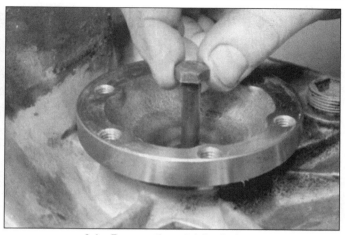

2.4a Remove the retaining bolt . . .

2 Dismantling into assemblies - 084 gearbox

1 Unscrew the drain and filler plug using a hexagon key and drain the remaining oil into a suitable container. Refit and tighten the plugs.
2 Remove the clutch release bearing and shaft.
3 Unscrew and remove the reversing light switch (see illustration).
4 Temporarily screw two bolts into each drive flange, and, using a bar to hold the flange stationary, unscrew each retaining bolt. Identify each flange left and right, then pull them from the differential (see illustrations). Extract the coil spring thrustwasher and taper

ring from the drive flange location in the differential housing and keep them with their respective drive flanges (see illustration).
5 The drive flange oil seals may be levered out and renewed, if necessary, either at this stage or later when servicing the differential unit. This job can also be done with the gearbox in situ once the drive flanges are removed, but note that the right and left-hand seals are dimensionally different.
6 Unscrew and remove the bolts securing the clutch housing to the gearbox housing. Make sure that all the bolts are removed from inside the clutch housing.
7 Support the gearbox with the clutch housing uppermost and, using a wooden mallet, tap the clutch housing from the gearbox housing and remove it (see

2.4b . . . and withdraw the drive flange

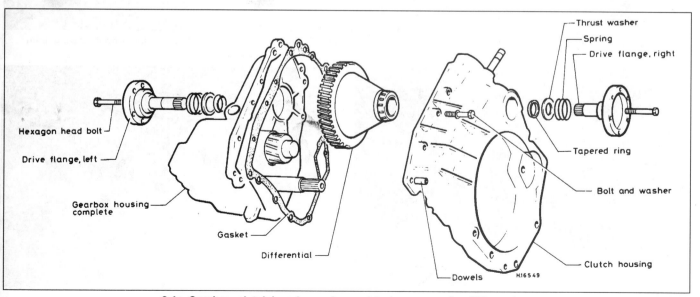

2.4c Gearbox, clutch housing and associated components - 084 gearbox

2.7 Clutch housing removal

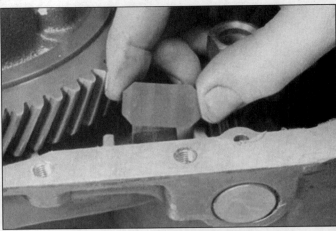

2.8 Remove the magnetic swarf collector

illustration). If it is difficult to free the housing from the dowels, tap out the dowels first using a soft metal drift.

8 Remove the gasket, if applicable, and take the magnetic swarf collector from the slot in the bottom of the gearbox housing (see illustration).

9 Lift the differential from the gearbox housing (see illustration).

10 Support the gearbox housing with the end cover uppermost.

11 Unscrew and remove the bolts and remove the bearing end cover (see illustration). Identify the input and output bearing shims then remove them (see illustration). Do not interchange the shims otherwise the shaft endfloats will need adjusting on reassembly. Remove the gasket.

12 Using circlip pliers, extract the circlip from the end of the input shaft and remove the small shim.

13 Check that the selector rods are in the neutral position then, using an Allen key, unscrew the gear detent plugs with their washers, and extract the sleeves, springs and plungers (see illustrations).

14 Unscrew the reverse relay cross-head bolt

2.9 Withdraw the differential unit

2.11a Removing the bearing end cover . . .

2.11b . . . and output bearing shim

2.13a Unscrew the gear detent plugs

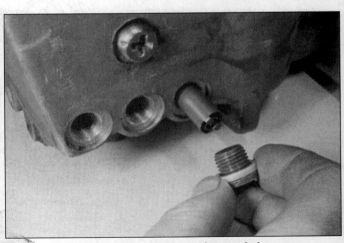

2.13b Extract the sleeves, springs and plungers

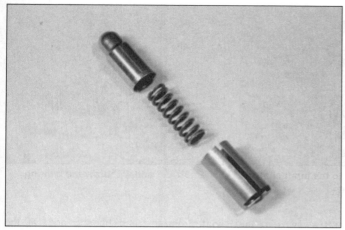

2.13c Detent sleeve, spring and plunger

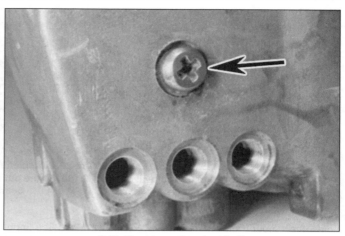

2.14 Reverse relay pivot bolt

next to the detent holes **(see illustration)**. The bolt is very tight and an impact driver will be required or, if not available, a cold chisel.

15 Invert the gearbox housing and remove the reverse selector rod and relay lever **(see illustration)**. The relay lever has slotted ends to engage the pin on the selector rod and the reverse gear.

16 The next stage is the removal of the input and output shafts, and the use of a bearing puller is described in the following paragraphs

(see illustrations). However, it is possible, with some difficulty, to remove the shafts simultaneously by tapping them through the end bearings without the use of a puller. This method is not recommended since damage to

the housing may occur and also the synchromesh units can easily come apart causing further damage.

17 Make up a support plate and bolt it to the housing, together with packing washers, to

2.15 Remove the reverse selector rod

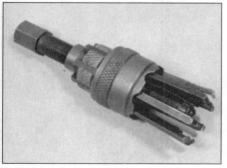

2.16a Suitable puller for removing the input shaft bearing

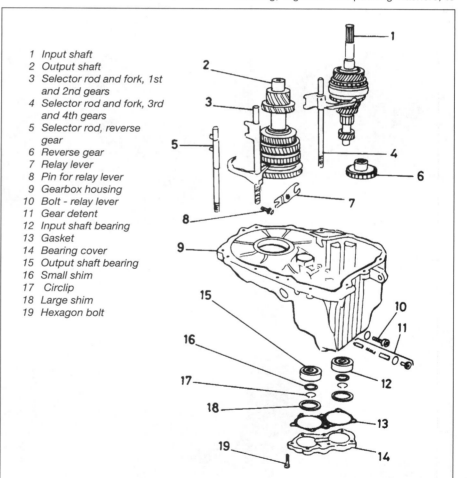

1 Input shaft
2 Output shaft
3 Selector rod and fork, 1st and 2nd gears
4 Selector rod and fork, 3rd and 4th gears
5 Selector rod, reverse gear
6 Reverse gear
7 Relay lever
8 Pin for relay lever
9 Gearbox housing
10 Bolt - relay lever
11 Gear detent
12 Input shaft bearing
13 Gasket
14 Bearing cover
15 Output shaft bearing
16 Small shim
17 Circlip
18 Large shim
19 Hexagon bolt

2.16b Input and output shafts and selector rod locations in the gearbox housing - 084 gearbox

9

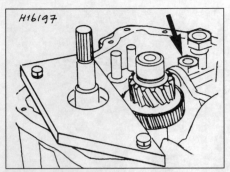

2.17 Support plate location for removal of the input shaft bearing. Jam gearshift shaft with M16 hexagonal nut (arrowed)

2.18a Fit the puller to the input shaft bearing . . .

2.18b . . . and withdraw the bearing

hold the input shaft stationary **(see illustration)**. Locate an M16 hexagonal nut (arrowed) between the gearshift shaft and housing to jam the shaft.

18 Support the gearbox with the end bearings uppermost, then using a puller remove the input shaft bearing from the housing **(see illustrations)**.

19 Remove the support plate.

20 Using a large nut, or piece of wire, retain the selector relay shaft against the spring tension.

21 Move the input shaft away from the output shaft then lift it from the gearbox housing, together with the 3rd/4th selector rod and fork **(see illustration)**. Lift the reverse gear slightly to allow the input shaft 1st gear to pass.

22 Remove the M16 nut or piece of wire used to jam the selector relay shaft.

23 Using circlip pliers, extract the circlip from the end of the output shaft and remove the small shim **(see illustrations)**.

24 Using the puller, press the output

shaft from the end bearing and, at the same time, remove the 1st/2nd selector rod and fork, and the reverse gear **(see illustrations)**. Make sure that the selector rod and reverse gear do not become jammed.

25 Extract the interlock plungers from the gearbox housing.

26 Using a soft metal drift, drive the output shaft bearing from the gearbox housing. Keep both input and output shaft bearings identified.

2.21 Input shaft and 3rd/4th selector rod removal

2.23a Extract the circlip from the output shaft . . .

2.23b . . . and remove the small shim

2.24a Pressing the output shaft from the bearing with a puller

2.24b Removing the output shaft and 1st/2nd selector rod

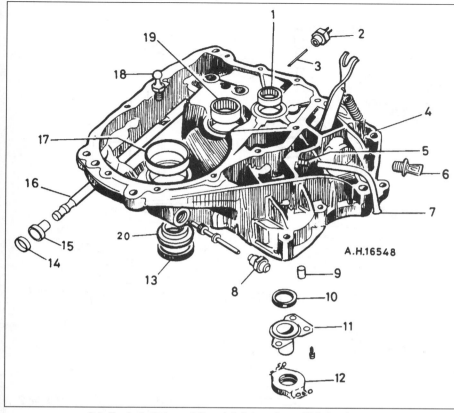

3.2a Inner shift lever oil seal location

3.2b Inner shift lever location in the clutch housing

3.1 Exploded view of the clutch housing - 084 gearbox

1 Needle bearing	8 Input shaft pinion	15 Bush
2 Switch	9 Starter bush	16 Inner shift lever
3 Extension pin	10 Input shaft seal	17 Outer race taper roller
4 Clutch housing	11 Guide sleeve	bearing
5 Breather connection	12 Release bearing	18 Selector finger
6 Plug	13 Driveshaft oil seal	19 Needle bearing
7 Breather pipe	14 Seal	20 Seal sleeve

3 Clutch housing (084 gearbox) - dismantling and reassembly

1 Clean the housing and examine it for damage or cracks **(see illustration)**. If evident it will have to be renewed, but note that this will necessitate readjustment of the differential unit, as described in Section 7.
2 Prise the seal from the inner shift lever. If the lever is not being removed smear the lip of the new seal with grease then drive it squarely into the housing until flush with the rim of the bush. To remove the lever, unscrew and remove the finger then slide out the lever **(see illustrations)**. Using a soft metal drift drive out the lever bush from the housing. Drive the new bush into position then smear the lever friction surfaces with molybdenum disulphide grease, slide it into the housing, fit the finger and tighten it to the specified torque. Fit the new seal as previously described.
3 Unscrew the speedometer pinion bush and withdraw the pinion. Examine the

components for wear and renew them if necessary. Insert the pinion then tighten the bush.
4 Check the starter bush in the housing. If necessary remove it with VW tools 228 b and 204 b, then drive in the new bush with a soft metal drift. Do not grease the bush.
5 Check the output shaft needle roller bearing and if necessary remove it with a puller.

Support the housing and drive in the new bearing, making sure that the end face with the lettering faces inside the gearbox **(see illustration)**.
6 Check the input shaft needle roller bearing. To remove it, prise out the oil seal then use a soft metal drive from the outside of gearbox to drive it out. Support the housing and drive in the new bearing flush, making sure that the end face with the lettering faces inside the gearbox **(see illustrations)**. Smear the lip of the new seal with grease then use a metal tube to drive it squarely into the housing as far as it will go. The fitted position of the seal is approximately 2.5 mm (0.099 in) below the housing surface.

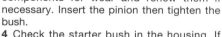

3.5 Output shaft needle roller bearing location in the clutch housing

3.6a Input shaft seal and bearing viewed from the engine side of the clutch housing

3.6b Input shaft bearing viewed from inside of clutch housing

4 Gearbox housing (084 gearbox) - dismantling and reassembly

1 Clean the housing and examine it for damage or cracks **(see illustration)**. If evident the housing will have to be renewed, and will necessitate readjustment of the differential, and input and output shafts (Sections 7 and 8 respectively).

2 Check the selector relay shaft for excessive play in the bushes **(see illustration)**. If evident unscrew the relay lever and withdraw the shaft from inside the housing. Remove the spring and use a soft metal drift to drive out the cap. Also use a drift to drive out the bushes. Note that they are of different lengths, the outer one being 9.5 mm long, the inner one 12 mm long. Drive in the new bushes flush then fit the shaft, insert the relay lever, and tighten it to the specified torque. Insert the spring and drive in the retaining cap.

3 Check the reverse gear shaft and if worn excessively use a soft metal drift to drive the shaft from the housing **(see illustration)** - heat the surrounding housing with a blowlamp if difficulty is experienced. Apply a liquid locking agent to the contact end of the shaft then heat up the housing and drive in the shaft from the outside until the inner end is 83.3 mm (3.280 in) from the mating face of the housing **(see illustration)**.

4 Check the input and output shaft bearings

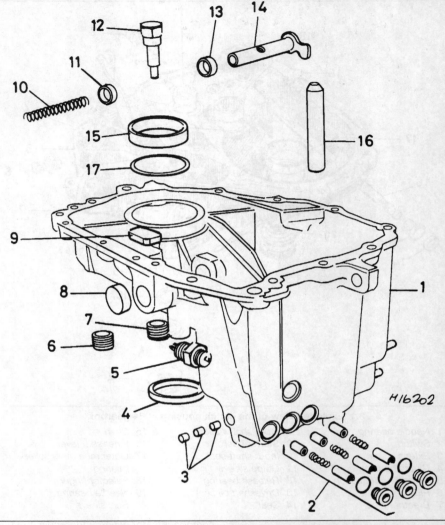

4.1 Exploded view of the gearbox housing - 084 gearbox

1 Gearbox housing	7 Oil filler plug	13 Inner bush for selector shaft
2 Gear detents	8 Cap	
3 Interlock plungers	9 Magnet	14 Selector shaft
4 Oil seal (left-hand drive flange)	10 Spring	15 Outer race taper roller bearing
	11 Outer bush for selector shaft	16 Reverse gear shaft
5 Reversing light switch	12 Relay lever	17 Shim
6 Oil drain plug		

4.2 Selector relay shaft location in the gearbox housing

4.3a Reverse gear shaft location in the gearbox housing

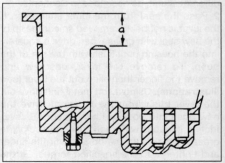

4.3b Reverse gear shaft fitting dimension
a = 83.3 mm (3.280 in)

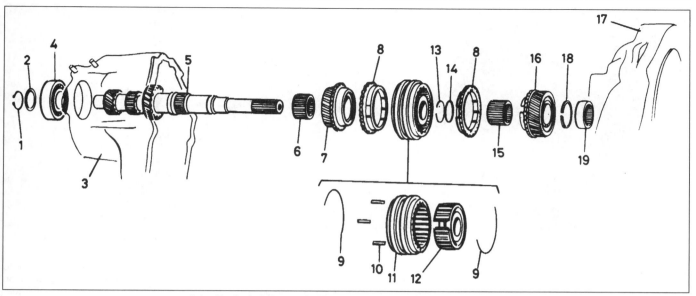

5.1a Exploded view of the input shaft assembly - 084 gearbox

1 Circlip	6 Needle bearing for 3rd gear	10 Key	15 Needle bearing for 4th gear
2 Shim	7 3rd speed gear	11 Sleeve	16 4th gear
3 Gearbox housing	8 Synchro rings for 3rd	12 Synchro-hub	17 Clutch housing
4 Grooved ball-bearing	and 4th gears	13 Circlip	18 Circlip
5 Input shaft	9 Spring	14 Thrust washer	19 Needle bearing

for wear by spinning them, and renew them if there is excessive play or any roughness evident. Also examine the end cover for condition.

5 Examine the selector rods and forks for damage and check the reverse gear for bore wear and chipping or pitting of the teeth. Renew the components as necessary.

5 Input and output shafts (084 gearbox) - dismantling and reassembly

Input shaft

1 Using circlip pliers extract the circlip from the splined end of the input shaft **(see illustrations)**.
2 Withdraw the 4th gear and needle bearing **(see illustrations)**.
3 Remove the 4th synchro ring **(see illustration)**.
4 Remove the thrustwasher **(see illustration)** then, using circlip pliers, remove the circlip from the 3rd/4th synchro unit **(see illustration)**. Do not overstretch the circlip.
5 Using a puller beneath the 3rd gear, pull off the gear, together with the 3rd/4th synchro

5.1b Extracting the circlip from the input shaft

5.2a Remove the 4th gear . . .

5.2b . . . and needle bearing

5.3 Removing the 4th synchro ring

5.4a Remove the thrustwasher . . .

9

5.4b . . . and circlip

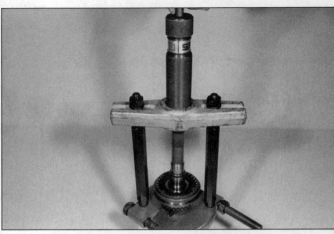

5.5 Pulling off the 3rd gear and 3rd/4th synchro unit

unit **(see illustration)**. When removed, separate the components and remove the 3rd synchro ring.

6 Remove the 3rd gear needle bearing **(see illustrations)**.

7 Clean the components in paraffin and examine them for wear and damage. Check the gearteeth for pitting, and similarly check the needle rollers. Renew the components as necessary.

8 Servicing of the synchro units is described in Section 6.

9 Commence reassembly by locating the 3rd gear needle bearing on the input shaft. Lubricate it with gear oil.

10 Fit the 3rd gear **(see illustration)**.

11 Locate the 3rd synchro ring on the 3rd/4th synchro unit with the cut-outs engaged with the keys. Then, using a puller, press the synchro unit onto the splines **(see illustration)**. Alternatively use a metal tube to drive it on. Make sure that the groove on the side of the hub will face the 4th gear position.

12 Fit the circlip in the groove followed by the thrustwasher.

13 Locate the 4th synchro ring on the 3rd/4th synchro unit with the cut-outs engaged with the keys.

14 Locate the 4th gear needle bearing on the

5.6a 3rd gear needle bearing location

5.6b Input shaft with gears removed

5.10 Fitting the 3rd gear on the input shaft

5.11 Fitting the 3rd gear synchro ring and 3rd/4th synchro unit to the input shaft

5.15 Circlip fitted to 4th gear

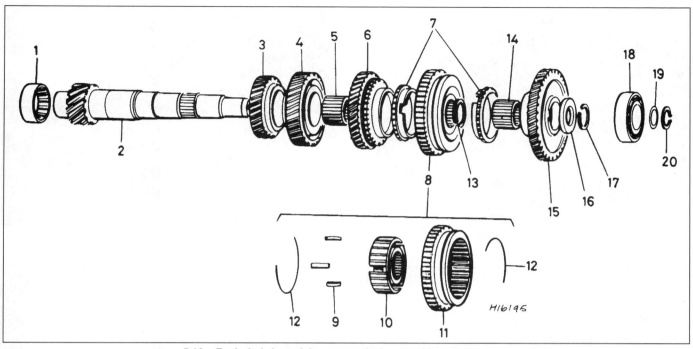

5.16a Exploded view of the output shaft assembly - 084 gearbox

1 Needle bearing
2 Output shaft
3 4th gear
4 3rd gear
5 Needle bearing for
  2nd gear

6 2nd gear
7 Synchro ring for 1st
  and 2nd gears
8 Synchro unit for 1st
  and 2nd gears
9 Key

10 Hub
11 Sleeve
12 Spring
13 Circlip
14 Needle bearing for
  1st gear

15 1st gear
16 Thrust washer
17 Circlip
18 Grooved ball-bearing
19 Shim
20 Circlip

shaft and lubricate it with gear oil, then fit the 4th gear.

15 Fit the circlip in the groove, making sure that it is correctly seated **(see illustration)**.

Output shaft

16 Using circlip pliers, extract the circlip from the end of the output shaft, and remove the thrustwasher **(see illustrations)**. Note that the circlip must be renewed on reassembly.

17 Remove the 1st gear and needle roller bearing **(see illustrations)**.

18 Remove the 1st synchro ring **(see illustration)**.

19 Remove the thrustwasher then, using circlip pliers, remove the circlip from

5.16b Remove the circlip

5.16c . . . and thrustwasher from the output shaft

5.17a Remove 1st gear . . .

5.17b . . . and needle roller bearing

5.18 Remove the 1st gear synchro ring

5.19a Remove the thrustwasher . . .

5.19b . . . and circlip

5.21a Remove the 2nd gear needle bearing

5.21b Output shaft with gears removed

the 1st/2nd synchro unit **(see illus-trations)**. Renew this circlip when reassembling.
20 Using a puller beneath the 2nd gear, pull off the gear, together with the 1st/2nd synchro

unit. When removed, separate the components and remove the 2nd synchro ring.
21 Remove the 2nd gear needle bearing **(see illustrations)**.

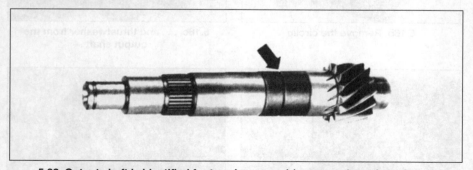

5.22 Output shaft is identified for type by groove(s) - arrowed - and number of final drive teeth

Ratio	Identification
4.27 (64 : 15)	No groove
3.88 (6 2: 16)	One groove
4.06 (65 : 16)	Three grooves

22 Clean the components in paraffin and examine them for wear and damage. Check the gearteeth for pitting, and similarly check the needle rollers. Renew the components as necessary. If the 3rd and/or 4th gears require renewal a press is necessary and the new gears must be heated to 120°C (248°F) before fitting. Note that the shoulders on the two gears are adjacent. The gear on the output shaft and the final drive crownwheel are not matched so, if necessary, the output shaft can be renewed separately, but it will be necessary to check and possibly adjust the output shaft endfloat adjustment, as described in Section 8. In addition, when fitting a new output shaft, ensure that the replacement has the correct number of final drive gearteeth by comparing with the old shaft **(see illustration)**.
23 Check the synchro rings and synchro units with reference to Section 6, paragraphs 3 and 4; however, there are no grooves or dot.
24 Commence reassembly by locating the 2nd gear needle bearing on the output shaft. Lubricate it with gear oil.

5.25 Fitting 2nd gear on the output shaft

5.26 Fitting the 2nd synchro ring and 1st/2nd synchro unit to the output shaft

5.27 Using a puller to press on the 1st/2nd synchro unit

25 Fit the 2nd gear **(see illustration)**.
26 Locate the 2nd synchro ring on the 1st/2nd synchro unit with the cut-outs engaged with the keys. The ring must be fitted on the reverse gear teeth end of the unit **(see illustration)**.
27 Using a puller, press the synchro unit onto

the splines **(see illustration)**. Alternatively use a metal tube to drive it on. When fitted the selector groove must be on the 1st gear end of the unit.
28 Fit the **new** circlip in the groove, followed by the thrustwasher.
29 Locate the 1st synchro ring on the 1st/2nd synchro unit with the cut-outs engaged with the keys.
30 Locate the 1st gear needle bearing on the shaft and lubricate it with gear oil, then fit the 1st gear.
31 Fit the thrustwasher and a **new** circlip, making sure that it is correctly seated.

6 Synchro units (084 gearbox) - dismantling and reassembly

1 Unless the gearbox is the victim of neglect or misuse, or has covered very high mileages, the synchro-hub assemblies do not normally need renewing. If they do, they must be renewed as a complete assembly. It is not

practical to fit an inner hub or outer sleeve alone - even if you could buy one.
2 When synchro baulk rings are being renewed, it is advisable to fit new sliding keys (blocker bars) and retaining springs in the hubs, as this will ensure that full advantage is taken of the new, unworn cut-outs in the rings.
3 Check the synchro rings by assembling them on their respective gears and using a feeler gauge to measure the gap between the dogs. If it is less than 0.5 mm (0.02 in), renew the rings **(see illustrations)**.
4 To dismantle the synchro unit, first mark the hub and sleeve in relation to each other, then press the hub out of the sleeve and remove the keys and springs.
5 Check the components then slide the sleeve onto the hub so that the marks are aligned. Note that the recesses in the inside of the sleeve must be aligned with the key grooves in the hub, and the dot on the sleeve applied during manufacture (where applicable) must face the same way as the

6.3a Checking the synchro rings for wear

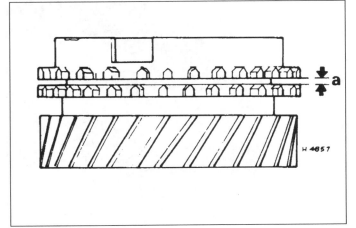

6.3b Synchro ring wear checking dimension (a)

9

6.5a Recess in synchro sleeve (arrowed) to align with key

6.5b Assembling the synchro sleeve to the hub

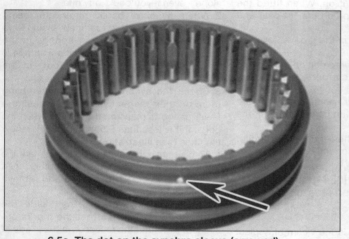

6.5c The dot on the synchro sleeve (arrowed) . . .

6.5d . . . must be on the long spline side of the hub (arrowed)

6.5e Insert the keys . . .

6.5f . . . and fit the springs

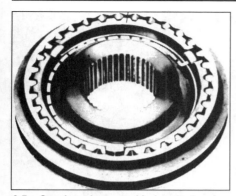

6.5g Synchro sleeve and hub unit showing correct fitting positions for keys and spring

groove on the side of the hub. The groove is on the same side as the longer splines on the hub. Insert the keys and fit the springs with the angled ends located in the keys. Note that the springs point in opposite directions with the angled ends 120° apart **(see illustrations)**.

7 Differential unit (084 gearbox) - dismantling and reassembly

1 Overhaul of the differential unit should not be attempted as special instrumentation is required; including the use of thermo pencils to obtain extremely accurate temperatures. However, if the gearbox or clutch housings are renewed, the differential bearing preload must be adjusted, and this procedure is included in the following paragraphs for the renewal of the differential taper bearings.
2 Examine the taper bearing rollers and races for pitting and scoring, and if evident renew the bearings as follows. Note that the bearings and races are matched so the new bearings must be fitted with their corresponding races.
3 Using a puller, pull the inner races and rollers from each side of the differential.

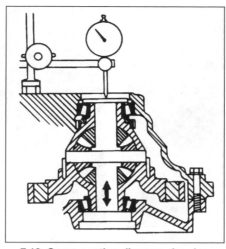

7.10 Cross-section diagram showing method of checking differential bearing endfloat

4 Wipe clean the bearing surfaces on the differential then heat the new inner races and bearings in boiling water and immediately drive them onto the differential using a metal tube on the races only. Make sure that the narrow diameter of the rollers faces away from the differential.
5 Using a metal tube, drive the outer races from the clutch and gearbox housings after prising out the oil seals. Drive them out from the outside of the housings then remove the shims. Keep the shim from the gearbox housing. This shim is 1 mm (0.04 in) thick and must be fitted to the gearbox housing during assessment of the bearing preload and when refitting the bearing on final reassembly.
6 Clean the recesses in the housings. If necessary, the seal sleeve in the clutch housing can be removed by levering out with a suitable screwdriver, but take care not to damage the housing. Once removed, a new seal sleeve must be refitted and this can be pressed in using a suitable tube drift.

7 Fit the 1 mm (0.04 in) shim into the gearbox housing and drive the new outer bearing race into position whilst supporting the housing on a block of wood.
8 Similarly drive the new outer race into the clutch housing without a shim.
9 Locate the differential in the gearbox housing then clean the mating faces and fit the clutch housing (together with a new gasket if applicable). Insert the bolts and tighten them to the specified torque in diagonal sequence.
10 Attach a dial gauge to the gearbox and, without turning the differential, measure the endfloat by pushing the differential in and out - dimension A **(see illustration)**.
11 The bearing preload is 0.30 mm (0.0118 in) - dimension B. Add dimension A to dimension B to obtain the thickness of the shim to fit in the clutch housing.
Example

Dimension A	1.50 mm (0.0591 in)
Dimension B	0.30 mm (0.0118 in)
Shim thickness	1.80 mm (0.0709 in)

12 Remove the clutch housing, drive out the outer race, then fit the correct shim and drive in the outer race.
13 Allow any water to dry from the taper roller bearings before the gearbox is reassembled, and fit new oil seals as described in Section 3.

8 Reassembly - 084 gearbox

Note: *Make sure that all components are clean and, during reassembly, lubricate all bearings and bearing surfaces with gear oil.*
1 Using a metal tube, drive the output shaft bearing into the gearbox housing with the closed side of the bearing facing in the gearbox.
2 Grease the interlock plungers and locate them in the housing - use a pen magnet if necessary **(see illustrations)**.

8.2a Using a pen magnet to insert the interlock plungers

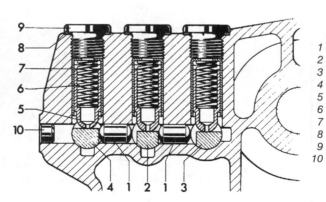

1 Interlock plunger
2 Shift rod 1st/2nd gear
3 Shift rod 3rd/4th gear
4 Shift rod reverse gear
5 Bush
6 Spring
7 Sleeve
8 Seal
9 Threaded plug
10 Plug in interlock bore

8.2b Cross-section of gear selector detents

8.3 Use a large nut to hold the selector relay shaft against the spring tension

8.8a Checking the output shaft bearing endfloat

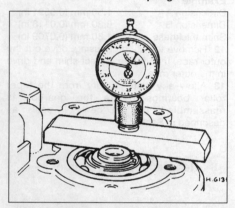

8.8b Using a dial gauge to determine the bearing preload shim thickness

3 Using a large nut or piece of wire, retain the selector relay shaft against the spring tension **(see illustration)**.
4 Locate the 1st/2nd selector rod and fork in the groove of the synchro unit on the output shaft.
5 Locate the reverse gear on its shaft, but retain it in a slightly raised position with a piece of wire.

6 Lower the output shaft and selector rod into the gearbox housing and at the same time feed the reverse gear in after the 1st gear.
7 With the output shaft entered fully in its bearing, check that the selector rod is in neutral and the reverse gear is free to move.
8 If a new gearbox housing, bearing or output shaft has been fitted, determine and fit the bearing preload shims as follows. Fit the circlip and using a feeler gauge determine the clearance between the circlip and bearing inner race **(see illustration)**. Select a small shim to set the clearance to between 0 and 0.05 mm (0 and 0.002 in) then fit the shim beneath the circlip. Using a dial gauge, or straight-edge and feeler gauge, determine the clearance between the housing face (without gasket) and bearing outer race **(see illustration)**. Add 0.27 to 0.31 mm (0.011 to 0.012 in) to the clearance for the thickness of the large shim to fit against the outer race. When assessing the large shim requirement, ensure that the bearing is fully seated in its housing and, if a dial gauge is used, it should be zeroed with a 2 mm (0.079 in) preload.
9 Locate the 3rd/4th selector rod and fork in the groove of the synchro unit on the input shaft.

10 Lower the input shaft and selector rod into the gearbox housing and mesh the gears with those on the output shaft. Lift the reverse gear slightly to allow the input shaft 1st gear to pass.
11 Support the output shaft using the plate described in Section 2 then remove the wire from the reverse gear.
12 Using a metal tube, drive the input shaft bearing into the gearbox housing and onto the shaft. The closed side of the bearing must face into the gearbox **(see illustration)**.
13 Refer to paragraph 8, and if necessary determine and fit the small and large shims to the end of the input shaft.
14 Remove the input shaft support plate.
15 Remove the nut or wire from the selector relay shaft.
16 Locate the relay lever on the reverse selector rod then lower them into the housing and engage the lever with the reverse gear. It will be necessary to lift the gears slightly.
17 Position the relay lever approximately 2.0 mm (0.08 in) away from the 1st/2nd selector rod. Make sure that the roll pin on the selector rod is flush with the fork **(see illustration)**.

8.12 Fitting the input shaft bearing to the gearbox housing

8.17 The fitted position of the reverse relay lever - arrowed

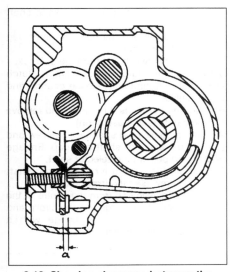

8.18 Showing clearance between the reverse relay lever and the 1st/2nd selector rod - arrow shows roll pin flush

a = 1.3 to 2.8 mm (0.051 to 0.110 in)

8.21a Bearing end cover gasket and large shims located on the bearings

18 Screw in the cross-head bolt and washer, and tighten it to the specified torque. Check that the clearance between the relay lever and selector rod is 1.3 to 2.8 mm (0.051 to 0.110 in) **(see illustration)**.

19 Insert the detent plungers, springs and sleeves in the housing apertures followed by the plugs and their washers. Tighten the plugs with an Allen key.

20 Move the relay shaft lever and check that each gear can be engaged easily. Also check that it is not possible to move two adjacent selector rods at the same time.

21 Locate the correct large shims on the input and output shaft bearings then fit the end cover, together with a new gasket **(see illustration)**. Apply a liquid locking agent to the bolt thread then insert the bolts and tighten them to the specified torque in diagonal sequence **(see illustrations)**.

22 Invert the gearbox and fit the differential unit into position in it **(see illustration)**.

23 Clean the mating faces of the gearbox and clutch housings. If applicable fit a new gasket, otherwise apply sealing compound to the faces.

24 Locate the magnetic swarf collector in the gearbox housing slot.

25 Check that the selector rods are in neutral, then lower the clutch housing onto the gearbox housing, making sure that the shift lever engages the relay shaft lever.

26 Tap in the dowels, then insert the bolts and tighten them evenly to the specified torque in diagonal sequence **(see illustration)**.

8.21b Apply a liquid locking agent to the bolt threads . . .

8.21c . . . then insert and tighten the bolts

8.22 Differential located in the gearbox housing

8.26 Tightening the clutch housing-to-gearbox housing bolts

9

8.27 Method of tightening the drive flange bolts

27 Insert the drive flanges into the differential, together with the taper ring, thrustwasher and spring. Insert the bolts and tighten them to the specified torque. Hold the flanges stationary with a bar between two bolts into adjacent holes **(see illustration)**. Note that the left and right flanges are different.

28 Insert and tighten the reversing light switch.

29 Refit the clutch release shaft and bearing.

30 Refill the gearbox with oil after fitting it to the engine.

9 Dismantling into major assemblies - 020, 4-speed gearbox

1 Proceed as described in paragraphs 1 and 2 of Section 2.

2 Prise free and remove the release shaft circlips.

3 Undo and remove the selector shaft peg bolt **(see illustration)**.

4 Remove the switch unit from the gearbox.

5 Remove the clutch release shaft, clutch lever, return spring and release bearing and guide sleeve.

6 Prise free the plugs then undo and remove the three nuts **(see illustration)**.

7 Using a spark plug spanner, unscrew and remove the selector shaft end cap. Engage neutral and pull out the selector shaft.

8 Undo and remove the reverse gear shaft retaining screw **(see illustration)**.

9 Prise the plastic cap from the centre of the left-hand drive flange, remove the circlip and washer and withdraw the flange with a suitable puller **(see illustrations)**.

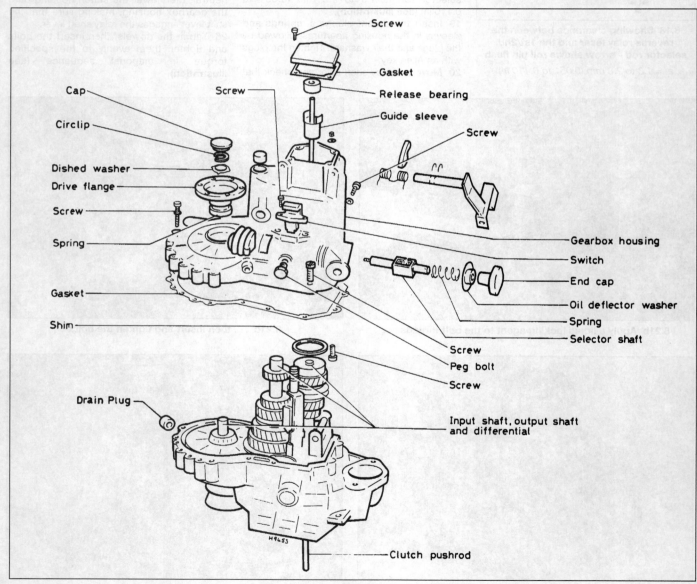

9.3 Exploded view of the 020, 4-speed gearbox

9.6 Undo the three nuts shown. Lever off the plugs (arrowed) where necessary

9.8 Removing the reverse gear shaft retaining screw

Torx type screw on later models

9.9a Remove the drive flange plastic cap

10 Unscrew the main casing-to-gear carrier (clutch housing) bolts then use a puller to draw the main casing away. Recover the bearing shim (if fitted) and remove the gasket and magnet from the gear carrier casing.

11 Withdraw the selector fork rod and remove the fork set sideways **(see illustration)**.

12 Remove the circlip securing 4th gear on the output shaft then withdraw the gear, using a puller if necessary.

13 The input shaft unit can now be withdrawn as a complete assembly.

14 The remaining removal and overhaul procedures are now the same as those

9.9b Drive flange circlip and washer

9.9c Using a puller to withdraw a drive flange

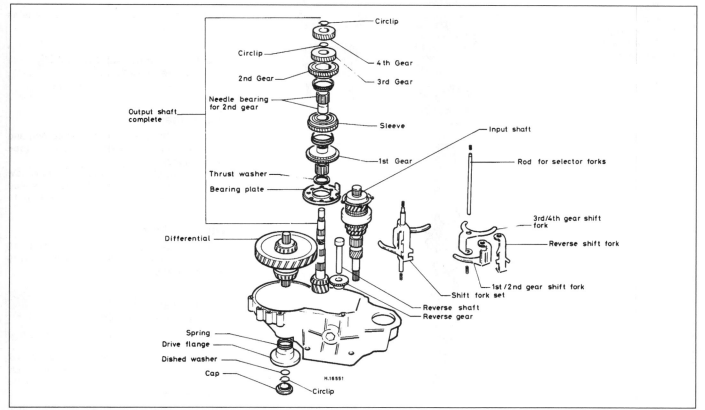

9.11 Exploded view of the gear assemblies and clutch housing components - 020, 4-speed gearbox

9

10.1a Remove 4th gear with the synchro ring . . .

10.1b . . . and the needle roller bearing from the input shaft

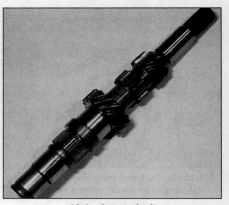

10.1c Input shaft

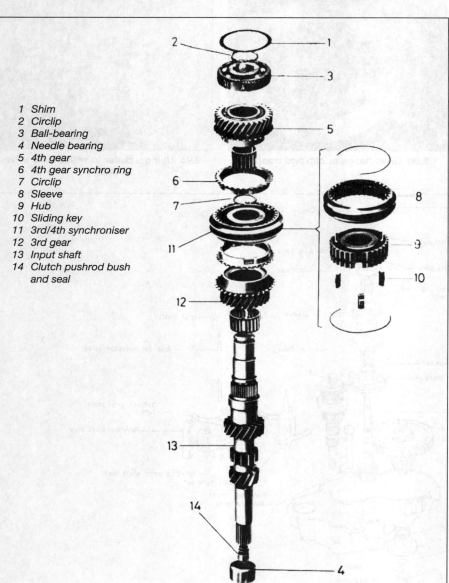

1 Shim
2 Circlip
3 Ball-bearing
4 Needle bearing
5 4th gear
6 4th gear synchro ring
7 Circlip
8 Sleeve
9 Hub
10 Sliding key
11 3rd/4th synchroniser
12 3rd gear
13 Input shaft
14 Clutch pushrod bush and seal

10.1d Exploded view of the input shaft - 020, 4-speed gearbox

described in paragraphs 17 and 25 inclusive in Section 12.

15 If the input shaft ball-bearing is to be removed from the main casing, unscrew the clamping screws then press or drift out the bearing and collect the shim (if fitted). When the new bearing is pressed into position the wide shoulder on its inner race must face towards 4th gear. If a shim was fitted, locate it into the housing before pressing the bearing into position. Fit the bearing clamping screws and tighten the nuts.

16 The input shaft and output shaft units can be serviced as described in the following Section.

17 The servicing of the differential unit is as described in Section 17.

10 Input and output shafts (020, 4-speed gearbox) - dismantling and reassembly

Input shaft

1 Remove 4th gear with its synchro ring and withdraw the needle bearing **(see illustrations)**.

2 The input shaft servicing procedure now follows that given for the 020, 5-speed gearbox in Section 13, paragraphs 4 to 11 inclusive.

Output shaft

3 Refer to Section 12, paragraphs 16 to 19 inclusive, and Section 13, paragraphs 15 to 19 **(see illustration)**.

11 Reassembly - 020, 4-speed gearbox

1 Proceed as described in Section 16, paragraphs 1 to 11 inclusive, then assemble the input shaft and the shift fork assemblies **(see illustrations)**.

2 If not already fitted, locate the input shaft ball-bearing with its original shim (if fitted) into

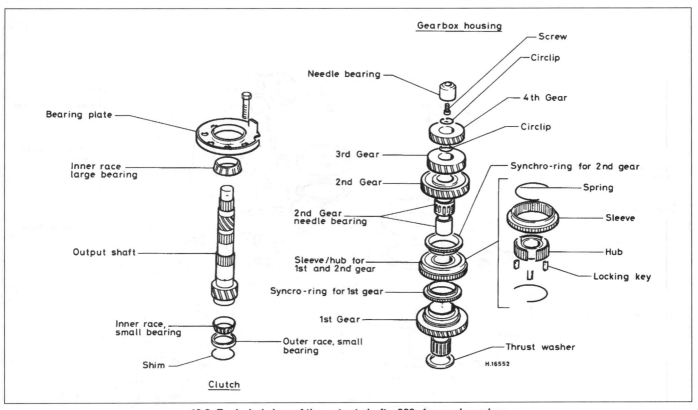

10.3 Exploded view of the output shaft - 020, 4-speed gearbox

11.1a Fitting the input shaft assembly to the gear carrier housing

11.1b Fitting the shift forks . . .

11.1c . . . and shift fork shaft

11.1d Fitting the reverse shift fork pivot posts

11.1e Reverse shift fork assembly

11.1f Reverse shift fork location on reverse idler gear

9

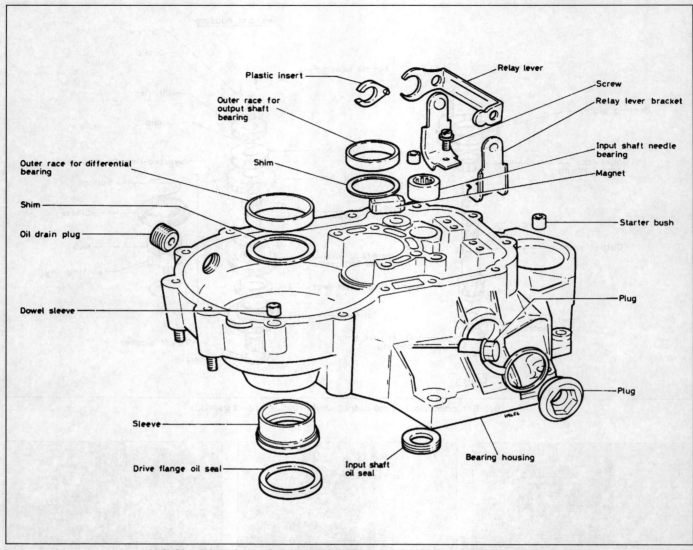

11.2 Clutch housing and associated components - 020, 4- and 5-speed gearbox

position in the main casing, as described in paragraph 15 of Section 9 **(see illustration)**.

3 Now refer to Section 16 again and proceed as described in paragraphs 12 to 18 inclusive.

4 Fit the left-hand drive flange, followed by the spring washer, retaining clip and cap.

5 With the shift forks in neutral, insert the selector shaft, spring and oil deflector washer. Tighten the end cap to the specified torque.

6 Refit the reverse light/consumption indicator switch.

7 Locate and tighten the selector shaft peg bolt to the specified torque.

8 Fit the circlip to the input shaft and check that it is fully engaged.

9 Refit the release bearing and guide sleeve. The release shaft, clutch lever and return spring can then be fitted, but ensure that the bent ends of the spring are in contact with the

housing and with the centre bridge hooked to the clutch lever.

10 Refit the release shaft circlips.

11 Locate a new end cover gasket then refit the cover.

12 With the gearbox reassembled, select each gear in turn to ensure correct and satisfactory engagement.

12 Dismantling into assemblies
- 020, 5-speed gearbox

1 Remove the clutch pushrod from the input shaft **(see illustrations)**.

2 Unbolt and remove the end cover from the main casing. Remove the gasket.

3 Remove the selector shaft detent plunger or

peg bolt, the 5th gear retaining screw, and the gearbox switch.

4 Using a spark plug spanner, unscrew the selector shaft end cap and remove the spring.

5 Engage neutral and withdraw the selector shaft. If difficulty is experienced, extract the circlip and drive out the shaft. However, this may cause damage to the shaft components.

6 Unscrew the reverse gear shaft lockbolt.

7 Prise the plastic cap from the centre of the left-hand side drive flange, remove the circlip and washer, and withdraw the flange with a suitable puller.

8 Engage 5th and reverse gears by removing the selector forks, then unscrew the 5th gear synchroniser retaining screw using a 12 mm Allen key. The screw is very tight and an assistant will be required to hold the main casing.

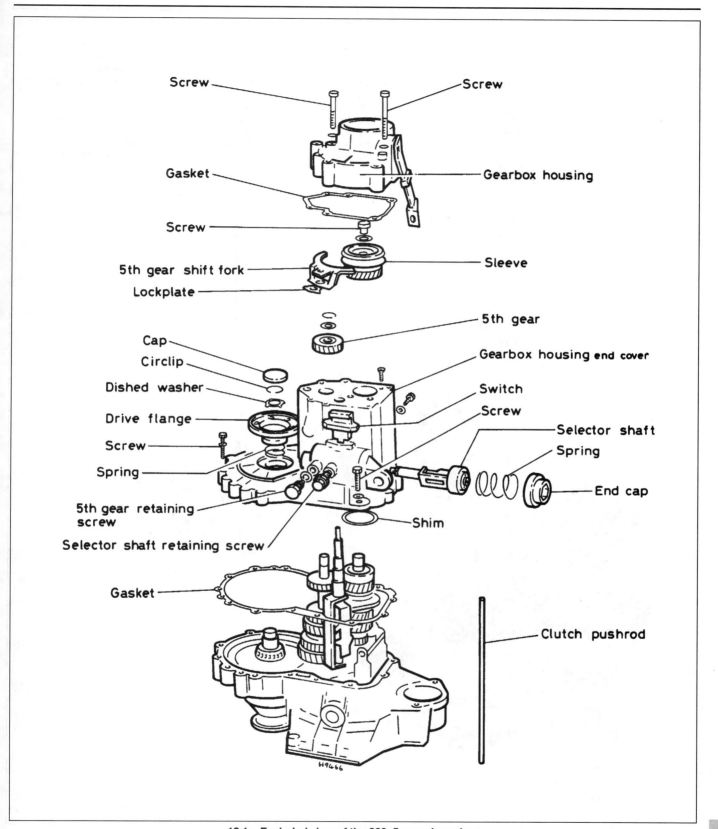

12.1a Exploded view of the 020, 5-speed gearbox

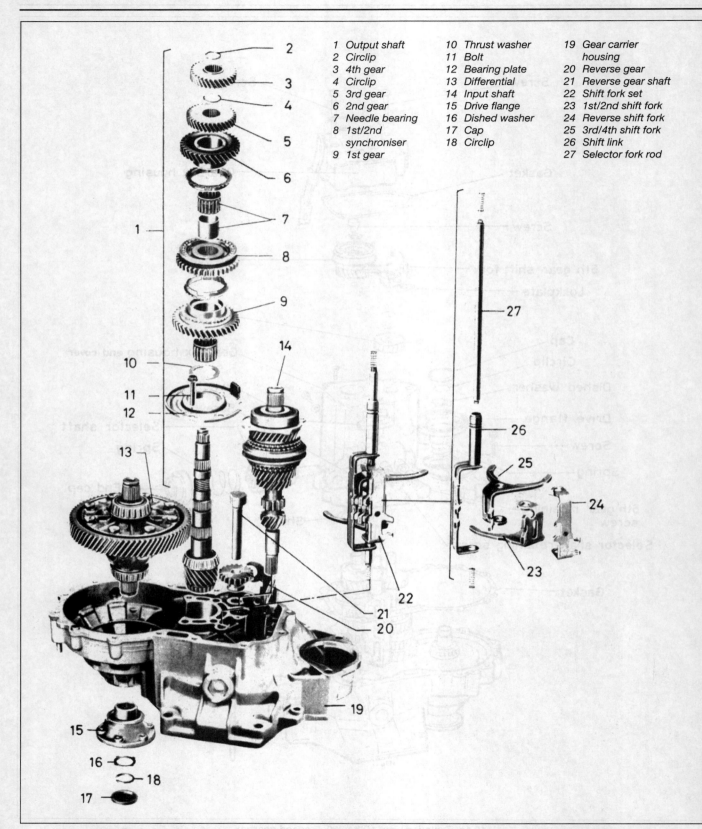

1 Output shaft
2 Circlip
3 4th gear
4 Circlip
5 3rd gear
6 2nd gear
7 Needle bearing
8 1st/2nd synchroniser
9 1st gear
10 Thrust washer
11 Bolt
12 Bearing plate
13 Differential
14 Input shaft
15 Drive flange
16 Dished washer
17 Cap
18 Circlip
19 Gear carrier housing
20 Reverse gear
21 Reverse gear shaft
22 Shift fork set
23 1st/2nd shift fork
24 Reverse shift fork
25 3rd/4th shift fork
26 Shift link
27 Selector fork rod

12.1b Exploded view of the gear carrier (clutch) housing and associated components - 020, 5-speed gearbox

9 Engage neutral, then unscrew the sleeve or prise out the locking plate from the end of the shift fork tube **(see illustration)**.

10 Unscrew the selector tube anti-clockwise from the 5th gear selector fork, but do not remove the selector rod.

11 Withdraw the 5th gear, together with the synchroniser and selector fork from the input shaft.

12 Extract the circlip from the end of the output shaft, then remove the 5th gear with a suitable puller.

13 Using a 5 mm Allen key, unscrew the bolts securing the input shaft bearing retaining plate.

14 Unscrew the bolts attaching the main casing to the gear carrier (clutch) housing, then use a puller to draw the main casing from the input shaft **(see illustration)**. Recover the shim located against the bearing outer track. Remove the gasket and the magnet from the gear carrier housing.

15 Pull the selector fork rod from the gear carrier housing and withdraw the fork set sideways.

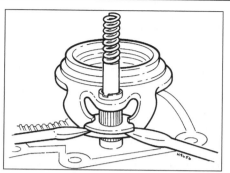

12.9 Selector fork tube locking plate removal method

16 Extract the circlip from the end of the output shaft, then remove the input shaft assembly from the gear carrier housing while removing the 4th gear from the output shaft.

17 Extract the remaining circlip from the output shaft and remove 3rd gear, 2nd gear, 2nd synchro ring and the needle bearing, using a puller if necessary **(see illustrations)**.

12.14 Main casing removal using VW tool 3042

12.17a Removing the 3rd gear retaining circlip (output shaft)

12.17b Removing 3rd gear from the output shaft

12.17c Removing 2nd gear from the output shaft

12.17d 2nd gear needle roller bearing location

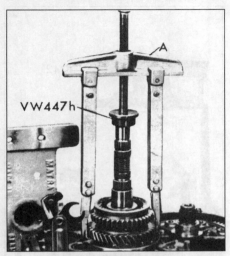

12.19a Showing suitable puller (A) required to remove the 1st gear, synchro-hub and sleeve assembly

18 Remove the reverse gear and shaft from the gear carrier housing.

19 Using a suitable puller, remove the 1st gear and 1st/2nd synchroniser from the output shaft, together with the 2nd gear needle bearing inner race. Remove the 1st gear needle bearing and thrustwasher **(see illustrations)**.

20 Unbolt the bearing retaining plate and remove the output shaft from the gear carrier housing. Note that the retaining plate incorporates the reverse gear stop which locates beneath the reverse gear **(see illustrations)**.

21 Remove the remaining drive flange, as described in paragraph 7, then lift out the differential unit. Overhaul of the differential unit should not be attempted (see Section 7).

22 To overhaul the gear carrier housing, no special tools are necessary and the procedures are similar to those described in Section 4. The drive flange housing on the gear carrier side also has a sleeve fitted. This can be levered out using a screwdriver, but take care not to damage the housing. Once

removed this sleeve must be renewed. Drive the new sleeve into position using a suitable tube drift.

23 The end cover retaining the clutch release components is separate from the main casing. The main casing is otherwise serviced as described in Section 3.

24 If the output shaft bearings (and/or differential unit or gear carrier housing) are to be renewed note that the large and small bearings locate the output shaft relative to the crownwheel, adjustment being by shim which is selected by one of sixteen different thicknesses available. If either bearing is defective then both must be renewed. In the removal process the bearings are destroyed. New ones have to be shrunk on and the shim under the smaller bearing changed for one of the correct size.

25 This operation is quite complicated and requires special equipment for measuring the preload of the shaft, and measurement of the torque required to rotate the new bearings; see Specifications.

12.19b 1st gear needle roller bearing location on the output shaft

12.19c Remove the 1st gear thrustwasher . . .

12.20a . . . undo the retaining bolts . . .

12.20b . . . and withdraw the bearing retainer plate

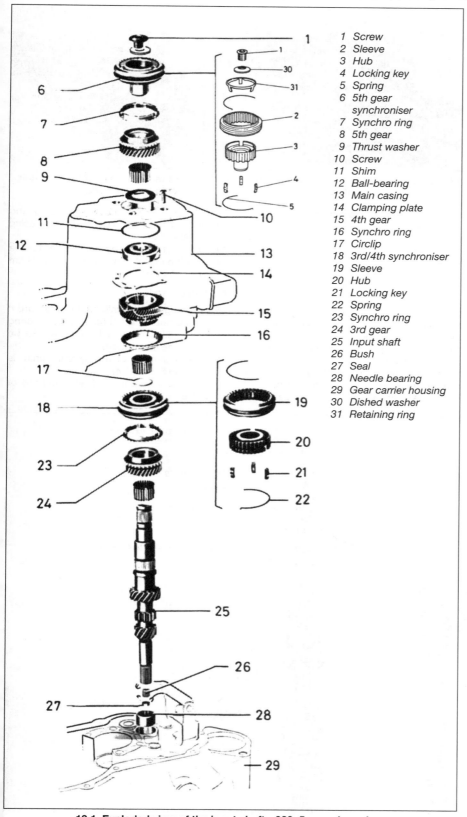

1 Screw
2 Sleeve
3 Hub
4 Locking key
5 Spring
6 5th gear synchroniser
7 Synchro ring
8 5th gear
9 Thrust washer
10 Screw
11 Shim
12 Ball-bearing
13 Main casing
14 Clamping plate
15 4th gear
16 Synchro ring
17 Circlip
18 3rd/4th synchroniser
19 Sleeve
20 Hub
21 Locking key
22 Spring
23 Synchro ring
24 3rd gear
25 Input shaft
26 Bush
27 Seal
28 Needle bearing
29 Gear carrier housing
30 Dished washer
31 Retaining ring

13.1 Exploded view of the input shaft - 020, 5-speed gearbox

13 Input and output shafts (020, 5-speed gearbox) - dismantling and reassembly

Input shaft

1 Remove the 5th gear needle bearing **(see illustration)**.

2 Use a suitable puller and withdraw the ball-bearing from the input shaft. If a shim was fitted on the 5th gear side of this bearing, keep the shim with the bearing, as it was selected during manufacture and must be re-used.

3 Remove the clamping plate, 4th gear and needle bearing, and 4th gear synchro ring.

4 Remove the circlip, then support 3rd gear and press the input shaft through the 3rd/4th synchro-hub. Tape the synchro unit together to prevent it from coming apart.

5 Remove the needle bearing to complete the dismantling of the shaft **(see illustration)**.

6 Should the clutch pushrod be loose in the input shaft, the bush may be driven out of the end of the shaft and a new bush and oil seal fitted **(see illustration)**. Press the new oil seal into position with the fitting plug supplied. When fitted, check that the oil seal depth in the shaft bore is 0.8 to 1.3 mm (0.032 to 0.051 in).

7 If gears on either shaft are to be renewed then the mating gear on the other shaft must be renewed as well. They are supplied in pairs only.

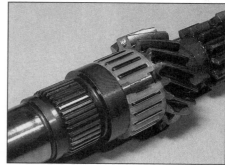

13.5 3rd gear needle roller bearing location on the input shaft

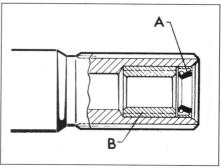

13.6 Clutch pushrod seal (A) and bush (B) location in the input shaft

13.10a Fit 3rd gear . . .

13.10b . . . and synchro ring onto the input shaft

13.10c Fit the 3rd/4th gear synchro unit onto the input shaft . . .

13.10d . . . and retain in position with a circlip

8 The inspection of the synchro units is dealt with in Section 14.

9 When reassembling the input shaft lightly oil all the parts.

10 Fit 3rd gear needle bearing and 3rd gear. Press on the 3rd/4th gear synchro-hub and fit a **new** retaining circlip. When pressing on the synchro-hub and sleeve, turn the rings so that the keys and grooves line up. The chamfer on the inner splines of the hub must face 3rd gear **(see illustrations)**.

11 Fit the 4th gear synchro ring, the needle bearing and 4th gear.

12 Locate the shim (if fitted) in the main casing, then press in the bearing with the inner race wide shoulder facing 4th gear.

13 Fit the plate to the main casing and tighten the bolts to the specified torque using a 5 mm Allen key.

14 Note that there is no adjustment for the input shaft endfloat and that the bearing shim remains constant.

Output shaft

15 Cleaning and examination of the output shaft components (dismantled during removal) will show which items are to be renewed **(see illustration)**.

16 The inspection of the synchro units is dealt with in Section 14.

17 Refer to paragraph 7 if renewing any of the gears.

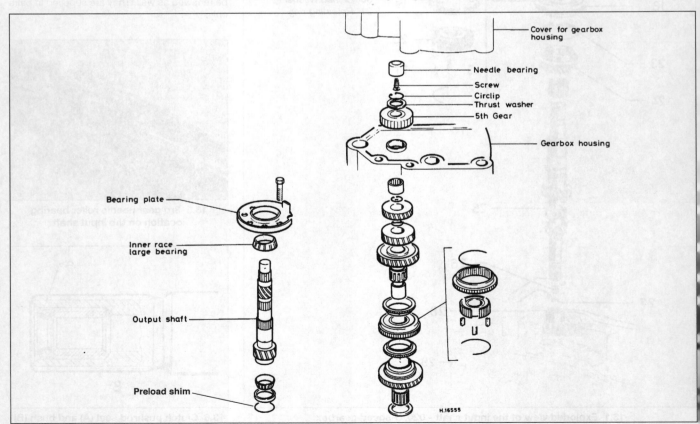

13.15 Exploded view of the output shaft - 020, 5-speed gearbox

Cover for gearbox housing
Needle bearing
Screw
Circlip
Thrust washer
5th Gear
Gearbox housing
Bearing plate
Inner race large bearing
Output shaft
Preload shim

H.16555

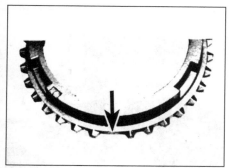

14.2 1st gear synchroniser ring - early type with tooth missing - 020 gearbox

16.1 Locate the differential unit into the gear carrier (clutch) housing

16.4 Tightening the output shaft bearing retainer plate bolts

18 If the output shaft is in need of renewal then the crownwheel must also be renewed as they are a matched pair (see paragraphs 24 and 25 in the previous Section).

19 Reassembly of the output shaft is in Section 16.

14 Synchro units (020 gearbox) - dismantling and reassembly

1 Refer to Section 6, but note the following points which are applicable to the 020 gearbox types.

1st/2nd synchro

2 The 1st gear synchro ring fitted during manufacture differs from the other synchro

rings in having a tooth missing **(see illustration)**. When refitting this synchro ring ensure that it is only fitted to 1st gear. When the synchro ring is renewed, a ring with full teeth will be supplied.

3 When assembling the hub and sleeve, the groove on the end face of the hub must face 1st gear, the assembly position is otherwise unimportant.

4 Assemble the keys and springs in the manner described in paragraph 5 of Section 6.

3rd/4th synchro

5 When assembling the hub and sleeve the chamfer on the hub inner splines must face towards 3rd gear with the outer groove on the end face towards 4th gear. The assembly position is otherwise unimportant.

6 Assemble the keys and springs in the manner described in paragraph 5 of Section 6.

5th gear synchro

7 Ensure when fitting that the chamfer on the splines of the synchro sleeve faces towards 5th gear.

15 Differential unit (020 gearbox) - dismantling and reassembly

Refer to Section 7 for details, but note that the following differences apply to the 020 gearbox:

a) *When assessing the preload allowance for the taper bearings, dimension B must be 0.40 mm (0.0157 in). A typical example will then be:*
   Dimension A = 0.90 mm (0.0354 in)
   Dimension B = 0.40 mm (0.0157 in)
   Shim thickness = 1.30 mm (0.0511 in)
b) *The 1 mm (0.04 in) shim must be fitted to the gear carrier (clutch) housing side and the adjustment shims to the main casing (gearbox housing) side.*

16 Reassembly - 020, 5-speed gearbox

1 Refit the differential unit in the gear carrier (clutch) housing **(see illustration)**.

2 Fit the right-hand drive flange followed by the spring washer, retaining circlip, and cap.

3 Fit the output shaft, complete with taper bearings, into the gear carrier housing and mesh it with the differential gear.

4 Fit the bearing retaining plate and tighten the bolts **(see illustration)**.

5 Locate the 1st gear thrustwasher on the output shaft with its shoulder facing the bearing plate.

6 Fit the needle bearing and 1st gear, followed by the 1st synchro ring. Press on the 1st/2nd synchroniser, making sure that the sliding keys locate in the synchro ring cutouts. Heat the synchroniser to 120°C (248°F) before fitting it **(see illustrations)**.

16.6a Fit 1st gear onto the output shaft . . .

16.6b . . . locate the synchro ring . . .

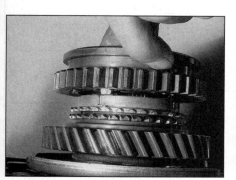

16.6c. . . and synchro unit (1st/2nd)

16.6d Using a metal tube to drive the 1st/2nd synchro unit onto the output shaft

9

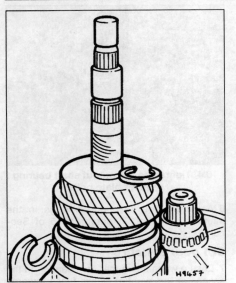

1619 Select suitable circlip to adjust play of 3rd gear

7 Insert the reverse gear shaft complete with the gear into the gear carrier housing, and at the same time engage the gear with the relay lever jaw.

8 Using a metal tube, drive on the 2nd gear needle bearing inner race, then fit the needle bearing, 2nd synchro ring, and 2nd gear.

9 Heat the 3rd gear and press it on the output shaft with its shoulder facing 2nd gear. Select and fit a **new** circlip. The circlip selected should be the thickest one possible that will fully engage in the location groove on the shaft and take up any play of 3rd gear **(see illustration)**. The circlips available vary in thickness and are colour-coded (see Specifications).

10 Fit the input shaft into the gear carrier housing and mesh the gears with the output shaft.

11 Heat the 4th gear and press it on the output shaft with its shoulder facing away from the 3rd gear. Fit the circlip.

12 Locate the selector fork rod spring in the gear carrier housing, then install the fork set. To do this engage the 1st/2nd fork in the synchro sleeve groove, then rotate the fork set around the shaft and engage the 3rd/4th fork and the reverse fork with the relay lever. On later models, the relay lever is tensioned by a coil spring, which is positively located between a lug on the relay lever and a pin in the clutch housing.

13 Push the selector fork rod into the gear carrier housing; and align the slots in the forks to the neutral position.

14 The gear carrier housing and shafts are now ready for the assembly of the main casing.

15 Check that the reverse gear shaft is in the correct position **(see illustration)** and set the gear train in neutral. Make sure that the spring is located on the end of the selector fork rod.

16.15 Reverse idle gear shaft alignment
$X = X$

16 Fit a new gasket on the gear carrier housing flange, and make sure that the magnet is in position.

17 Lower the main casing over the shafts and selector rod, then use metal tubing to drive the bearing inner race onto the input shaft while supporting the shaft on a block of wood.

18 Insert and tighten the reverse gear shaft lockbolt, then insert and tighten the bolts attaching the main casing to the gear carrier housing.

19 Check the input shaft bearing retaining plate bolts for tightness.

20 Fit the 5th gear thrustwasher on the input shaft with the chamfer facing the bearing, followed by the needle bearing.

21 Heat the 5th gear to 100°C (212°F) and press it onto the output shaft with the groove facing away from the main casing.

22 Fit the thrustwasher and a **new** circlip to the output shaft.

23 With the selector fork engaged with the groove in the 5th gear synchroniser, fit the 5th gear, synchro ring, and synchroniser onto the mainshaft and selector fork extension together with the locking plate. Note that the locking plate should be renewed.

24 Without displacing the selector fork rod, screw the selector tube (clockwise) into the fork, then screw it out until it projects by 5.0 mm (0.2 in) **(see illustration)**. Take care not to pull the selector fork rod from the tube during this operation or the shift forks within the gearbox will be disengaged; in which case the gearbox will have to be partially dismantled again to re-engage them.

25 Coat the threads of a **new** 5th gear synchroniser retaining screw with locking compound then screw it into the mainshaft. Engage 5th and reverse gears by moving the selector forks (front fork slot down), then tighten the screw to the specified torque. In view of the high torque loading required, a 12 mm, 12-point socket-head screw wrench

16.24 Selector tube fitting dimension
$X = 5.0$ mm (0.2 in)

should be used if available, but failing this try using a 12 mm Allen key.

26 Engage neutral and insert the selector shaft. The gearbox is best positioned on its side for this operation so that the selector shaft can be lowered into position vertically.

27 Fit the spring and tighten the selector shaft cover (using a spark plug box spanner).

28 Insert and tighten the reverse light/consumption indicator switch unit.

29 Locate and tighten the selector shaft peg bolt to the specified torque.

30 Fit and adjust the 5th gear retaining screw. To do this first fit the shift linkage lever to the selector shaft. With the gears in neutral, remove the cap and loosen the locknut. Tighten the sleeve until the central plunger just starts to move, then loosen the sleeve 1/2 a turn and tighten the locknut **(see illustration)**.

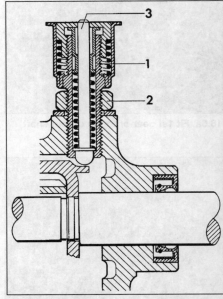

16.30 Sectional view showing 5th gear detent plunger

1 Adjusting sleeve   *3 Plunger*
2 Locknut

31 Adjust the 5th gear selector fork as follows, taking care not to allow gear disengagement. First check that the selector tube projection is as shown **(see illustration 16.24)**. Engage 5th gear with the aid of a lever if necessary, then press the synchroniser sleeve away from the gearbox to eliminate any play and check that the sleeve overlaps the hub by 1.0 mm (0.039 in) **(see illustration)**. If not, turn the selector tube as necessary.

32 Fit the new locking plate into position. Support the shift fork with a pair of open-ended spanners (19 mm and 24 mm) or other suitable tool(s) about 12 mm (0.5 in) thick and knock the plate on.

33 Locate a new end cover gasket and then refit the end cover (with the release bearing) and tighten the retaining bolts.

34 Lubricate the clutch pushrod and insert it in the input shaft.

35 Fit the left-hand drive flange followed by the spring washer, retaining circlip and cap.

36 Gearbox reassembly is now complete. Select each gear in turn to ensure satisfactory and correct engagement.

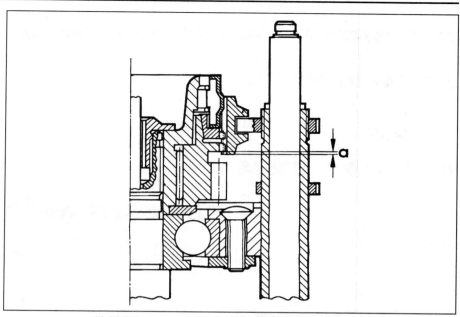

16.31 5th gear selector fork adjustment dimension (a)

Haynes Manuals – The Complete List

Title	Book No.
ALFA ROMEO	
Alfa Romeo Alfasud/Sprint (74 - 88)	0292
Alfa Romeo Alfetta (73 - 87)	0531
AUDI	
Audi 80 (72 - Feb 79)	0207
Audi 80, 90 (79 - Oct 86) & Coupe (81 - Nov 88)	0605
Audi 80, 90 (Oct 86 - 90) & Coupe (Nov 88 - 90)	1491
Audi 100 (Oct 76 - Oct 82)	0428
Audi 100 (Oct 82 - 90) & 200 (Feb 84 - Oct 89)	0907
AUSTIN	
Austin Ambassador (82 - 84)	0871
Austin/MG Maestro 1.3 & 1.6 (83 - 95)	0922
Austin Maxi (69 - 81)	0052
Austin/MG Metro (80 - May 90)	0718
Austin Montego 1.3 & 1.6 (84 - 94)	1066
Austin/MG Montego 2.0 (84 - 95)	1067
Mini (59 - 69)	0527
Mini (69 - Oct 96)	0646
Austin/Rover 2.0 litre Diesel Engine (86 - 93)	1857
BEDFORD	
Bedford CF (69 - 87)	0163
Bedford Rascal (86 - 93)	3015
BL	
BL Princess & BLMC 18-22 (75 - 82)	0286
BMW	
BMW 316, 320 & 320i (4-cyl) (75 - Feb 83)	0276
BMW 320, 320i, 323i & 325i (6-cyl) (Oct 77 - Sept 87)	0815
BMW 3-Series (Apr 91 - 96)	3210
BMW 3-Series (sohc) (83 - 91)	1948
BMW 520i & 525e (Oct 81 - June 88)	1560
BMW 525, 528 & 528i (73 - Sept 81)	0632
BMW 5-Series (sohc) (81 - 91)	1948
BMW 1500, 1502, 1600, 1602, 2000 & 2002 (59 - 77)	0240
CITROEN	
Citroen 2CV, Ami & Dyane (67 - 90)	0196
Citroen AX Petrol & Diesel (87 - 94)	3014
Citroen BX (83 - 94)	0908
Citroen CX (75 - 88)	0528
Citroen Visa (79 - 88)	0620
Citroen Xantia Petrol & Diesel (93 - Oct 95)	3082
Citroen XM Petrol & Diesel (89 - 97)	3451
Citroen ZX Diesel (91 - 93)	1922
Citroen ZX Petrol (91 - 94)	1881
Citroen 1.7 & 1.9 litre Diesel Engine (84 - 96)	1379
COLT	
Colt 1200, 1250 & 1400 (79 - May 84)	0600
DAIMLER	
Daimler Sovereign (68 - Oct 86)	0242
Daimler Double Six (72 - 88)	0478
DATSUN (see also *Nissan*)	
Datsun 120Y (73 - Aug 78)	0228
Datsun 1300, 1400 & 1600 (69 - Aug 72)	0123
Datsun Cherry (71 - 76)	0195
Datsun Pick-up (75 - 78)	0277
Datsun Sunny (Aug 78 - May 82)	0525
Datsun Violet (78 - 82)	0430

Title	Book No.
FIAT	
Fiat 126 (73 - 87)	0305
Fiat 127 (71 - 83)	0193
Fiat 500 (57 - 73)	0090
Fiat 850 (64 - 81)	0038
Fiat Panda (81 - 95)	0793
Fiat Punto (94 - 96)	3251
Fiat Regata (84 - 88)	1167
Fiat Strada (79 - 88)	0479
Fiat Tipo (88 - 91)	1625
Fiat Uno (83 - 95)	0923
Fiat X1/9 (74 - 89)	0273
FORD	
Ford Capri II (& III) 1.6 & 2.0 (74 - 87)	0283
Ford Capri II (& III) 2.8 & 3.0 (74 - 87)	1309
Ford Cortina Mk IV (& V) 1.6 & 2.0 (76 - 83)	0343
Ford Cortina Mk IV (& V) 2.3 V6 (77 - 83)	0426
Ford Escort (75 - Aug 80)	0280
Ford Escort (Sept 80 - Sept 90)	0686
Ford Escort (Sept 90 - 97)	1737
Ford Escort Mk II Mexico, RS 1600 & RS 2000 (75 - 80)	0735
Ford Fiesta (inc. XR2) (76 - Aug 83)	0334
Ford Fiesta (inc. XR2) (Aug 83 - Feb 89)	1030
Ford Fiesta (Feb 89 - Oct 95)	1595
Ford Fiesta Petrol & Diesel (Oct 95 - 97)	3397
Ford Granada (Sept 77 - Feb 85)	0481
Ford Granada (Mar 85 - 94)	1245
Ford Mondeo 4-cyl (93 - 96)	1923
Ford Orion (83 - Sept 90)	1009
Ford Orion (Sept 90 - 93)	1737
Ford Sierra 1.3, 1.6, 1.8 & 2.0 (82 - 93)	0903
Ford Sierra 2.3, 2.8 & 2.9 (82 - 91)	0904
Ford Scorpio (Mar 85 - 94)	1245
Ford Transit Petrol (Mk 1) (65 - Feb 78)	0377
Ford Transit Petrol (Mk 2) (78 - Jan 86)	0719
Ford Transit Petrol (Mk 3) (Feb 86 - 89)	1468
Ford Transit Diesel (Feb 86 - 95)	3019
Ford 1.6 & 1.8 litre Diesel Engine (84 - 96)	1172
Ford 2.1, 2.3 & 2.5 litre Diesel Engine (77 - 90)	1606
FREIGHT ROVER	
Freight Rover Sherpa (74 - 87)	0463
HILLMAN	
Hillman Avenger (70 - 82)	0037
HONDA	
Honda Accord (76 - Feb 84)	0351
Honda Accord (Feb 84 - Oct 85)	1177
Honda Civic (Feb 84 - Oct 87)	1226
Honda Civic (Nov 91 - 96)	3199
HYUNDAI	
Hyundai Pony (85 - 94)	3398
JAGUAR	
Jaguar E Type (61 - 72)	0140
Jaguar MkI & II, 240 & 340 (55 - 69)	0098
Jaguar XJ6, XJ & Sovereign (68 - Oct 86)	0242
Jaguar XJ6 & Sovereign (Oct 86 - Sept 94)	3261
Jaguar XJ12, XJS & Sovereign (72 - 88)	0478

Title	Book No.
JEEP	
Jeep Cherokee Petrol (93 - 96)	1943
LADA	
Lada 1200, 1300, 1500 & 1600 (74 - 91)	0413
Lada Samara (87 - 91)	1610
LAND ROVER	
Land Rover 90, 110 & Defender Diesel (83 - 95)	3017
Land Rover Discovery Diesel (89 - 95)	3016
Land Rover Series IIA & III Diesel (58 - 85)	0529
Land Rover Series II, IIA & III Petrol (58 - 85)	0314
MAZDA	
Mazda 323 fwd (Mar 81 - Oct 89)	1608
Mazda 626 fwd (May 83 - Sept 87)	0929
Mazda B-1600, B-1800 & B-2000 Pick-up (72 - 88)	0267
MERCEDES-BENZ	
Mercedes-Benz 190, 190E & 190D Petrol & Diesel (83 - 93)	3450
Mercedes-Benz 200, 240, 300 Diesel (Oct 76 - 85)	1114
Mercedes-Benz 250 & 280 (68 - 72)	0346
Mercedes-Benz 250 & 280 (123 Series) (Oct 76 - 84)	0677
Mercedes-Benz 124 Series (85 - Aug 93)	3253
MG	
MGB (62 - 80)	0111
MG Maestro 1.3 & 1.6 (83 - 95)	0922
MG Metro (80 - May 90)	0718
MG Midget & AH Sprite (58 - 80)	0265
MG Montego 2.0 (84 - 95)	1067
MITSUBISHI	
Mitsubishi 1200, 1250 & 1400 (79 - May 84)	0600
Mitsubishi Shogun & L200 Pick-Ups (83 - 94)	1944
MORRIS	
Morris Ital 1.3 (80 - 84)	0705
Morris Marina 1700 (78 - 80)	0526
Morris Marina 1.8 (71 - 78)	0074
Morris Minor 1000 (56 - 71)	0024
NISSAN (See also *Datsun*)	
Nissan Bluebird 160B & 180B rwd (May 80 - May 84)	0957
Nissan Bluebird fwd (May 84 - Mar 86)	1223
Nissan Bluebird (T12 & T72) (Mar 86 - 90)	1473
Nissan Cherry (N12) (Sept 82 - 86)	1031
Nissan Micra (K10) (83 - Jan 93)	0931
Nissan Micra (93 - 96)	3254
Nissan Primera (90 - Oct 96)	1851
Nissan Stanza (82 - 86)	0824
Nissan Sunny (B11) (May 82 - Oct 86)	0895
Nissan Sunny (Oct 86 - Mar 91)	1378
Nissan Sunny (Apr 91 - 95)	3219
OPEL	
Opel Ascona & Manta (B Series) (Sept 75 - 88)	0316
Opel Ascona (81 - 88)	3215
Opel Astra (Oct 91 - 96)	3156
Opel Corsa (83 - Mar 93)	3160
Opel Corsa (Mar 93 - 94)	3159
Opel Kadett (Nov 79 - Oct 84)	0634

Title	Book No.
Opel Kadett (Oct 84 - Oct 91)	3196
Opel Omega & Senator (86 - 94)	3157
Opel Rekord (Feb 78 - Oct 86)	0543
Opel Vectra (88 - Oct 95)	3158
PEUGEOT	
Peugeot 106 Petrol & Diesel (91 - June 96)	1882
Peugeot 205 (83 - 95)	0932
Peugeot 305 (78 - 89)	0538
Peugeot 306 Petrol & Diesel (93 - 95)	3073
Peugeot 309 (86 - 93)	1266
Peugeot 405 Petrol (88 - 96)	1559
Peugeot 405 Diesel (88 - 96)	3198
Peugeot 406 Petrol & Diesel (96 - 97)	3394
Peugeot 505 (79 - 89)	0762
Peugeot 1.7 & 1.9 litre Diesel Engines (82 - 96)	0950
Peugeot 2.0, 2.1, 2.3 & 2.5 litre Diesel Engines (74 - 90)	1607
PORSCHE	
Porsche 911 (65 - 85)	0264
Porsche 924 & 924 Turbo (76 - 85)	0397
PROTON	
Proton (89 - 97)	3255
RANGE ROVER	
Range Rover V8 (70 - Oct 92)	0606
RELIANT	
Reliant Robin & Kitten (73 - 83)	0436
RENAULT	
Renault 5 (72 - Feb 85)	0141
Renault 5 (Feb 85 - 96)	1219
Renault 9 & 11 (82 - 89)	0822
Renault 12 (70 - 80)	0097
Renault 15 & 17 (72 - 79)	0763
Renault 18 (79 - 86)	0598
Renault 19 Petrol (89 - 94)	1646
Renault 19 Diesel (89 - 95)	1946
Renault 21 (86 - 94)	1397
Renault 25 (84 - 92)	1228
Renault Clio Petrol (91 - 93)	1853
Renault Clio Diesel (91 - June 96)	3031
Renault Espace (85 - 96)	3197
Renault Fuego (80 - 86)	0764
Renault Laguna (94 - 96)	3252
Renault Mégane Petrol & Diesel (96 - 97)	3395
ROVER	
Rover 111 & 114 (95 - 96)	1711
Rover 213 & 216 (84 - 89)	1116
Rover 214 & 414 (89 - 96)	1689
Rover 216 & 416 (89 - 96)	1830
Rover 618, 620 & 623 (93 - 97)	3257
Rover 820, 825 & 827 (86 - 95)	1380
Rover 2000, 2300 & 2600 (77 - 87)	0468
Rover 3500 (76 - 87)	0365
Rover Metro (May 90 - 94)	1711
SAAB	
Saab 90, 99 & 900 (79 - Oct 93)	0765
Saab 9000 (4-cyl) (85 - 95)	1686

Title	Book No.
SEAT	
Seat Ibiza & Malaga (85 - 92)	1609
SIMCA	
Simca 1100 & 1204 (67 - 79)	0088
Simca 1301 & 1501 (63 - 76)	0199
SKODA	
Skoda Estelle 105, 120, 130 & 136 (77 - 89)	0604
Skoda Favorit (89 - 92)	1801
SUBARU	
Subaru 1600 & 1800 (Nov 79 - 90)	0995
SUZUKI	
Suzuki SJ Series, Samurai & Vitara (82 - 97)	1942
Suzuki Supercarry (86 - Oct 94)	3015
TALBOT	
Talbot Alpine, Solara, Minx & Rapier (75 - 86)	0337
Talbot Horizon (78 - 86)	0473
Talbot Samba (82 - 86)	0823
TOYOTA	
Toyota Carina E (May 92 - 97)	3256
Toyota Celica (Feb 82 - Sept 85)	1135
Toyota Corolla (fwd) (Sept 83 - Sept 87)	1024
Toyota Corolla (rwd) (80 - 85)	0683
Toyota Corolla (Sept 87 - 92)	1683
Toyota Corolla (Aug 92 - 97)	3259
Toyota Hi-Ace & Hi-Lux (69 - Oct 83)	0304
Toyota Starlet (78 - Jan 85)	0462
TRIUMPH	
Triumph Acclaim (81 - 84)	0792
Triumph Herald (59 - 71)	0010
Triumph Spitfire (62 - 81)	0113
Triumph Stag (70 - 78)	0441
Triumph TR7 (75 - 82)	0322
VAUXHALL	
Vauxhall Astra (80 - Oct 84)	0635
Vauxhall Astra & Belmont (Oct 84 - Oct 91)	1136
Vauxhall Astra (Oct 91 - 96)	1832
Vauxhall Carlton (Oct 78 - Oct 86)	0480
Vauxhall Carlton (Nov 86 - 94)	1469
Vauxhall Cavalier 1300 (77 - July 81)	0461
Vauxhall Cavalier 1600, 1900 & 2000 (75 - July 81)	0315
Vauxhall Cavalier (81 - Oct 88)	0812
Vauxhall Cavalier (Oct 88 - Oct 95)	1570
Vauxhall Chevette (75 - 84)	0285
Vauxhall Corsa (93 - 97)	1985
Vauxhall Nova (83 - 93)	0909
Vauxhall Rascal (86 - 93)	3015
Vauxhall Senator (Sept 87 - 94)	1469
Vauxhall Vectra Petrol & Diesel (95 - 98)	3396
Vauxhall Viva HB Series (ohv) (66 - 70)	0026
Vauxhall Viva & Firenza (ohc) (68 - 73)	0093
Vauxhall/Opel 1.5, 1.6 & 1.7 litre Diesel Engines (82 - 96)	1222
VOLKSWAGEN	
VW Beetle 1200 (54 - 77)	0036
VW Beetle 1300 & 1500 (65 - 75)	0039
VW Beetle 1302 & 1302S (70 - 72)	0110

Title	Book No.
VW Beetle 1303, 1303S & GT (72 - 75)	0159
VW Golf Mk 1 1.1 & 1.3 (74 - Feb 84)	0716
VW Golf Mk 1 1.5, 1.6 & 1.8 (74 - 85)	0726
VW Golf Mk 1 Diesel (78 - Feb 84)	0451
VW Golf Mk 2 (Mar 84 - Feb 92)	1081
VW Golf Mk 3 Petrol & Diesel (Feb 92 - 96)	3097
VW Jetta Mk 1 1.1 & 1.3 (80 - June 84)	0716
VW Jetta Mk 1 1.5, 1.6 & 1.8 (80 - June 84)	0726
VW Jetta Mk 1 Diesel (81 - June 84)	0451
VW Jetta Mk 2 (July 84 - 92)	1081
VW LT vans & light trucks (76 - 87)	0637
VW Passat (Sept 81 - May 88)	0814
VW Passat (May 88 - 91)	1647
VW Polo & Derby (76 - Jan 82)	0335
VW Polo (82 - Oct 90)	0813
VW Polo (Nov 90 - Aug 94)	3245
VW Santana (Sept 82 - 85)	0814
VW Scirocco Mk 1 1.5, 1.6 & 1.8 (74 - 82)	0726
VW Scirocco (82 - 90)	1224
VW Transporter 1600 (68 - 79)	0082
VW Transporter 1700, 1800 & 2000 (72 - 79)	0226
VW Transporter with air-cooled engine (79 - 82)	0638
VW Transporter (82 - 90)	3452
VW Vento Petrol & Diesel (Feb 92 - 96)	3097
VOLVO	
Volvo 66 & 343, Daf 55 & 66 (68 - 79)	0293
Volvo 142, 144 & 145 (66 - 74)	0129
Volvo 240 Series (74 - 93)	0270
Volvo 262, 264 & 260/265 (75 - 85)	0400
Volvo 340, 343, 345 & 360 (76 - 91)	0715
Volvo 440, 460 & 480 (87 - 92)	1691
Volvo 740 & 760 (82 - 91)	1258
Volvo 850 (92 - 96)	3260
Volvo 940 (90 - 96)	3249
YUGO/ZASTAVA	
Yugo/Zastava (81 - 90)	1453
TECH BOOKS	
Automotive Brake Manual	3050
Automotive Carburettor Manual	3288
Automotive Diesel Engine Service Guide	3286
Automotive Electrical & Electronic Systems	3049
Automotive Engine Management and Fuel Injection Systems Manual	3344
Automotive Tools Manual	3052
Automotive Welding Manual	3053
In-Car Entertainment Manual (3rd Edition)	3363
CAR BOOKS	
Automotive Fuel Injection Systems	9755
Car Bodywork Repair Manual	9864
Caravan Manual (2nd Edition)	9894
Haynes Technical Data Book (89 - 98)	1998
How to Keep Your Car Alive	9868
Japanese Vehicle Carburettors	1786
Small Engine Repair Manual	1755
SU Carburettors	0299
Weber Carburettors (to 79)	0393

CL05.01/98

Preserving Our Motoring Heritage

< *The Model J Duesenberg Derham Tourster. Only eight of these magnificent cars were ever built – this is the only example to be found outside the United States of America*

Almost every car you've ever loved, loathed or desired is gathered under one roof at the Haynes Motor Museum. Over 300 immaculately presented cars and motorbikes represent every aspect of our motoring heritage, from elegant reminders of bygone days, such as the superb Model J Duesenberg to curiosities like the bug-eyed BMW Isetta. There are also many old friends and flames. Perhaps you remember the 1959 Ford Popular that you did your courting in? The magnificent 'Red Collection' is a spectacle of classic sports cars including AC, Alfa Romeo, Austin Healey, Ferrari, Lamborghini, Maserati, MG, Riley, Porsche and Triumph.

A Perfect Day Out

Each and every vehicle at the Haynes Motor Museum has played its part in the history and culture of Motoring. Today, they make a wonderful spectacle and a great day out for all the family. Bring the kids, bring Mum and Dad, but above all bring your camera to capture those golden memories for ever. You will also find an impressive array of motoring memorabilia, a comfortable 70 seat video cinema and one of the most extensive transport book shops in Britain. The Pit Stop Cafe serves everything from a cup of tea to wholesome, home-made meals or, if you prefer, you can enjoy the large picnic area nestled in the beautiful rural surroundings of Somerset.

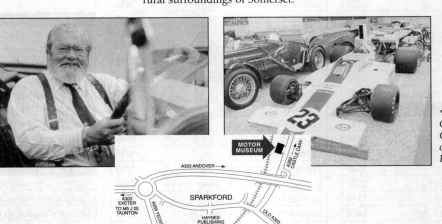

John Haynes O.B.E., > *Founder and Chairman of the museum at the wheel of a Haynes Light 12.*

< *Graham Hill's Lola Cosworth Formula 1 car next to a 1934 Riley Sports.*

The Museum is situated on the A359 Yeovil to Frome road at Sparkford, just off the A303 in Somerset. It is about 40 miles south of Bristol, and 25 minutes drive from the M5 intersection at Taunton.
Open 9.30am - 5.30pm (10.00am - 4.00pm Winter) 7 days a week, *except Christmas Day, Boxing Day and New Years Day*
Special rates available for schools, coach parties and outings Charitable Trust No. 292048